A HISTORY OF THE MODERN AGE

A HISTORY
OF THE
MODERN AGE

Julian K. Prescott

GARDEN CITY, NEW YORK

Doubleday & Company, Inc.

1971

BIOGRAPHICAL NOTE ON JULIAN K. PRESCOTT
BY
PROFESSOR NEAL F. MORRISON

I first met Julian K. Prescott sometime in October 1956, soon after completing my doctorate in American diplomatic history at Johns Hopkins. Mr. Prescott, then Undersecretary of State for Political Affairs, had asked my department chairman, Professor Medford L. Clark, to recommend a part-time research assistant. Professor Clark kindly recommended me.

Before going down to Washington to see Prescott, I learned from *Who's Who in the United States Department of State* that he had been born in 1913 in Plymouth, Massachusetts, had attended Groton and Harvard (where he had excelled as an athlete), and had received a degree from Harvard Law School. He had worked briefly for the Boston *Times-Beacon* and had written a novel (*The Betrayal*) before entering government service. Imagine therefore my surprise when I met a Chekhovian-looking character—a sallow, paunchy man who seemed much older than his forty-three years. His eyes were heavy, grey, and sad, even when they smiled (as they did when he greeted me), and his rumpled suit seemed to have been made for someone else. I must say that I was put off by his appearance, by the weary sense of defeat he exuded, and I even thought of turning down his offer. But the moment we talked I knew that I would not turn it down, that I wanted to get to know him better.

He informed me that he was working on a history of the modern age, beginning roughly with the Cold War. He compared the United States to Athens in the fifth century B.C., following its defeat of Persia. "What we need," he said, "is a latter-day

Thucydides who could chronicle the events from the inside, from the perspective of a participant-observer."

I asked him if he thought the United States was headed for a tragic fall, too. He smiled, or rather winked, and said he had not yet made up his mind. "In any case, the fall, should it come, would probably be farcical. We don't live in tragic times. We therefore don't need anyone as good as Thucydides to be our reflected image."

I then wondered how such a busy man found the time and energy to write a project of this sort. He faithfully worked two hours every evening, he said, and most of Saturday. "My commitment to this history is very deep, and I lay up a tiny amount every night. It has grown over the years into something quite huge and unmanageable. It's my own leviathan."

As Julian Prescott's sometime assistant, my task was to supply such information—exact dates, names, situations, etc.—as he might need to refresh his memory from time to time. Our professional relationship continued for two years. By 1958 I I had a family of my own, and I had been appointed assistant professor of history at Johns Hopkins. Though I no longer worked for him, we corresponded regularly, and occasionally we met. I should add that I never saw his manuscript while he was writing it.

In December 1962 Prescott retired from the State Department to devote full time to his history. By then I was seeing little of him. Between his retirement and his death on September 12, 1968 I met him only once, in October 1964 when he came up to New York for a brief visit with friends. He told me his work was progressing well, but he did not know how to end it, and would like someday to discuss his "quandary" with me.

We never did discuss it. Two months later he had a nervous breakdown, and upon his release from the hospital he became a recluse and hardly communicated with the outside world. In 1969, a year after his death, his brother asked me if I would accept a manuscript that Julian, in his will, had requested me to have and to use as I saw fit. That was how *A History of the Modern Age* came into my possession.

I take full responsibility for its publication. I think it deserves to be read. In a hastily written note appended to the manuscript

Prescott declared: "I write this not merely as a witness to the past but as a citizen of the future. Its public, I hope, will be young people and generations unborn. If it does not reach them I have pursued an *ignis fatuus;* I have failed."

Whether he had failed remains to be seen. The future will be his judge.

The reader, however, should be forewarned. This is no conventional history. Farthest from it. The events described are real, but the conversations, settings, and explanations are invented, sometimes out of whole cloth, and the personages (many of *them* fictitious) move in and out of the action like characters in a complicated play. I have read every sentence of the manuscript and I have found not one quote that can be authenticated. Often, I confess, I was unable to separate "fact" from "invention," so deftly did Prescott weave them together to give the illusion of veracity.

For a historian like myself this was a heady brew indeed! Reading Prescott's *History* I sometimes felt as if I were on a whirligig, the universe a white blur of paranoid fantasy. Was Prescott mad, I wondered? Was he taking revenge on innocent readers like myself for the grotesqueries that *he* had experienced in international politics, for the deceptions and lies *he* had swallowed?

Then again, reflecting further, I wondered if Prescott might not have been right. His *History* is, to be sure, his private version of historial facts. Nonetheless, he does what historians should do—and what Herodotus, Thucydides, Josephus, Polybius, Seutonius, ibn-Khaldun, and a host of other great historians have done who also have relied on hearsay, gossip, myth, and, most important, their own unfettered imaginations to supply the deficiencies of their material; Prescott successfully gives us the substance, the underlying meaning, of historical events as they transpired before his eyes.

And so he raises anew the questions: What is history? What is an objective rendering of the past? Is the past as rational, as well-ordered, as historians since the seventeenth century, when modern history-writing began, have traditionally made it out to be? Perhaps reality itself is a white blur of paranoid fantasy. Perhaps Prescott's *History* more closely approximates the truth—the insanities of modern politics and affairs of state —than those that pass themselves off as "true." Perhaps his *History* will serve as a model for the history-writing of the future. With this possibility in mind I present it in the pages below just as he wrote it.

Contents

Biographical Note on Julian K. Prescott
  by Professor Neal F. Morrison   v

Foreword   xi

BOOK I: THE COLD WAR

1. The Big Three   3

2. The Rift   12

3. Hostile Alliances   23

4. China and Korea   34

5. The Great Crusade   54

BOOK II: THE THAW

1. Transitions   71

2. Transitions (*cont'd*)   83

3. Rollback   97

4. Rollback (*cont'd*)   112

5. Indochina   125

6. Peaceful Coexistence   139

7. Ancient Legacies   155

8. Hegemony   163

9. Hegemony (*cont'd*)   184

10. Khrushchev   205

11. Khrushchev (*cont'd*)   213

12. Eisenhower   228

BOOK III: JOHN F. KENNEDY AND THE AMERICAN EPOCH

1. Election   247

2. Grandeur   259

3. Cold War Redivivus   275

4. Paris and Vienna   291

5. Berlin   306

6. Indochina   319

7. The Edge of Armageddon   338

8. Thaw Redivivus   368

9. Insurgency in America   372

BOOK IV: HUBRIS [?]

1. Transitions   389

2. Indochina   392

Index   409

FOREWORD

I, Julian K. Prescott, was privileged to attend important international conferences since 1938, the year I joined the United States Department of State as a specialist in international politics. I sought the position (which I obtained through the good offices of a college classmate, Mr. Harold Berrington, then an adviser to President Franklin D. Roosevelt) because I sensed that the world was about to undergo deep convulsions—the birth pangs of a new era in international politics. I decided that I would write about the era from the inside—that is, from the point of view of one who would bear personal witness to great events.

I was not, of course, present at the making of all those events, but I knew, or came to know, many others who were, from heads of state to "faceless" functionaries, such as interpreters, bodyguards, valets, cooks, waiters, and chauffeurs. Over the years, they have sent me several file cabinets full of highly confidential notes, memoranda, and messages, much of it in code. I also have summaries of interviews and conversations with them comprising nearly four dozen volumes of closely packed notes. There is a saying among the diplomats: "Fear not that the walls have ears. Fear that they have tongues." Some day, long after my death, the names and testimonies of my informants will be made public. Until then, the reader must accept my word as to their reliability.

Though this history depends largely on information supplied by others, it will, I trust, become itself a "primary source" for future students of the subject. To me has fallen the sad privilege of [. . .]*

---

* Prescott's introductory remarks break off here. Subsequently, whenever there is a break or discontinuity in the narrative it will be indicated by brackets enclosing an ellipsis followed by a new paragraph.—N.F.M.

"So that half of our life being passed in sleep, we have on our own admission no idea of truth, whatever we may imagine. As all our institutions are then illusions, who knows whether the other half of your life, in which we think we are awake, is not another sleep a little different from the former, from which we awake when we suppose ourselves asleep?"

Pascal, *Pensées*

"(*He murmurs.*) . . . swear that I will always hail, ever conceal, never reveal, any part or parts, art or arts . . . (*He murmurs.*) in the rough sands of the sea . . . a cabletow's length from the shore . . . where the tide ebbs . . . and flows . . ."

Joyce, *Ulysses*

"The influences that have formed the writers ['original historians' such as Herodotus and Thucydides] are identical with those which have molded the events that constitute the matter of his story. The author's spirit, and that of the action he narrates, is one and the same. He describes scenes in which he himself has been an actor, or at any rate an interested spectator. It is short periods of time, individual shapes of persons and occurrences, single, unreflected traits, of which he makes his picture. And his aim is nothing more than the presentation to posterity of an image of events as clear as that which he himself possessed in virtue of personal observation, or lifelike descriptions."

Hegel, *Philosophy of History*

"It is not impossible that it should fall to the lot of this work, in its poverty and in the darkness of this time, to bring light into one brain or another—but, of course, it is not likely."

Wittgenstein, *Philosophical Investigations*

* Appended to the first page of Prescott's manuscript are a number of epigraphs. Since there is no way of knowing how many of them he intended to use, it was thought best to publish all of them.—N.F.M.

"Fortune has no divinity, could we but see it: it's we,
We ourselves, who make her a goddess, and set her in the
heavens."

Juvenal, Satires

"Eternity is in love with the productions of time."

Black, Proverbs of Hell

"To be both a speaker of words and a doer of deeds."

Homer, The Iliad

". . . So we'll live,
And pray, and sing, and tell old tales, and laugh
At gilded butterflies, and hear poor rogues
Talk of Court news. And we'll talk with them too,
Who loses and who wins, who's in, who's out,
And take upon's the mystery of things
As if we were God's spies. And we'll wear out,
In a wall'd prison, packs and sects of great ones
That ebb and flow by the moon."

Shakespeare, King Lear

De omnibus dubitandum!

BOOK I

The Cold War

I

THE BIG THREE

OPINIONS will differ on when the modern age began. Some trace it back to the Renaissance and Reformation, others to the industrial and political revolutions of the late eighteenth and early nineteenth centuries, still others to the First World War. Each of these opinions would be correct within its own limits; it depends on the historical perspective, or standard of measurement, one wishes to employ. I maintain that the Second World War ushered in the modern age, for it decisively, permanently, recast the structure of international politics.

Western Europe and Japan ceased after the war to be arbiters of world affairs. In their place two continental giants have contended for mastery: the Soviet Union, which occupies the Eurasian land mass from Vladivostok to the Elbe River; and the United States, which embraces the central portion of North America and dominates the rest of the hemisphere like a colossus. The size, population, and wealth of each staggers the imagination. Each is a universe in itself. Their relations, or conflicts, have defined the history of the modern age. The United States and the Soviet Union have [. . .]

They first became aware of the magnitude of their differences during a conference of their wartime leaders in Iran, at the end of November 1943.

Until then, they and Great Britain, the other member of the "Big Three" alliance, had presented a united front against their common enemy. Only Nazi Germany, a tyranny unexampled in history, could have induced them to set aside the deep distrust they felt for each other, the representatives of liberal democracy on the one hand and authoritarian Communism on the other. After 1941 Germany had controlled an empire compassing almost all of Europe, from the English Channel to the Dnieper, from the Aegean to the Baltic, along with a strip of North Africa extending fifteen hundred miles from Tunis to El Alamein. But by 1943 the tide had turned. German armies had been pushed out of North Africa. American and British troops had landed in southern Italy. Soviet troops had begun to go on the offensive. At the extremities of the empire Allied armies stood poised for the great assault into its interior.

The end of the war could be discerned in the distance when the leaders of the Big Three met for the first time* at Teheran in the Palace of the Mighty Shahs.

Fifty-three statesmen, diplomats, and high military officers were seated around the huge turquoise-inlaid table (dating back to the Seljuk invasions) set in the middle of the Grand Ballroom. At its head sat President Franklin D. Roosevelt of the United States, who was deeply tanned from a recent Caribbean fishing trip and looked especially handsome. He had been smiling and joking ebulliently since his arrival at the Palace. Suddenly he became grimly serious as he cleared his throat to deliver the opening remarks.

"The first order of business, gentlemen, should be Allied war aims. I propose the following statement as the basis of discussion: 'We are engaged in a worldwide struggle against assassins of international law, against the deadliest enemies of humanity in history. Out of that struggle we will create a new world free of aggression, or the threat of aggression, a world in which all peoples shall be free to work out their own destinies, choose their own governments, and live in fraternal peace with each other. We, the people of the United Nations, hereby consecrate ourselves to fulfilling the immemorial hopes of mankind. This, indeed, shall be the war to end all wars.'

"I think, gentlemen, that this statement can serve as the preamble to the doctrine of our war aims. You can suggest any changes. I have no author's pride. Are there any objections?"

Josef Stalin, the Premier and military dictator of the Soviet

* The leaders of the United States and Great Britain had already met several times.—N.F.M.

Union, raised his finger to speak. "No, Mr. President," he said slowly, "we of the Union of Soviet Socialist Republics have no objection to these words. But, with all due respect to you, they are no more than empty generalities. What we would like to know is whether this conference will declare its opposition to all forms of colonialism, all empires, all imperialisms. If this conference fails to do so, we will have wasted our time, and we had better forget about defining our war aims and simply discuss our strategy for destroying the Hitlerite aggressors."

While Stalin spoke, Winston Churchill, the British Prime Minister, grew redder and redder in the face, until it seemed he would burst. He shot up from his chair the second Stalin completed his remarks.

"I object to this outrage. If it is the intention of this conference to discuss the liquidation of His Majesty's empire, then His Majesty's First Minister should have stayed home. As the distinguished Premier must realize, it is His Majesty's empire that has borne the heat and burden of struggle against the common foe. For one whole year we of the Commonwealth and the Empire held the fiend at bay. Had we submitted—and who in those perilous days believed we would not submit?—had we done so, I say, none of us would now be sitting here, and all our peoples would groan under the monster's knout.

"Let us be candid. Remember, a copy of the Kornilov Memorandum fell into our hands. We know its contents. We know that the Soviet Union intends to dominate every one of its neighboring countries, to secure them as Communist states, by force if necessary. Gentlemen, the Soviet Union will become an empire far greater and more expansionist than anything dreamt by the czars. It ill behooves the architect of that empire-in-process to throw stones at His Majesty, who rules his multitudinous peoples—a veritable league of nations in miniature—with tolerance, justice, and compassion. I beseech you, let us get on with the work at hand."

Throughout Churchill's speech, Stalin sat expressionless, looking straight ahead, calmly smoking a cigarette. He waited a full minute after Churchill had sat down before speaking.

"Gentlemen, we of the USSR do not want to engage in

fruitless polemics. This is not the House of Commons. I am afraid that the rhetoric we have just heard from Mr. Churchill was wasted. All right, we shall put our cards on the table. When Soviet armies drive out the aggressors and advance into neighboring countries, they will install regimes friendly to the Soviet Union, representing the will of the masses. No longer will our land be surrounded by capitalist enemies bent on our destruction.

"Does the Prime Minister say that this too is an empire? Let him say what he wishes. These countries lie on our borders. Time and again—in the seventeenth, eighteenth, and nineteenth centuries and twice in the twentieth century—they have conspired with Western powers to do us injury. We will see to it that this never happens again. We will see to it that the masses rule, not foreign imperialists. Should a fascist clique rise up in Poland, Hungary, Bulgaria, etc., again, it will be liquidated. We will do everything to support our Socialist comrades. This is our answer. I say no more."

A long silence fell over the conference. President Roosevelt, who had been shaking his head throughout the colloquy, finally spoke:

"Gentlemen, I'm dismayed. This meeting is beginning to sound like the Congress of Vienna, or a Tammany conclave. Let me say in behalf of the United States that we want no territories, no colonies, no national reward of any kind from this war. And we steadfastly oppose any existing, or any future colonial-imperial arrangement, anywhere. Will we rid the world of one injustice only to fasten another on it? Will victory in this war make no difference in the lives of the common people?

"Gentlemen, we of the United States assume that this earth will be a freer, happier, juster place when Hitler, Mussolini, and Tojo are sent to everlasting perdition. We want India and Indochina to be just as independent and self-respecting as England and France, and we want Poland to be just as independent and self-respecting as Russia. Yet we recognize that independence confers on no country the right to be hostile to its neighbor. That, my friends, is what this war is all about. Neighboring countries must act like neighbors. This is the policy the United

States has followed, I think with some success, in the Western Hemisphere.

"Gentlemen, we must give humanity something to hope and fight for. Let us here set a standard of right and justice and neighborliness from which the world can, in its moment of deepest agony, take courage."

The Teheran Conference settled down after the President's remarks. Stalin and Churchill refrained from taking up controversial issues. Without acrimony the Allies agreed on their war aims, making only slight changes in the text of the preamble that Roosevelt had read. They agreed that Germany's armed forces had to be destroyed, that in the peace to come all nations, "large and small" would participate as equals, and that all peoples "will live according to the dictates of their desires and consciences." "We arrived here with the highest hopes," the Teheran communiqué concluded. "We depart friends in fact, in purpose, in spirit."

A year after the conference Churchill and his Foreign Minister, Anthony Eden, paid an unexpected visit to Moscow, where they enjoyed a cordial stay at the Kremlin Palace. For three days Churchill and Stalin feasted and drank, toasting each other well into the morning.

One evening, as they and their retinues were taking a steam bath (in a converted dungeon of the early Czars), Stalin, his small, grey body glistening with sweat, turned to Churchill: "Mr. Prime Minister, we have been beating around the bush for three days. We, the Soviet Union and Great Britain, are great powers. We have interests in common. We did not wish to become great powers; fate wished it upon us, and we must act accordingly. The idealism of the Atlantic Charter which you and the President signed is unimpeachable. We Socialists have always defended the rights of nations and peoples. But, alas, not all nations are equal in size and strength. Nor have they all suffered equally. It has fallen to us, to Russia and England in particular, to suffer much for our greatness.

"Mr. Prime Minister, I come to the point. Let the distant future take care of itself. Meanwhile, we must respect each other's sphere, like planets spinning in their orbits. There is a

saying in Georgian: 'He lives best who lets others live well.'
So it should be between the British and Soviet spheres."

When he heard these words from the interpreter, Churchill's
face lit up in a moist glow. Naked, he looked like a pink
cherub. He had come to Moscow to hear precisely these words.
"Premier Stalin," he said in a rumbling, resonant voice, "I
propose a toast to your triumphant wisdom. The Georgian people have given the world an archangel of destiny. You shall
find the United Kingdom ready."

They clinked their champagne glasses, drank up, and called
for more. The next day Churchill flew home.

According to the secret agreement drafted in Moscow (it was
so secret that even the United States did not know its terms until
much later), Britain consented to Soviet hegemony over the
Balkans (Greece excepted) and Eastern Europe. The Soviet
Union consented to leave His Majesty's empire undisturbed: it
would not encourage insurgency in the colonies, nor would it
seek to gain a foothold in Southeast Asia, the Middle East, and
Africa.

"There will be a Soviet empire now," Churchill told Eden
the day after the steam room conference, "but it will not be at
our expense. There is room for the Bolsheviks, Anthony, provided they know their limits."

Differences between the Allies emerged again in their last
conference of the war, held in Potsdam in July 1945. Germany
and Italy had been defeated and were occupied by Allied armies.
Hitler and Mussolini, with their mistresses, had died like hunted
animals, one by his own hand in an underground shelter, the
other at the hands of his countrymen. Only Japan held out,
waiting for its own Götterdämmerung.

Meanwhile, the Allied "Big Three" had undergone a radical
change of leadership. Roosevelt had suddenly died of a stroke in
April 1945. In his place was the ex-Vice President, Harry S.
Truman. The contrast between the undistinguished-looking little
man who had risen to prominence from humble beginnings in
Missouri politics and his illustrious predecessor could not have
been more pronounced. Hardly less pronounced was the contrast
between the new British Prime Minister, Clement Attlee, and
his illustrious predecessor. Attlee, bland and self-effacing, could

have passed for a country school teacher. Actually, he was a tough Socialist politician, the leader of a Party that had just received an overwhelming mandate to democratize Britain. Josef Stalin was the only one of the wartime giants to survive the ravages of death and circumstance.

The Potsdam Conference went smoothly at first. The division of Germany and Berlin into zones of occupation, the procedures for trying Nazi war criminals, these and other matters were resolved easily enough. But on the third day, the Soviet Foreign Minister, Vyacheslav Molotov—known to Western diplomats by such names as "Stony-Face," "Mr. Implacable," "Old Hard-and-Fast," and "Old Iron-Pants"—asked to be heard.

"Gentlemen," he said in his rasping, staccato voice, "I must bring up a question that is of profound urgency to the Soviet Union and to the world. We know that the United States will soon unleash atomic bombs on Japan. We do not raise any objections against the decision to do so. We hope it will bring the fascist aggressor to his knees. The Soviet Union is concerned about what the United States intends to do with the atomic bomb after Japan is defeated.

"We address that concern directly to President Truman. Last week the Soviet Foreign Ministry sent a message to the Department of State and the Foreign Office asking that the United States and Great Britain share their secret formula for the manufacture of the atomic bomb with their Soviet ally, preparatory to the establishment of a system of controls. The reply to us was vague. It implied that the United States and Great Britain will presently develop a plan for the comprehensive control of atomic weapons and atomic energy in general. I should like to know here and now what the two governments mean by that."

Molotov's speech caught the conference by surprise and a recess was called to enable the two countries to draw up a reply. Later in the day the Big Three and their foreign ministers met in secret session. Truman slowly read from a paper:

"I will be brief. The United States, I am told by my advisers, is working on a treaty to ban all atomic weapons and to disseminate data on the production of atomic energy. However, this treaty will contain iron-clad safeguards. Only after the most careful inspection procedures have been agreed upon will we

yield up our secrets and destroy our bombs. Let me state further"
—here he looked directly at Stalin and Molotov—"that I have
not made up my mind yet about dropping any atomic bombs on
Japan. That depends on what Japan does."

Stalin, looking as imperturbable as ever, replied. His voice
was inaudible to everyone except the translator.

"Mr. President, the Soviet Union awaits your plan very anx-
iously. But if your statement is any indication of your intentions,
the future bodes ill for our friendship. We are allies. We bled
and died together. Now you tell us that you will withhold valuable
information from us until we sign a treaty with you that binds our
hands but leaves yours free. It will regulate our production of
atomic energy, but leave you with stockpiles of weapons. The
United States and Great Britain can keep faith with the Soviet
Union by a full, open sharing of knowledge, accompanied by the
destruction of all stockpiles of bombs. Then and only then will
we allow inspection teams and the like to enter our country and
spy about."

"I can hardly believe my ears," Truman shot back at once.
"Premier Stalin, do you think we'll sign a treaty to tie your
hands? In other words, you think the United States is an enemy,
or a potential one. You think we want to tie your hands and then
slit your throat. Is that it? [Here Stalin smiled slightly under his
grey mustache.] I want to emphasize this point. Look, we're
willing to give our secrets away, destroy our bombs, allow ourselves to be inspected by impartial observers. And they'll have to
be impartial observers. Listen here, distrust cuts both ways. What
assurance do we have if we give our secrets to you first, that you
won't refuse later to sign an inspection treaty? Come on, what's
your answer?"

Stalin shrugged his shoulders and flicked the ash from his
cigarette. "I will be brief too. The answer, Mr. President, is
self-evident. If you give us atomic secrets and we then refuse to
sign an inspection treaty, both of us—all three of us—will possess the same secret, and, in time, the same weapons. Will the
Soviet Union be stronger than the United States? At most we
will be your equal. Make us your equal and you shall have your
treaty."

Attlee had been looking down his glasses, glaring discreetly at the protagonists. "I trust you don't mind if I speak plainly?" he said gently. "I should like to state that I agree implicitly with the President. Consider our position, Premier Stalin. Suppose the United Kingdom and the United States were to give you the information on atomic energy before securing guarantees concerning its use. How much of an advantage the Soviet Union would have! You already possess, or occupy, a significant portion of southern and Eastern Europe, and your armies are poised on the threshold of the West. In the event of a conflict—highly improbable, to be sure—what can we of the West fall back on? You will be our equal in atomic warfare and our superior in conventional warfare. This is the compelling reason why the United Kingdom and the United States insist on fool-proof supervision of atomic production before anything else."

With these words, the secret session of the Potsdam Conference broke up for a sumptuous dinner at Soviet Army Headquarters on Mommsen Platz, and no more was said about the atomic question.

In August 1945, Truman ordered atomic bombs dropped on Hiroshima and Nagasaki. Both cities were obliterated. Two weeks later Japan surrendered and was placed under American military rule. [. . .]

2

THE RIFT

ON a severely cold morning in Moscow in November 1945, Stalin summoned his chief ministers and advisers to meet him at once in his bedchamber. He often chose the middle of the night for important discussions of state policy, and they had anticipated such a meeting. For weeks he had been brooding, staring into space for long periods, giving cryptic replies to questions. Bleary-eyed and nervous, they assembled in their leader's bedroom.

"As you know," he told them, articulating each word in his distinct Georgian accent, "we're becoming disillusioned with our Western friends. We suspect them of treachery. The Americans and British speak with forked tongues. On the one hand, they profess the keenest friendship with us, insist that they wish to maintain their wartime alliance with us, and offer us spectacular credit and trade advantages. On the other, they're plotting against us. Yes, plotting. They haven't given up their desire to strangle us, to liquidate the Communist movement everywhere by liquidating us. They're again conspiring to ring us with a band of steel. They think their atomic bombs will intimidate us. They think they can undermine our troops with capitalistic propaganda, turn them against the Party and the state. Well, we'll give our Western comrades cause to think twice.

"I've reached a decision. First, our relations with our Western allies will be less naïve. We'll look at them with narrow eyes. Intercourse between our side and theirs will be held to a minimum. Our troops and theirs will no longer fraternize, nor will our troops fraternize with the civilian populations. We'll have Communist regimes in all our occupied countries. We'll develop our own atomic bombs, by any means necessary and at any cost. And not only bombs, but rockets as well. I want the German rocket people brought to us at once. We must build rockets that will travel over continents and oceans. We'll resume the program of industrialization so that we may never be tempted by capitalist offers of money and trade.

"Our goal, comrades: complete self-sufficiency, complete independence. The era of relaxed discipline is to end this minute. There will be no disloyalty, no backsliding, no questioning of decisions, no weakness. The Western idols are to be smashed. The camps are to be filled with the enemies of the state and the Party."

Stalin spoke deliberately, without once raising his voice, emphasizing his points with puffs of his cigarette. His audience had known that a somewhat harder policy toward the West was in the offing. They had no idea it would go so far or be so sweeping.

After a long, tense pause, Stalin looked at them and said, "All right, you can go to your ministries now. Later in the day I will send you special directives." He nodded to them and they left.

The world was soon introduced to a stridency of language in international relations reminiscent of the days of Hitler and Mussolini. The Soviet Union accused the West in general, the United States especially, of being "imperialist warmongers," of seeking to "unleash fascist aggressors" upon "the Socialist camp," of serving "the ruling clique" of businessmen and financiers. Soviet delegates walked out of the various international agencies dealing with labor, health, welfare, agriculture, etc. It became commonplace for the Soviet Union to veto resolutions passed in the UN Security Council. Increasingly, it refused to take part in the debates, maintaining that the United Nations and its subsidiary bodies were so many "tools" of the West.

Setting aside the hyperbole, the Soviet point was well taken. The United Nations was certainly pro-Western. Of the fifty-odd nations in the General Assembly only ten were Communist; a handful were neutral. And of the five "Great Powers" that sat in the eleven-member Security Council, four were in the Western "camp."

The American attitude toward the Soviet Union had begun to harden or "freeze" even before the public tirades and insults.

Early in 1946 the State Department sent a note to the Soviet Foreign Ministry "requesting"—really insisting—that Soviet troops leave Iran at once, in conformity with the Allied agreement at Teheran three years before. According to that agreement the United States, Great Britain, and the Soviet Union were to pull their troops out of Iran by March of 1946. (They had originally been ordered in because the Shah of that strategic country had declared his support of the Axis powers.)

The reason the Soviet Union had not removed its army was apparent enough: Iran was a neighboring country; moreover, it contained enormous oil deposits. It was a foregone conclusion that Iran would go over to the West if Soviet troops left. When the United States received no reply to its note, it brought the issue before the United Nations. While the Assembly debated the issue, each side castigating the other for breaking faith with the wartime alliance, the foreign chancelleries were busy. The notes that passed back and forth grew warmer and warmer.

At last, President Truman called in his Secretary of State, James F. Byrnes of South Carolina, who had for some time advocated a "get tough" policy toward the Soviet Union. It was Byrnes who had said several months before: "Let them have their big army. We'll make big bombs. Don't rush for agreements. If there's a snake in the grass don't try to beat him with a stick: get a gun."

"I want those bastards out of there," Truman said. "No more pussyfooting with them. Tell the Russian ambassador we mean business. If their soldiers aren't out of there within a month, we're going to go in and flush them out. I mean that. You can tell him that I'm going to alert the European command to get its men ready. If the Russians want a fight they'll have it."

In more genteel language, the President's threat was communicated to the Soviet ambassador. For three weeks the State Department and the President waited tensely for the response. Then they read a dispatch in the press quoting an announcement over Moscow Radio that Soviet forces would shortly leave Iran in accordance with the terms of a previous agreement with the United States and Great Britain. By mid-May they had all gone. Here then was the first fruit of the "get tough" policy.

At the end of the year Byrnes received an analysis of the

"Iran affair" from his chief adviser, Undersecretary of State Dean Acheson. "The Russians will negotiate," Acheson wrote, "only when they feel or taste—literally taste in their mouths—the strength of their adversaries. This being so, why should we, who are stronger, negotiate away even a tiny portion of our vital national interests? We have given away too much already. First let us build up our strength. Then let us see about negotiating."

On an unseasonably hot and humid day in March 1947 President Truman called his entire cabinet to his office in Blair House. He was seated at his desk, a sheaf of papers in his hand.

"This is the gist of the speech on Greece and Turkey I plan to deliver to the Congress, in person, next week," he said. "I want all of you to listen carefully, and if you have any suggestions to make don't hesitate to make them. I'll put in whatever changes are necessary. Just point them out. Remember, the people have got to understand the argument. I've got to persuade them to take a big step. I've got to educate them to what's happening. It won't be easy.

"My fellow Americans," he said, assuming his rhetorical mode of address (a sharp nasal voice, choppy pronunciation, emphatic hand gestures), "I speak to both houses of the Congress because once again the interests of the United States are under threat. Not only the interests of our country, but the freedom of humanity. I repeat, the freedom of humanity.

"A dark specter haunts the earth, my friends—the specter of Communism as promulgated by the Soviet Union. In many parts of the earth the forces of Soviet Communism have lain siege to the habitations of free men. To the United States has been given the sacred responsibility of safeguarding the free world. To fail in that responsibility is to fail ourselves, to serve notice that we do not value our own freedom. Bitter experience has taught us what our fate must be if we fail in our responsibilities.

"The United States does not welcome enmity from any quarter, least of all from the Soviet Union. We were allies in the last war. We recognize the bravery of the Russian people, who lost so much, who suffered so greatly.

"But neither can we tolerate a repetition of the events that brought on that war. Appeasement is the surest road to war. We shall not appease those who perpetrate or encourage aggression.

This means internal aggression, or armed subversion, as well as external. The Soviet government has encouraged both kinds. This must stop. We have repeatedly warned Moscow to stop. Our warnings have been met with condemnations and insults.

"Specifically, I propose to this Congress that the United States initiate a vast military and economic aid program to two countries that need it desperately, Greece and Turkey. In Greece, civil war is now raging between the legitimate government and Communist guerrillas, abetted by surrounding Communist states. Great Britain can no longer help the Greek government. Therefore, we must help it. And Turkey is at this moment utterly defenseless from attack by its hostile neighbor, the Soviet Union. The Turkish army needs to be strengthened and brought up to date. We must waste no time, for the hour of reckoning for these two nations fast approaches. I expect the American people to give its unstinting support to the program I have recommended."

Truman's speech to Congress, a modified and much expanded version of the one he read in his office, was warmly praised throughout the country. The only major criticism came from Senator ———, a well-known political maverick. "Why," he asked, "does the President presume to call the Greek government legitimate? That government was imposed on the Greek people by the British in 1945. I think the legitimate Greek government is fighting up there in the hills, against a usurping king, against big landowners and businessmen. Are we going to pour in our money, maybe our men, to save those reactionaries? As for Turkey, how the deuce will strenthening its army stop the Russians, if they want to march in? It would be the signal for another war. Does Russia want another war—over Turkey? This is insane. I say vote down the appropriations request."

But Congress quickly approved the "Truman Doctrine," and authorized, as a start, the spending of hundreds of millions of dollars in military and economic aid to Greece and Turkey.

Later in the year the administration mounted a vastly more ambitious foreign aid program, prompted by the deepening crisis in the European economy. Two years after the war much of the Continent still lay in rubble. Millions of people still lived in shacks or bombed-out houses or caves. In Italy, Germany, and France, about 20 per cent of the work force was unemployed.

Yet it was not so much the suffering of the masses that gave statesmen cause for alarm. It was the possibility that if their suffering were unrelieved, they would throw their full weight behind the Communist movement. As it was, the movement commanded enormous power in Italy and France where it dominated the trade unions and secured no less than a fifth of the vote. The liberal Catholic regimes of Western Europe required immediate economic assistance, and on a scale commensurate with the problem. As Premier Alcide de Gasperi of Italy put it, "Après nous, le déluge."

With the deluge in mind, the American Secretary of State, George C. Marshall, set forth the administration's intended program in a private memorandum to the Foreign Policy League of New York. It became the basis, later, of his famous "Marshall Plan" speech at Harvard University.

After detailing the problem that Europe faced—the destruction of factories and homes, the high rate of unemployment, the pervasive hopelessness and fear—the memorandum declared: "We of the United States, fortunate in not having suffered the ravages of war, pledge to provide whatever help is needed to put the nations of Europe back on their feet. We will deliver the tools. They will do the job. We know that they will recover in time, that their prosperity will return, that they will experience a rebirth of hope as they re-build their cities and homes and factories. And I want to emphasize that we will offer our assistance to every nation in Europe, those in the so-called Eastern bloc as well as those in the Western, those that are Communist as well as those that are not. Our program will be open-handed. It will be based on need and the desire to get on with the job, nothing else."

Though a man of the highest probity, Secretary Marshall was artfully disingenuous. He presented the aid program as though it transcended politics and was universal in scope. Actually, it was designed by State Department experts to combat Communism in Western Europe, and he knew that the Eastern bloc would have nothing to do with it. At any rate, the European Recovery Program, or Marshall Plan, passed Congress with surprising ease despite its incredible cost: some seventeen billion dollars to be distributed, over a five-year period, among sixteen countries.

The Marshall Plan sowed confusion in the Eastern bloc. Some of the Soviet Union's "satellite" nations were inclined to join the Plan's Committee for European Economic Cooperation on the promise that large amounts of capital would be forthcoming. But of course they had to have Moscow's approval to do so.

The fact is, Moscow had not completely turned down the Marshall Plan. The question was debated by Soviet officials. Gregory Vargara, the country's chief economist, who had never been known to fawn on authority, told the Minister of Industrial Development that the Communist states might, on balance, gain much more than they would lose by signing up with the Committee. "Let them give us capital and credits," he maintained. "What can they take from us for security? Our sovereignty? They are fools if they expect something in return. If American capitalists want to give money away to their enemies we should not stop them."

Persuaded, the Minister of Industrial Development took up the matter with Stalin himself. Impassive as always, the dictator nodded once or twice as he listened to the minister's argument. The minister, marveling at his own eloquence (he repeated Vargara word for word), believed that he had convinced Stalin.

For a time, it seemed that Stalin might bring the Soviet Union into the Marshall Plan. To everybody's surprise, Foreign Minister Molotov showed up in Paris at the preliminary meeting of the Committee for European Economic Cooperation. Molotov was so cordial at first, the delegates began discussing the resumption of East-West friendship.

Suddenly, on the third morning of the meeting, Molotov launched a withering assault on the whole proceeding. It was, he declared, nothing more than a "scheme" to draw all of Europe into the American sphere. "You," he shouted to the delegates at one point, "you are selling your people for a mess of pottage, for thirty pieces of silver. The United States is the imperialist mammon who will subjugate and rob you as slaves."

He stalked out of the hall, and that evening boarded a plane for Moscow.

Stalin had revealed to no one his motive for the sudden *volte-*

face. At five A.M. of the day he delivered his fiery speech, Molotov had received the following message: "The Marshall Plan is an American plot. Expose and denounce it. Come right home. J. Stalin."

At the same time the Minister of Industrial Development was demoted to a clerk. The economist Vargara disappeared, or was silenced. Anyone who had shown the slightest sympathy for the Plan was spirited away to a labor camp for "rehabilitation."

Stalin ordered Andrei Vyshinsky, the Assistant Foreign Minister and the chief Soviet representative at the United Nations (he had been the state prosecutor in the great purges of the 1930s), to assail the United States and the West even more vituperatively than before. Vyshinsky, as everyone knew, was a master of vituperation. For hours on end he would smite the Soviet's enemies hip and thigh before the Security Council, treating them as though they too were on the witness stand, drugged and beaten and ready to confess their sins.

Stalin issued two further orders. The Western Communist parties were to step up their opposition, carry the battle into the streets and shops of the major cities, and eliminate from their ranks the last vestiges of independence and heterodoxy. And the "satellite" regimes were to purge themselves of their own "reactionary elements" and reduce contact between their countries and the West to the barest minimum. These orders were carried out with ferocious dispatch. No longer could anyone doubt the existence of an "iron curtain."

Czechoslovakia, however, posed a problem to Stalin. He could not take its loyalty for granted. In fact, it was not a satellite at all. It was a flourishing democracy, where various parties freely competed for votes, where the rights of the people were guaranteed by custom and law. Throughout its history as an independent nation—that is, from the end of the First World War to the beginning of the Second—Czechoslovakia had been a democracy on the Western model, and after its liberation by both American and Soviet troops in 1945, it re-established its political system as a matter of course. The Czech people were grateful to the Soviet Union for all that it had done for them in the past, and the Communist Party was one of the largest in the country. But it was definitely not the party of the majority. It had the support of no more than a third of the electorate.

The liberal Czech government of Eduard Beneš did not follow the Soviet Union and the peoples' democracies in opposing the Marshall Plan. Indeed, by the end of 1947 it still seemed interested in joining the Committee for European Economic Cooperation, despite objections from Moscow. Molotov sent a personal note to the Czech Foreign Minister, Jan Masaryk (son of the country's founding father, Thomas Masaryk), demanding that Czechoslovakia keep clear of Western "imperialism." "The people of Czechoslovakia," Molotov warned, "will indignantly repudiate their betrayal. They have not forgotten Munich. Let the Prime Minister and his accomplices take heed."

The Czech government did not know what to make of such a note, and they debated its meaning endlessly. Was it a threat? Would the Soviets bring in troops? Would Stalin risk war? Should the government back down? And if it did, would it ever again be independent?

Meanwhile, Stalin arrived at a decision. At six one frosty morning in late February 1948, he drove to Molotov's apartment, woke up the Foreign Minister and told him: "I want Beneš and his lackey regime liquidated. Czechoslovakia must become a people's republic at once. I leave the task to you and Zorin, not to the army. I don't want a war or an international cause célèbre. Do the deed."

The next day, Molotov, disguised as an animal trainer (he shaved off his mustache and hair), and his Deputy Foreign Minister, Valerian Zorin, flew to Prague to direct the Czechoslovakian Communist Party's overthrow of the "illegitimate" government. The exact arrangements were made on the spot by Molotov, members of the Soviet secret police (the MVD), and Czechoslovakian Communist Party.

The deed was carried out with hardly a hitch. The leaders of the government, the army, the trade unions, the churches, and other major institutions were routed from their homes in the middle of the night and "detained." The next day a new government was formed under Premier Klement Gottwald, boss of the Communist Party. And so for the second time in ten years Czechoslovakia lost its freedom and autonomy without a struggle.

The world was surprised to learn that Jan Masaryk, a liberal democrat, was staying on as Foreign Minister. The truth was, he had to stay on. Valerian Zorin told him on the day of the coup d'état that he dare not resign or flee. "You are needed to assure those people who may be unreconciled to the new regime that they have nothing to fear if they obey the law." "What will happen if I do resign?" Masaryk asked. "Then there will be a purge, I'm afraid," Zorin said with a smile. "A big one. I think you agree, Czechoslovakia wants no violence, no terror. You're a sensible man."

In the weeks that followed Masaryk said nothing during his rare public appearances, not even at state functions, and wore an expression of unrelieved sadness. The officials at the ministry called him the "fallen knight of the mournful countenance."

One evening Masaryk was awakened by a loud knocking on the door to his apartment in the Foreign Ministry Building. Gottwald and Vladimir Klementis, the Deputy Foreign Minister, entered, accompanied by three secret policemen. "Sorry to wake you," said Gottwald, "but we just heard disturbing news. We hope it's false. We heard you were planning to leave for West Germany."

They stared at each other for some time. "Yes," Masaryk said, pursing his lips, "I was going to escape from this prison and tell the world what is going on here, how you are converting Czechoslovakia into a concentration camp, a society of inmates and guards. Jail me, shoot me, do what you like with me now."

Gottwald had drawn close to Masaryk, his paunchy, pock-marked face a deep apoplectic red. "You bourgeois scum. You think you can defy the will of the people? You would betray the proletariat and join the imperialist clique? No, you are going into the trashcan of history, you and your whole class."

Gottwald slapped Masaryk resoundingly on the face. "You're finished. Say good-bye." He called to the others, "Go ahead, you know what to—."

Masaryk had been standing with his eyes closed and fists tightly clenched at his sides. Suddenly, he threw himself at Gottwald. The two men fell to the thickly carpeted floor. The others rushed over, knocked Masaryk unconscious, dragged him to the bathroom, opened the narrow window, and with difficulty pushed him through to his death three floors below.

That day Premier Gottwald announced the "tragic suicide of our great patriot" and declared a period of national mourning during which *Te deums* would be played on the radio and all public buildings would be draped in black.

3

HOSTILE ALLIANCES

BY 1948 the Soviet Union, only shortly before a beleaguered, isolated country, a pariah in the international community, ruled over a host of nations. In fact, it dominated the life of each of them. If, for example, the Soviet Union needed more oil, it promptly "requested" Romania to sell it oil at a price it alone determined. Or if it needed machinery, it bought machinery under similar terms from Czechoslovakia. The people of Eastern Europe were forced to work for the development of the Soviet Union. The leaders of the Soviet bloc repeatedly condemned Western imperialism. Meanwhile a new form of colonialism had grown up under the guise of "Socialist solidarity."

One of the peoples' democracies, Yugoslavia, expressed reservations about the Soviet equivalent of the Marshall Plan, the so-called Committee for Mutual Prosperity. In July 1948, Marshal Tito, the Yugoslav President and Communist Party boss, sent Stalin the following message: "Last week Yugoslavia received its import and export quotas from the Committee for Mutual Prosperity. We have reviewed the matter very carefully and have concluded that the quotas fail to take our special needs into account. Beyond the quotas themselves we object to the whole procedure, for we were not consulted. I propose to meet you at your convenience to discuss this matter further."

Stalin read the message in his office, mulled it over for a few moments, and called in Molotov and Lavrenti Beria, the chief of secret police. "Comrades, a very serious question has come up. Tito is striking a pose. He seems to object to our economic program. I suspect his asswipers, especially the Jew Pijade, are trying to turn him against me. Go to Belgrade and put Tito back on the rails."

Molotov and Beria argued strenuously with Tito. At one point they even threatened him. "You will remember what happened in Czechoslovakia," Molotov said. "The Yugoslav masses will not tolerate treason by their regime."

"You dare say that to me," Tito shouted, standing up, his huge fists clenched. "I have a mind to personally throw both of you out on your asses. I'll tell Comrade Stalin that you were rude and insulting and that I expect an abject apology from both of you."

A week later came Stalin's reply: "It is you, Comrade Tito, who have been rude and insulting. It is you who owe the apology —not to Beria and Molotov, but to your own people, whom you have disappointed. After making the apology, you will accept, 'abjectly,' the quotas that the Socialist states have agreed on."

Tito wrote back: "Your quotas, like your words, Comrade Stalin, mean nothing to us. The people of Yugoslavia fought for their independence against the fascist beasts. They will not surrender it to you. We are holding high the banner of Marxism-Leninism which you have abandoned."

Soon the break was in the open. The Soviet Union cut off all aid programs to Yugoslavia, removed its trade, military, and cultural missions, and recalled its ambassador. The peoples' democracies followed suit. All over Eastern Europe the press and radio referred to Tito and his associates as villains and renegades, enemies of the people.

There were no Soviet troops on Yugoslav soil. This was why, apart from his personal courage and pride, Tito could defy Stalin. Led by Tito's Partisan guerrillas, Yugoslavia had liberated itself from the Germans and Italians. To subdue Yugoslavia, Stalin would have had to send in armies of soldiers. Had Stalin done this at once, when the hammer was on the anvil as it were, he might have succeeded in his purpose. But he hesitated, keeping himself incommunicado in his apartment for a whole week after his break with Tito, while two divisions of crack airborne troops were on alert, waiting for orders to attack Belgrade.

During that critical week, the United States became a protagonist in the drama. George F. Kennan, one of the State Department's foremost theoreticians on Soviet affairs, advised the President to offer Tito unconditional American support. "Let the Russians take us into account, too," Kennan said. "If Tito holds fast with our help, we will have penetrated the iron curtain. And after the penetration has been effected, who knows what may happen? The opportunity is too propitious to let pass."

Truman acted swiftly. He notified Tito that the United States was interested in Yugoslavia's independence, as it was in that of every nation, and asked what assistance the United States might render. By the fall, abundant American economic and military aid was flowing to Yugoslavia. By then, the threat of a Soviet invasion had receded and finally disappeared.

Yugoslavia's defection was a victory for the West in the Cold War. Here was a Communist nation that had stood up to Stalin and gotten away with it. Before long Yugoslavia was developing its own kind of "revisionist" Communism, more decentralized, freer, less bureaucratic than the orthodox Soviet kind. This much was universally acknowledged: should "Titoism" survive, it would sooner or later undermine Soviet hegemony all over Eastern Europe.

The West also enjoyed an important residual benefit from Yugoslavia's defection: it brought the Greek civil war to an end. Since 1945 Yugoslavia had provided arms and sanctuary for the Greek insurgents. That it cease doing so was the sole condition under which it received American aid. Their primary source of help cut off, the Greek insurgents were driven deeper and deeper into the mountains of Thrace and Macedonia; many were captured (and thereupon executed or given long prison terms); others fled to nearby Communist countries.

The threat to Greek conservative, oligarchic rule and to the monarchy was put down, at least for the time being.

President Truman was immensely pleased by the success of his Doctrine. "I guess we taught those sons of bitches a lesson," he told one of his aides on the day the Greek king officially proclaimed the civil war to be over. "Communists understand only force, and that's what we'll give 'em from now on."

Germany was of course the main theatre of conflict between East and West. Germany was where they met and shared responsibilities. Its strategic location, its large population (more than sixty-five million), and its huge industrial potential made it the great prize of the Cold War. As relations between the two camps deteriorated, the two zones of occupied Germany—the Soviet and the combined American, British, and French—inevitably grew increasingly antagonistic toward each other. Two Germanies were emerging from the gutted ruins, one Communist, the other liberal-constitutional.

Berlin, which was also divided into four zones, found itself in a peculiar situation. It lay deep within Soviet occupied territory, and as the Western zones of the city drew closer to the Western zones of Germany, the city became correspondingly dependent on the Soviet Union, which controlled its access routes. But the Soviet Union had little cause to be obliging. Hundreds of East Germans, primarily professional people, were emigrating to West Berlin every day. Furthermore, the United States, Great Britain, and France were using their zones in the city as valuable espionage and propaganda outposts.

The Soviet Union was losing its patience. Stalin was heard to say to his brother-in-law, Lazar Kaganovitch: "My greatest regret, do you know what it is? Giving them part of Berlin in 1945. I was too generous, too trusting. I wanted to make a grand gesture. Now I must pay the price for it, maybe with blood."

For some time the four occupying powers had been debating what kind of currency should be used in Berlin. The Soviets maintained that it should be theirs, since theirs was the currency in use in surrounding East Germany. The Western powers (or Allies as they now called themselves) demanded that a special "Berliner" currency be circulated. In late June of 1948, the Allies summarily broke off talks and established the Berliner currency in their three zones.

The Soviets were indignant. Molotov rushed to Stalin's office with the news. "They have done it. It has come to pass. The pigs are uniting their zones. What shall we do?"

Stalin stood up. "Send in Malinowski and Beria at once."

The four men—Stalin, Molotov, Beria, and Marshal Rudyan Malinowski, the Army Chief of Staff (he had been one of the heroes of the Great Patriotic War)—huddled around a small table. Stalin asked them how they thought the Allies might be stopped, "nipped in the bud," as he put it.

Malinowski, trembling with anger, stated that the Allied act was a clear violation of the Big Four agreement, "a slap in the face." The Soviet army, he declared, should march into West Berlin. "We can take it in an hour, and the West will do nothing about it. It will be a *fait accompli*. They won't like it, but they will have to lump it."

Molotov agreed. "This is a Western base, a thorn in our side. We must pull it out, and if we draw blood, so be it."

Beria (sometimes nicknamed "Moloch" because he lusted for young girls, sometimes "Dr. Caligari" because he was so scholarly looking and soft spoken) demurred.

"Comrades, let's not be hasty. It's a question of means, not ends. Why smash anything? Why provoke a possible conflict— and I assume you admit the possibility of conflict. Instead of marching into West Berlin suppose we cut Berlin off from the West. We can do that just by stopping the access routes. It will have to submit to us peacefully or die of starvation. If the West wants to make something of it, that's up to them. Let them be the provocateurs."

A long silence followed while Stalin stared at the ceiling and puffed slowly on his white Georgian pipe. "We will try Beria's plan," he announced at last. "Berlin is to be blockaded tonight, and the blockade is to continue until the city surrenders."

Six hours later, all overland traffic to the Western zones of Berlin was halted.

On the day of the blockade President Truman met with the National Security Council, which included the leading members of his cabinet, the head of the intelligence apparatus, and the Joint Chiefs of Staff, in the Rutherford B. Hayes Room of the White House to discuss the American response to "the most provocative deed by the Communists since the Cold War began," as *The New York Traveler* phrased it.

Three positions emerged from the discussion. James V. Forrestal, the Secretary of Defense, spoke for one group. Forrestal (whom his critics had once labeled "mentally unbalanced") represented the most extreme "hard line" tendency in the administration.

"Can anyone doubt now that the Russians are bent on taking over the world?" he asked. "The pregnant question is whether they should be stopped now or later, whether we or they are going to choose the time and place. I submit we should choose it —right now. I propose we send an ultimatum to them, telling them that if they don't end their blockade forthwith, we'll give them all we have. If we wait, they'll have the bomb. You know they're on the verge of developing one. Let's strike the anvil now, while we still have the hammer."

The opponents of this position, led by George F. Kennan, argued that dropping the atom bomb was "counterproductive."

"All right," said Kennan, "you destroy Russian cities. What then? The Russians will overrun Western Europe. Are you going to send in troops? Are you going to fight them on the Eurasian continent? And after you defeat them—if you do—will you occupy Russia? It's madness."

"What's your position, then, Mr. Kennan," Admiral Harley B. Kingston asked. "How are you going to stop them?"

Kennan admitted he had no answer yet. "My position is that we wait, consult our allies, bring the issue before the United Nations, and try to end the blockade diplomatically."

The argument between Kennan and Forrestal went on for some time. President Truman said nothing. His lips were pursed and bloodless.

"There may be a third way, gentlemen," the Chairman of the Joint Chiefs, Air Force General Hoyt Vandenberg, suddenly volunteered. "The Russians have cut off the overland routes to Berlin, and we're powerless to stop them unless we do so physically. But what about air routes? We can supply the city by air transport. Berlin's only a half hour from our zone of Germany. Each plane can make twenty trips a day. If the Russians try to stop us, we'll shoot them out of the sky. That'll be our kind of war, fought on our terms."

President Truman interposed: "You have the planes and personnel to do this? Right now?"

"Yes, Mr. President," the general replied, "you give us the word and we'll do it."

All the members of the National Security Council except Forrestal and Admiral Kingston came over to Vandenberg's position.

Truman said that it seemed to be the right solution, since it "flings the ball right back into their goddamed teeth," and he adjourned the meeting.

Later Truman informed the British and French Prime Ministers of his decision, and secured their agreement along with a promise from each of the fifty air transports.

The next day the great "Berlin Airlift" got under way. Within hours, one plane per minute was landing at Templehof airport with food and fuel and clothing. The Soviet Union, though it denounced the operation as a violation of the Big Four agreement and a dangerous provocation, did nothing more than send up planes to make certain that the Allies remained within the assigned airspace. Day after day, week after week, month after month, the airlift continued, and the two and a half million people of West Berlin survived, despite an unusually harsh winter. "We'll fly 'em in until hell freezes over," Truman said, exulting over the success of his policy.

Actually, the airlift and the breakdown in relations between the two sides in Germany served the Western powers very well. It gave them the grounds they sought to go ahead with their "Master Plan" for Germany. Drawn up by Undersecretary of State Acheson and Arthur Thiebold, dean of the Harvard School of International Law, the Master Plan called for the integration of the three Western zones of Germany into a new military alliance that would embrace all the nations (except Spain) of the North Atlantic tier. As General Elias V. Henderson of the War College explained it, when asked to comment on the Plan: "The Germans can fight. They know the Russians. They'll be our best ally. We can trust them."

During the period of the Berlin Airlift the Western governments pursued a twofold strategy to put the Master Plan into effect. First, they established the North Atlantic Treaty Organization (NATO), consisting of the United States, Great Britain, France, Canada, Italy, the Netherlands, Belgium, Luxembourg, Denmark, Norway, and Iceland. Second, they set about unifying their occupation zones and allowing the West Germans to have their own sovereign and independent government. Under the timetable worked out by the State Department and the British Foreign Office, these moves were to be completed by May 1949.

A year or two later West Germany was to come into the North Atlantic Treaty Organization as a full-fledged partner, an equal among equals.

"It would be criminal on our part," Acheson wrote in his "Prologue" to the final draft of the Plan, "to neglect Germany's immeasurable resources and talents during these critical days in the history of Western civilization."

The Master Plan alarmed the Soviet Union. Especially alarming was the West's decision to unify West Germany, grant it autonomy, and eventually arm it. For two days Stalin heard Vyshinsky, Gromyko, Shepilov, Gretchko, Molotov, and the ambassadors to the United States, Great Britain, and France discuss every side, every implication of the German question. They were convinced that the West wanted to prepare Germany for a possible future war, and they recommended—this was the upshot of the discussion—that the Soviet Union try to reach an accord with the West to neutralize all of Germany, both the Eastern and Western zones, and so convert it into a gigantic buffer state.

"Our task," said Andrei Gromyko of the Foreign Ministry, speaking for the rest, "is to keep fifty million Germans from joining the imperialist camp. We can do this by unifying the whole country and then neutralizing it under joint occupation. Should we fail, should the West go ahead with its plan, then we must make our zone of Germany a buffer state to protect ourselves and the peoples' democracies from the revanchists."

"I have one thing to add," said Stalin. "I have ordered the production of the atomic bomb speeded up. It should be ready any day. This, too, will be our answer to the revanchists."

The Soviet ambassadors returned to their respective countries with the following message: "The Soviet Union will, on May 12, 1949, permit the resumption of traffic to and from the Western zones of Berlin. Before it does so, it requests agreement by the United States, Great Britain, and France to a meeting of the foreign ministers to take up the issues of Berlin and Germany."

"O.K.," Truman said to his cabinet when he learned of the Soviet request, "let's see what those sons of bitches have up their sleeves. We'll meet 'em, but we'll keep our planes ready to fly again at a second's notice. People sometimes don't know when they're licked."

The West officially agreed to the Soviet proposal, and the blockade was called off on the day promised.

Later that month, the Big Four foreign ministers met in Paris, at the sumptuously elegant Palais des Roses. On the morning of the first session, Foreign Minister Andrei Vyshinsky (who had been uncharacteristically amiable and "open" at President Herriot's dinner the night before) offered the Soviet Union's proposal. His speech, free of epithets, came right to the point. All of Germany was to be unified under Big Four control. Free elections were to be held shortly thereafter to choose a German government. And whatever the government's "tendency, capitalist or Socialist, it was solely for the Germans to determine," the country was to be neutral and to have no sizable army. Also, each of the presiding Big Four was to have the right to veto.

"If this proposal is accepted by this council," Vyshinsky concluded, "Germany will cease henceforth to be a threat or a source of discord. If we solve the German question, we will have world peace. All other problems will solve themselves. According to St. Vladimir, 'Lend him [. . .]' "*

At the next session the Allies presented their counterproposal. They insisted on an all-German election *before* the country was unified. The German government was to decide its own future "without the constricting threat of veto by each of the occupying powers." The Allies furthermore [. . .]

"The German people should not start out on the road to maturity encumbered by conditions, qualifications and suspicions," said British Foreign Minister Ernest Bevin, a former trade unionist, who gave the Allied position. "They shall choose wisely and well, don't doubt it for a minute, if they are allowed to choose freely." [. . .]

The Western foreign ministers knew exactly how the Soviet Union would react to their counterproposal. They knew that in a free election of German people would very likely vote for a pro-Western government, and that the Soviet Union would hardly surrender its zone of Germany without receiving something of equivalent value. And so, as anticipated, Vyshinsky excoriated

* The entire following page of Prescott's manuscript is difficult to make out.—N.F.M.

the West for "playing with fire," for "seeking to unleash the Nazi beasts against the peoples' democracies," for [. . .]

The Western powers were thus free to go ahead with their Master Plan. By the end of 1949 West Germany—now the German Federal Republic—had acquired its own government, dedicated to European unity, Christianity, and business enterprise, under a constitution modeled on that of the United States. The Soviet zone had simultaneously become the German Democratic Republic, a certified people's democracy, led by Walter Ulbricht, one of Stalin's most faithful protégés. His participation in the Spanish Civil War earned him such titles as "The Executioner," "Lupus," "Beelzebub," "The Minotaur," and others.

The Soviet Union, meanwhile, had exploded its first atomic bomb in central Siberia, an event that sent shock waves reverberating around the [. . .]

When Vyshinsky returned from Paris, Stalin withdrew to his private study at his dacha in Yalta and saw no one for five days. His long absence sent a shudder through the Kremlin a thousand miles away. Everyone there knew that his "crisis" portended a new policy, new trials, new suffering for the Russian people. They remembered his last five-day withdrawal in 1934, preceding the terrible purge that lasted four years and took the lives of millions.

A mood of deep gloom enveloped the Soviet bureaucracy when it learned that Stalin had emerged from seclusion and was meeting with Beria and other officials of the MVD. Beria had not seen Stalin so pale since that memorable day when he fainted away after being told of the German invasion. Stalin was heavy-lidded, and a light film seemed to cover his eyes. He spoke in a very slow, listless monotone.

"We must destroy the plot against the Soviet Union. The imperialist dogs have friends in our midst, comrades. Their mission is to sap our strength, demoralize us, castrate us. I refer especially to the Jews. They are born foreign agents. Let us admit it; disloyalty is in their blood. Hitler had a point. The Jews scorn our fatherland. They give their allegiance to the West, to America, to Palestine. Every Jew in our country and in the peoples' democracies who is not completely loyal to us, who is not a sworn patriot and Marxist-Leninist, is to be purged, imprisoned in the

Arctic, liquidated. I don't care what you do with them. Just get them out of my sight. They offend me."

Within twenty-four hours Soviet, Romanian, Hungarian, Czech, and Bulgarian newspapers began denouncing the "petty bourgeois" and "cosmopolitan scum." Soon the names of the "scum" appeared in the papers, even as the persons named disappeared forever, "like rabbits in the forest," as the Russian saying went. Many of the names were prominent: professionals, Communist party officials, intellectuals—above all, intellectuals. The peoples' democracies held spectacular show trials of the "traitors," that is, men and women who had been devoted Communists throughout their lives. Now, on the witness stand, they confessed that they had always been perfidious and that most recently they had conspired with the imperialists and the Zionists against the working class, the Communist Party, and the principles of Marxism-Leninism. After their confessions they were usually shot and buried in unmarked graves, the symbol of their total obliteration. They had become non-persons. Publicly, they had never lived.

4

CHINA AND KOREA

BY the end of 1949 the attention of the world had turned from Europe to Asia, where an event of seismic dimensions had taken place. The Communist revolutionaries had seized power in China, the most populous nation on earth.

To anyone familiar with China's recent history this came as no surprise. The regime of Generalissimo Chiang Kai-shek, which had ruled since the mid-1920s, had been weak and incompetent even before Japan attacked in 1937. Its weakness and incompetence had grown steadily during and after the war. Corruption was a way of life, particularly at the highest levels of the government. Above all, Chiang was powerless against the landowners who ground the faces of the peasants into the dust, and against the warlords who ran their provinces with haughty contempt for central authority.

The Communist insurgents had entrenched themselves in the mountain fastnesses of Yunan after their heroic "long march" of 1934–35. Led by Mao Tse-tung, a onetime school teacher and an invincible pedagogue in all he said and wrote, even in his poetry, the Communists gradually extended their area of conquest. They treated the peasants with respect, not contempt; they eliminated usurious interest rates and oppressive taxes; they punished crimes swiftly and impartially; and they were always efficient, incorruptible, and well organized. For good reason, then, the Communists inspired trust and gratitude. Foreign observers, irrespective of ideology, were impressed. General George C. Marshall could say in 1946, after concluding a fact-finding trip to China for the President, that the Communists were essentially "agrarian reformers."

Full-scale civil war broke loose the moment the Japanese left in 1945. The Communists were no longer a band of renegades hiding in the mountains, restricted to occasional forays. Thanks to captured Japanese and American arms and to expert military leadership under General Chu Teh, they advanced relentlessly eastward toward the large cities and the river deltas. Their armies swelled with the addition of recruits drawn from the ranks of "liberated" peasants. The Nationalist armies were no match for them. The United States tried mightily to stem the tide. Massive quantities of American arms and foodstuffs reached the Nationalists in 1947 and 1948—only to fall into the hands of Mao's armies.

When it was apparent that nothing could stop them, President Truman summoned his foreign policy advisers for a conference in the Millard Fillmore Room of the White House: Secretary of State Acheson (who had replaced Marshall); two long-time confidants, Bernard Baruch and Averell Harriman; Clark Clifford, the strategist of Truman's extraordinary 1948 electoral victory; Senators Tom Connally of Texas and Arthur Vandenberg of Michigan, collaborators in the bipartisan Cold War policies of the administration; and General Omar Bradley, universally respected as level-headed, wise, and judicious.

"The problem is this," the President explained to them gravely. "Our military and diplomatic men in China tell me that it's all over for Chiang Kai-shek. No amount of our help will save him. Let me say off the record, I'm angry as all get-out with him for the bum job he's done. But we're stuck with him. What should we do now? What do you think, gentlemen?"

After long deliberation, they unanimously decided that further American involvement in Asia would be a "dreadful mistake." "It's a sink," said General Bradley, "from which we'd never extricate ourselves." Harriman even suggested that "we should begin sounding out the Communists. Maybe we can live with them. Maybe it will be easier for us to live with them than it will be for the Russians."

Truman concluded that the United States would do nothing more than continue sending arms and material to Nationalist China. He was resigned to its defeat.

In September 1949, Chiang, his retainers, and the battered

remnants of his army fled the mainland to the island of Taiwan, where he set up a Nationalist government in exile. His parting words to the Chinese people were: "Be of good faith, my children. I shall return to throw out the usurpers. Our ancestors shall be avenged."

Meanwhile, he avenged himself on any Taiwanese who dared question his presence on their island. Thousands of them were slaughtered or imprisoned by their liberator.

The triumphant Communists held a two-week celebration in Peking. Night and day the city gave itself over to parades and feasts and carnivals. Not since the fall of the Manchus had there been anything like it. "The long sleep is over," Mao announced to the guests assembled in the Great Hall of the Emperor's Palace. "The people of China are reborn. They now consecrate their lives to Marxism-Leninism."

That evening, at an official state dinner, Mao proudly spoke of the impending alliance between the People's Republic of China and the Soviet Union. "Our two nations will march arm in arm against the imperialists. Together we will carry the war of liberation into the enemy camp and release their peoples, too, from the thralls of capitalism. History awaits us. We cannot fail."

Molotov, who had flown to Peking for the dinner, clenched his teeth when he heard these words. Was Mao actually implying the equality of the two nations? "We shall see, we shall see," Molotov muttered to himself, as he drank a toast to Mao and the Communist Party.

On the very day Mao declared China a people's republic, the recently appointed Secretary of State, Dean Acheson, delivered a top-secret verbal report to the highest officials of the State and Defense departments on the significance of the Communist takeover of China.

Acheson, an impeccably well-dressed and mannered New England Brahmin, had long been active—and enormously influential—in government and Democratic Party affairs. Winston V. Larouche, a retired foreign service officer, who knew and worked with him for years, described Acheson "as the closest thing we've ever had to a Talleyrand in this country. He's at once charming and abrasive. Neither he nor the fools he always has to deal with suffer each other gladly." One paper referred to him as "the quintessential diplomat, the archetypal man in the striped suit, the first real professional to occupy the post since Hamilton Fish back in the 1870s." His demeanor often put people off, but no one doubted his talents. He had the ability, rare in a public official, of making issues lucid and of placing them in perspective. Just how lucid he was may be judged from his report, excerpted below, on the "loss of China."

"It is a grievous blow to us, though it comes as no surprise. Every aspect of international politics is or will be affected by this monumental cataclysm, and we must be honest and forthright in our discussion of it. Let us assume that the Chinese Communist regime survives and consolidates its power, much as the Soviet Union has done since 1917. Let us assume further that it, too, succeeds in rapidly industrializing the country. If these assumptions are borne out I must say in all candor that the prospects for world peace are not very good.

"Are you familiar with the writings of the leading geopoliticians of our time? I see some of you are nodding. Well, you know what is in store for us, then. You know the famous formulation of Mackinder and Haushofer: 'Whoever controls the Eurasian heartland controls the World Island. Whoever controls the World Island controls the world.' Well, the two states dedicated to the same principle of expansion in the name of international Communism now occupy the World Island.

"Consider these facts, gentlemen: Between them, China and Russia contain a total of nearly fifteen million square miles—a land area equivalent to the whole Western Hemisphere. We don't know exactly what their combined population is. The best recent estimate is that Russia has two hundred million and China five hundred. We think China has many, many more, perhaps as many as a billion. Startling isn't it? And need I mention the inexhaustible natural resources to be found in the World Island? Need I tell you what we can expect when the World Island is industrialized?

"The critical question is what we are to do now. The most pressing task is to stop the Communist powers from expanding any farther. What that means, concretely, is that they must be prevented from gobbling up the remainder of the World Island. Their primary goal is to absorb the western or Atlantic extremity of the Eurasian land mass—the seat of civilization, the center of industry, intelligence, culture. Western Europe is the prize of international Communism: it would be the workshop of the World Island.

"Now at the eastern extremity there is Indochina and the Malay Peninsula, both coveted by China for their raw material and foodstuffs. To counter this threat radiating out from the center of the World Island to its circumference, the Department of State is devising a grand counterstrategy under Mr. George Kennan's direction. This much I can reveal to you now. We will be setting up a defensive ring around the World Island. We will be serving notice to the Communist bloc: 'Thus far and no farther. Know what you are risking. We who represent the culture and heritage of the West have no intention of allowing you to become masters of the world because you are now the masters of the World Island.'"

For some reason Acheson had failed to mention Korea, though Korea was very much on his mind. He was receiving daily reports on the deteriorating situation there. The latest report, which he had read only minutes before giving his talk, predicted war "within a year."

In 1945 Korea, like Germany, had been divided into Soviet and American zones (the armies of both countries having liberated it from Japan). The Soviet zone extended from the Yalu River in Manchuria south to the 38th parallel. The American zone took in the remainder of the peninsula, including the ancient capital of Seoul. As the Cold War progressed, the division became permanent. By 1949 two Koreas had emerged: the People's Republic in the north, headed by an old-line Communist named Kim Il Sung, and the Republic of Korea in the south, headed by the grand old man of the country, conservative, Western-educated Syngman Rhee, then in his early eighties.

The situation was highly dangerous because both governments claimed to represent the country as a whole; both declared that they would not rest until they had unified their people. Apart from the epithets—imperialists and colonialists on the one side, totalitarian and atheist enemies of freedom on the other—the statements of Kim Il Sung and Syngman Rhee sounded exactly alike. Accompanying the statements were aggressive actions by both governments, the 38th parallel being the scene of continuous skirmishes and raids back and forth. It was the increasing violence of these conflicts that worried the State Department so much.

The effects of the 1949 revolution in China were felt at once in Korea. North Korea now had a friendly neighbor. More than a friendly neighbor, a comrade, a kindred regime. Before the end of the year China was shipping vast quantities of arms to the North Korean army. Similarly, the United States was equipping and training the South Koreans.

One day in December 1949, Stalin received a dispatch from Kim Il Sung: "I need your heaviest tanks and guns. I have word that Rhee and his swine are preparing to attack us."

Stalin replied at once: "The arms are on the way. If they attack, rebuff them. Avoid provocations. Consult [Vassily N.] Lebyadkin [the Soviet ambassador]. Let the swine drown in their own swill."

The tanks and guns came across China and by sea, and by the spring of 1950 the North Korean army was clearly superior to the South Korean. In mid-June Kim informed Lebyadkin that his forces would soon launch a drive to clear the 38th parallel of enemy troops. "It is a cleansing operation, nothing more," Kim explained, smiling. "Comrade Mao has already expressed his approval. What does Comrade Stalin think?"

For several days Stalin, Molotov, Gromyko, and Lebyadkin conferred on the Korean problem, which was beginning to alarm them. "I don't care what he does," Stalin said, "so long as he doesn't go too far. We want no war over Korea. I'm afraid Comrade Kim is trying to keep us in molasses.* Is he going to make a war?"

Just as Stalin was instructing Lebyadkin to give qualified approval to the "cleansing operation," he received word that the North Korean army had invaded South Korea along a broad front, and that Kim Il Sung was proclaiming the liberation of the Korean people.

"That Asiatic motherfucker," Stalin cursed under his breath in Georgian, "has made a fool of me."

President Truman was awakened from his sleep on Sunday

---

* A Georgian saying. It would be equivalent to our "pulling the wool over our eyes."—N.F.M.

morning, June 25, 1950, and told of the invasion. After ordering
the armed forces in the Pacific placed on alert, he summoned his
advisers. Late that afternoon Secretary Acheson, Generals
Bradley and Dwight D. Eisenhower (the commander of Allied
forces in Europe during the Second World War and now president
of Columbia University), Secretary of Defense George C. Marshall, Bernard Baruch, and Chief Justice Fred Vinson, an old
political crony of the President's, arrived at the White House.

As soon as they had seated themselves around a huge mahogany
table in the Chester A. Arthur Room, Truman strode in. He
spoke at once.

"I'm goddamned mad at those sons-of-bitches. They learn
nothing. Well, we'll have to teach 'em a lesson again. I have a
mind to issue an ultimatum: either they get out now or we'll
bomb them to smithereens. Maybe Jim Forrestal was right back
in '48. He looks more and more like a prophet, God save his
soul."

There was a long silence. Then, one by one, all of his advisers
counseled a more cautious response. The consensus of opinion
was that a charge of aggression and a demand for sanctions against
North Korea should be brought before the UN Security Council,
and that if the United States must act, it should do so in the name
of international law. "The nations of the earth shall evince their
abhorrence for this dastardly deed," said Chief Justice Vinson.

They further counseled that the Soviet Union should be urged
to use its influence with the North Koreans to restore peace. Only
when these attempts had failed, should the United States "unilaterally" send troops to South Korea. Truman did not comment
during the discussion. He simply said he agreed with them and
would implement their suggestions "posthaste."

That same evening the UN Security Council met in emergency
session. Without much debate it condemned the People's Republic of Korea as an aggressor and authorized member states to
help the Republic of Korea any way they could. The Council was
able to pass this resolution so effortlessly because the Soviet Union
was just then in the midst of one of its walkouts. At the very
moment that the emergency session was going on, Andrei
Gromyko was at the Soviet UN mission, sleeping off a heavy
meal.

In later years, American political scientists often would wonder what the United States would have done had Gromyko attended the session and vetoed the resolution. (The Soviet Union for its part came to realize that its boycotts were self-defeating, and it gave up the practice for good.)

Stalin smiled when he was informed of the American request that he use his influence to stop the fighting. He asked Georgi Malenkov, one of his favorite retainers, "Which is worse, a fool or a scoundrel?"

Malenkov answered: "I would rather deal with a scoundrel. With him at least you know what to expect."

"Well," Stalin said, "our friends are scoundrels, our enemies are fools. The American fools really think that I control everything, that I need only say the word and the sun stands still. Maybe so, but I can't control that scoundrel Kim. I could not stop him from going to war. How can I stop him from winning it? Have Molotov tell Washington that this is not our affair, that the imperialist lackeys of Syngman Rhee started it and must be punished, and so forth. I wash my hands of it."

"But Comrade Stalin," Malenkov asked, "suppose the Americans bring in atomic bombs? What then?"

"Malenkov, pray to God that their folly doesn't turn into insanity."

The next day President Truman ordered American troops into South Korea to carry out the UN resolution. He also declared a "national emergency," thereby placing the United States on a semiwartime footing. Reserves and national guard divisions were hastily pressed into service, and the draft call was greatly enlarged. To head the UN armed forces (actually American, since the U.S. supplied nearly all of the troops and equipment), Truman appointed none other than General Douglas MacArthur, the son of military heroes and a hero himself.

MacArthur was a brilliant and imperious man, as aloof and awesome as a god, who inspired intense devotion from his aides and intense distrust from everyone else. Few episodes in the last war compared to his spectacular escape from the Philippines in a torpedo boat early in 1942 and his triumphant return three years later. As American proconsul in occupied Japan he was responsible for bringing a measure of democracy to that conservative, martial, and submissive people. Now seventy years old, but as vigorous as ever, he took charge of the defense of South Korea.

When he received word of his appointment in Tokyo, he wired the President immediately: "I accept your charge with mingled pride and humility."

MacArthur was confident that once American troops went into combat the invasion would be turned back. "I think I know the Asian mind as well as anyone alive," he said to one of his chief aides, General Lemuel Birchby, on the eve of his departure for South Korea. "They'll take flight when they meet our boys. We'll strike them hard and they'll crumble into dust."

But the North Koreans broke through all the lines of defense that MacArthur threw up against them. They captured Seoul, then swept across the peninsula in a pincers movement that cut off a sizable part of the South Korean army. The defeat was staggering. By August only the southeast tip of Korea remained to the UN forces, and MacArthur prepared to evacuate his men.

When (during a routine cabinet meeting) Truman received word that the UN army had been driven to the beaches of Pusan, he thumped the table with his fist and threatened to "press the button and blow those little people to kingdom come."

That evening the Prime Ministers of Great Britain, France, and Italy pleaded with Truman to refrain at all costs from introducing atomic weapons into the war. His answer to each of them was that he would "wait and see" but that he found it hard to "play the game" against enemies like the Communists. They agreed, but they also reminded him that even the loss of Korea was not worth a war in Europe, which was certain to break out if the United States dropped atomic bombs on Korea.

It was his concern about the danger of a war in Europe, should the Asian conflict get out of hand, that prompted Truman to confer at length with his senior foreign policy advisers and with congressional leaders. The upshot of the highly secret conference (which took place in August in the basement of Blair House) was that the NATO alliance must be built up immediately. A large standing army was to be created in Western Europe and deployed on the East-West frontier. That army, moreover, was to include substantial German contingents.

Secretary Acheson summarized the findings and recommendations of the conference to the President. "Our mistake in Korea —I admit my own culpability, sir—was not to give the enemy the clear and emphatic message that we and the rest of the free world will fight for their territory. We have also learned that merely saying we will fight in the event of aggression is not enough. It does not intimidate the Communists. We must back up our words with men. We pulled our troops out of Korea early in '49. We should not have done that. It was a catastrophic error.

"Well, sir, we recommend that we now put our troops in Europe. If the Russians invade they will have to hit us too. They will know the risks—as probably the North Koreans did not— and so there will be no chance of miscalculation on their part. I should like, finally, to point out one more advantage of putting an American army in Europe: it will strengthen the European resolve to resist. It will be an invaluable psychological fillip. I'm sure—and Generals Bradley and Eisenhower agree with me —that had our men been in Korea, the South Korean army would have fought better than they did. At any rate, we should not permit a repetition of the Korean disaster in Germany.

"The conference has gone along with my proposal that we bolster NATO with five hundred thousand of our men, eight to ten divisions, that number to be doubled by the combined contributions of the other member states. With one and one-half million soldiers in readiness against them, the Russians will have to think long and hard before mounting an assault."

"How the hell am I going to convince the Congress and the people to support this kind of commitment?" Truman complained. "Half a million in Europe, half a million in Japan and Korea. And if the public does approve, it'll want to know how long it's going to have to pay for such a big army."

The congressional leaders who had attended the conference assured Truman that they would do all in their power to persuade Congress to go along with the request. "Half a million men is a little high," said Senator Connally, "but I think we might just do it. Nobody thought we could put through the Marshall Plan, but we put it through."

The results of the secret conference somehow were leaked to

the press, provoking a storm of criticism against the administration. Ex-President Herbert Hoover denounced the plan as a surrender of American principles. "We should convert America into an impregnable fortress," he stated in a widely publicized interview, "otherwise we shall disperse our strength. The Communists would like nothing more than that."

Senator Robert Taft of Ohio, "Mr. Republican" to his colleagues in Congress, spoke out against "entangling alliances." "Let the Europeans help themselves for once. They have taken our paternalism too much for granted. We would not help them by doing their job for them. The President," he went on, "has usurped too much power. Our entangling alliances have invested him with the authority of a despot. He can send our boys into battle, declare a national emergency, appropriate the nation's resources. Perhaps the next step is martial law. Congress must resume its historic prerogatives."

Siding with the administration on the issue were those who opposed a return to isolationism. There was, for example, Governor Thomas E. Dewey of New York, the titular head of the Republican Party, who twice had run unsuccessfully for the presidency. Now he was defending a Democratic administration against criticisms made by men of his own party. "Isolationism," he asserted, "is dead and should be respectfully buried. The only way to protect the United States is by honoring our commitments abroad, by sending American troops wherever they are needed to stop aggression. Fortress America lies across the two oceans, on other continents, in other lands."

John Foster Dulles, a special adviser to the State Department (foreign affairs having been the province of his family for six generations), was another influential Republican who defended the administration. "Atheistic communism would like nothing better than to know that we have retreated into ourselves," Dulles wrote in the prestigious magazine, *International Relations*. "We are sending forth a New Model army to do the battle of the Lord. We will not wait for the enemy to break in upon us as we huddle in our Cave of Adullam."

And General Eisenhower, probably the most popular and most highly respected of all Americans, came down from Columbia University to address both houses of Congress. Speaking as usual with great sincerity, Eisenhower explained how from a military point of view America would benefit from deploying its troops in Europe.

By now the administration had clearly won its case. After Eisenhower's speech the only remaining question was how many soldiers Congress would agree should be shipped to Europe. [. . .]

After much tacking and veering the number specified was left at four divisions (two regular army and two national guard), some two hundred fifty thousand men in all. Even before Congress voted appropriations for the enlarged army, the NATO military organization, with headquarters outside Paris, had been formed and a commander in chief appointed: Dwight Eisenhower.

The Soviet Union, as expected, condemned the NATO build-up as a preparation for a new attack on the East. When Eisenhower officially assumed his post, Communist-sponsored demonstrations broke out in Europe, and "Yankee Go Home" became the refrain of the European far left.

But in fact Stalin and his counselors were not so much worried about the NATO allies, nor even about the presence of an American army, as they were about West Germany. Soviet intelligence had reported some time back that blueprints were being drawn up in Washington and Bonn (the West German capital) to fashion a "democratic," "European-oriented" West German army.

These reports were borne out in September 1950, during a meeting in New York City of the Western Big Three foreign ministers. It was then that Acheson openly proposed the incorporation in NATO of no less than ten West German divisions. "Here is our opportunity," he told his skeptical auditors, who represented nations that twice in the last forty years had fought against the Germans. "Germany can now be encouraged to participate in the defense of Western civilization. Not only Germany itself, but the West as a whole. Here is a grand opportunity to Europeanize Germany once and for all. I propose this completely apart from the need to have the German Federal Republic help protect all of us against the common threat from the East."

It was thus decided, a little more than five years after the Second World War, that West Germany should rearm.

"What should we do?" Stalin asked Molotov, Beria, and Malenkov, the men to whom he felt closest. "You know that a large number of traitors among us are plotting with the Nazis. They think there will be a second round. They are waiting for the revanchists to enter the gates of Moscow. I ask you, what should we do?"

Malenkov suggested that the Soviet Union issue an ultimatum forbidding the West to rearm Germany.

"And if they reject it?" Beria asked sarcastically, with a trace of a smile. "Will you follow it with another ultimatum, then another? No, I oppose ultimatums."

"Correct, Comrade Beria," Molotov added. "Instead we should send our own divisions into the Communist lands contiguous to West Germany. Then we—"

Stalin interrupted: "All right, that is what we will do. We will form our own military alliance. We will send new divisions into Germany, Poland, Czechoslovakia, and Hungary. We will draw our allies yet closer to us economically and politically. We will give no quarter, show no mercy. Let the West make one wrong move and it will 'Know the mountain frosts.'*

"First, I want Berlin ringed with our troops. Berlin, remember, is our hostage. Second, I want the poison squeezed out of our system. Beria, I want you to shoot anyone suspected of treason. No compunction. Shoot them right and left. Watch the Jews carefully. Shoot them if they raise their heads an inch, or make a single demand, for matzos, for synagogues, books, burial grounds, whatever. Comrades, we will gird our loins."

Pale and shaking slightly, Stalin rose, nodded, and left the room.

Beria was efficient, as usual. The purges were stepped up. The labor camps overflowed with "criminal elements." What little autonomy the peoples' democracies had had disappeared as they were swept into the Soviet vortex. All the Communist nations of Eastern Europe, Yugoslavia excepted of course, were compelled to join the Warsaw Pact, the Soviet answer to NATO. Their armies were staffed by Russian officers. Strict orders came

* A Georgian proverb that implies great suffering.

down to each of the satellite governments: the slightest resistance to Soviet control was to call forth swift and total retribution. In fact, hundreds of Polish, Czech, and Hungarian officers were shot as examples because they had disobeyed their Soviet "comrades."

In the meantime the Korean War passed through a series of extraordinary reversals of fortune for both sides. The American, or UN, forces managed to hold on to the Pusan perimeter. Having stabilized the situation there, General MacArthur planned a daring feat. An attack would be launched to break out of the Pusan perimeter at the same time as Marines landed at Inchon, on the western coast of Korea, some twenty miles below Seoul. A massive vise would close on the fleeing enemy.

The plan worked to perfection, or rather beyond perfection. At the end of September 1950, within ten days after the offensive had begun, the UN army had recaptured Seoul and decimated the North Koreans. The way was open to the north.

MacArthur's communiqué to the American people was more eloquent than usual: "We have met the enemy and he is ours. We advance to our objective secure in the knowledge of our rectitude, certain that posterity will crown our cause as the cause of righteousness and justice."

MacArthur was hailed—and even his severest detractors could not deny it—as the greatest general of modern times and one of the greatest who ever lived. "He is Hannibal and Scipio rolled into one," said one enthusiast.

With the UN army marching unimpeded across the 38th parallel and through the People's Republic of Korea, MacArthur and Truman met on Wake Island to discuss future policy. One critically important question was on Truman's mind: Would the Chinese Communists intervene in the war? The State Department had heard disturbing reports from India, Sweden, and other countries that China would intervene if the UN army advanced beyond the North Korean capital of Pyongyang. Several days before, when the army had crossed the 38th parallel, Chinese Foreign Minister Chou En-lai had stated, "We won't stand by twiddling our thumbs while the imperialists approach our gates." Truman decided to consult General MacArthur in person without delay.

MacArthur answered the President's question about China's intensions as the two men sat on the veranda of a small stucco house overlooking the Pacific Ocean and sipped iced tea.

"Mr. President, I have thought hard on this matter, and I am convinced beyond peradventure of doubt that Red China will not intermeddle. First of all, our defensive positions in the mountainous terrain of North Korea will be impenetrable, and they know it. We shall also take up strong defensive positions on the rivers, the Yalu and the Tumen, that divide Korea from China. Second of all, I think it inconceivable that the Chinese would dare take us on. They dare not test *our* mettle. I think I know the Chinese mentality pretty well, sir, and I can guarantee that we will be safe—provided we do not show them we are overcautious, timorous, or diffident. They will utter threats and imprecations, but they will back down in the teeth of our power. We must not forbear, equivocate, or temporize."

This (in less stately language) was the message Truman carried back to Washington, and after discussing the question again with his Council, he gave MacArthur permission to take all of North Korea.

At the end of October the UN army occupied Pyongyang. They met no resistance, for the North Koreans had fled into China. As the advance continued, though at a slower pace— MacArthur having instructed his men to "dig into the hills and raise up impregnable barriers"—word filtered through that Chinese "volunteers" were surreptitiously crossing the Yalu and grouping for an attack. MacArthur reassured the State and Defense departments, which had sent him anxious queries. "At most, the merest token show of force, designed only to announce their presence," he informed them.

And to dispel the "nefarious speculations" about what the Chinese were up to, he held a press conference at which he promised to end the war very shortly. "The time of jubilee approaches," he said. "I am pleased to announce that the war will soon be over. And I further pledge that several of my divisions will be available for duty in Western Europe. Seasoned in battle, they will turn the NATO alliance into a mighty fortress of freedom."

Two days after this press conference hundreds of thousands

of well-equipped Chinese "volunteers" descended on the UN army. MacArthur ordered a retreat to more defensible positions, but the retreat became a rout and the Chinese broke through American lines, cutting off avenues of escape for countless numbers of troops. The Communist armies recaptured Pyongyang as the UN army fell back in headlong flight. At a point slightly above the 38th parallel the UN and Chinese "volunteer" forces fought each other to a stalemate.

The American people were stunned. First their boys had snatched victory from the jaws of defeat; now they had suffered another defeat, as humiliating as the first, this time at the hands of the Chinese. For a while it seemed that they would be driven to the beaches of Pusan again.

"If they surround our boys," General Bryce Higman, the Army Chief of Staff, advised the President, "I would recommend that we use atomic weapons. We have about one hundred fifty thousand men on the line over there and twice as many in the rear. I don't think we'd have much choice, Mr. President. Either we stop them or they'll destroy our boys."

Truman bit his lower lip and said nothing. When he met with Acheson that same day (he had just learned that the Chinese were advancing on the high road to Seoul) he was obviously angry. His face was flushed and he blinked his eyes repeatedly.

"That pompous, overconfident ass," he said, sounding more nasal than usual. "If the situation wasn't so tragic I would've been happy to see that supercilious so-and-so get his comeuppance. Couldn't he prepare for the attack? He was so sure when he spoke to me at Wake. I'll never forget what he said: 'They dare not test *our* mettle. I think I know the Chinese mentality pretty well.' He didn't know his ass from his elbow. Look at the stew we're in now. Dean, I might have to use atomic arms and order the bombing of Manchuria."

"Mr. President," Acheson replied. "I strongly urge you to discuss the matter first with Attlee and Pinay. It would be awkward in the extreme if we found ourselves isolated now, if we broke faith with our allies, if we divided the UN."

Truman spoke on the telephone to the British and French Prime Ministers, both of whom pleaded with him again to neither enlarge the war by bombing Manchuria nor intensify it by introducing atomic weapons. "The war must be contained at all costs," Attlee said, in his high-pitched voice.

Truman promised them that he would wait. "I'll tell you this much," he said, before hanging up, "I'm going to do everything I can to keep our boys from being wiped out."

By the spring of 1951 it was obvious that the Korean War had settled into a stalemate, and that the stalemate would persist indefinitely. Accordingly, Truman gave up any thought of widening the war. Containment was his fixed policy. "Let us not assume that we have lost because we have not won in a conventional sense," General Omar Bradley explained to the Joint Chiefs of Staff. "We have won our original objective, which was to save South Korea. We have vindicated the principle of collective security. I regret that the Chinese gave us a licking up there. But we mustn't lose sight of what this thing is all about. It would be insanity, sheer lunacy, to go all out and try to beat the enemy, destroy their army, take their territory and the like. What for? We're not fighting a crusade against these people. And if we were we should attack Russia. So I say let the stalemate go on. We've got to have the strength to persevere. This is a new kind of war, gentlemen, and the sooner we Americans recognize that fact the better off we'll be."

Bradley thus effectively summarized the administration's position.

But it was not General MacArthur's position. He sent a stream of messages to the Joint Chiefs pleading for permission to resume the offensive. By resuming the offensive he meant attacking the Chinese "in their stronghold, the staging areas of Manchuria." "Must I tell my men," he wrote in one of his messages, "that they are to fight but not to win? It is indeed a sad moment for myself, for my men, for my country."

Soon congressmen and newspapers were taking up the refrain, accusing the government, as Senator Everett M. Dirksen of Illinois put it, of "deliberately pursuing a no-win policy in Korea." The senator spoke for many when he said: "I have never known our nation to fail its fighting men. It is failing them now. I am ashamed."

Secretary Acheson was the chief target of administration critics.

His reserve, his fastidious manner, his brilliance, contributed to the bad impression he made. "You pulled us out of Korea in 1949," shouted Senator Homer Capehart of Indiana during a secret Foreign Relations hearing at which Acheson was testifying, "now you want to keep us there forever. This is criminal. You should be impeached." At the same hearing Senator John Bricker of Ohio wondered why "you and the President are letting the Chinese Reds get away with it, why you are so solicitous of their welfare—more solicitous than you are of our boys or our honor."

While the hearing was held, MacArthur was quoted by a reporter for a news agency as saying that "we could win this war if we could get at their bases in Manchuria. In war as in life, not to have won is to have lost."

The President read MacArthur's remarks and called in General Bradley and the Army Chief of Staff. "I'm fed up to here with him," he said, running his right hand across his neck. "Omar, I want you to order him to clear all of his public statements from now on with the Defense Department. I'm hopping mad. You can tell him that. He's not bigger than the President and he never will be. He had his chance to win this thing and he flubbed it. I'm not going to expand the war for the sake of his pride."

MacArthur received the order directly from General Bradley. "The President enjoins me to silence," MacArthur said to his aide, Birchby, at his headquarters in Tokyo. "He is my superior and I will obey him. But not since I was a second lieutenant at Fort Meade, serving under an illiterate, inebriated, utterly incompetent company commander have I had so much contempt for a superior."

But MacArthur obeyed only the letter, not the spirit of the order. A number of congressmen who visited Korea and met with MacArthur (his headquarters being open house to them) accused the administration of tying his hands. A few of them even suggested that men in high places were conspiring to deny the United States a victory. In late March 1951, following the enemy's capture of a strategic hill just north of Seoul, MacArthur lost his temper and publicly threatened to bomb Manchuria. Some newspapers predicted that an American assault on Chinese sanctuaries was imminent. The next day, Chou En-lai warned that if Manchuria were bombed "all of Southeast Asia would go up in smoke."

For the third time Truman heard pleas from the British and French leaders to refrain from widening the war. He then asked Acheson, Bradley, Marshall, and others in his cabinet if they had any objections to his "firing" MacArthur on the spot. None objected, but Attorney General J. Howard McGrath thought that the country "would be up in arms over the fight," that MacArthur's friends would hail him as "a conqueror and martyr, like Caesar."

"Nonsense," Truman replied, "the American people won't go for that. I don't think they especially like that so-and-so. Anyway, I have my duty. He defied me and I'm going to chuck him out of there."

In early April MacArthur received a direct order from the White House. "You are hereby relieved of your command and of all further services in the armed forces of the United States."

MacArthur returned to America later that month for the first time since well before the Second World War. The police estimated that as many as seven million people greeted him in New York City.

Especially impressive was the speech he delivered before a joint session of Congress. The old-time members claimed that Congress gave him a longer and more enthusiastic ovation than it gave Churchill in 1942 and Lindbergh in 1927.

He spoke poignantly of his long stay in Asia, of his knowledge, respect, and devotion for the Chinese people, now "yoked to Communist masters who respect neither the laws nor the simple hopes of humanity." He lectured his distinguished audience on the differences between Confucianism, which bred on obedient and virtuous people, and Communism, which preached class war, nihilism, and rule by might.

"We must prepare for a long siege. Communism is a satanic force in the world, seizing as it does on the ignorance, confusion, and credulity of the masses, and then imposing its iron grip on them, destroying all compassion, all idealism, all that mankind cherishes. The struggle, I daresay, will persist beyond my lifetime

and yours as well. It will shape the destiny of our people for the
remainder of this century and longer."

Yet MacArthur did not attempt to present an *apologia pro
vita sua* or to condemn the President. Instead, in sad and moving
tones, he announced that he would retire at last and withdraw
to quiet obscurity, waiting for the death that was near at hand.

Three months after MacArthur's recall the UN and the North
Koreans (the Chinese being only "volunteers") agreed to discuss
the terms of an armistice. The fighting continued during the
arduous, often interrupted negotiations. Neither side made much
progress on the battlefield or at the conference table. The primary
dispute was over the North Korean demand that the UN repatriate North Korean prisoners, whether they wanted repatriation
or not. The UN of course refused, the negotiations remained
deadlocked, and the stalemated war went on.

5

THE GREAT CRUSADE

FROM the beginning of the Cold War the Truman administration had to deal with an uncomfortable problem: how to arouse the nation to oppose Communism abroad and at the same time restrain it from launching an irresponsible anti-Communist crusade at home.

During the crisis with Iran in 1946 one of the President's special assistants, a young New York lawyer (he shall be called Reuben Hoffman here)* suggested in a memorandum to his immediate superior on the White House staff that an executive committee be set up to preserve the balance between national security and civil liberties.

"We should remember that even the Democratic Party is vulnerable to attack from the far right. Not long ago FDR's enemies were calling him a Bolshevik, a revolutionist, and what not, because he was a reformer. And we all remember the Dies Committee. Under the circumstances, with Russia looming up as our enemy, I think it entirely possible that reactionaries will exploit a new red scare to get at us, at the liberals, at the vital center of American life. I therefore suggest that the President create an executive committee to recommend measures against subversives, while protecting the innocent and upholding our most precious inheritance, our civil liberties."

The memo reached Truman, who liked the idea, and he promptly established the White House Committee on Freedom and Security with instructions to meet and report to him regularly.

But as the Cold War deepened, as the American people passed

* Why Prescott relied on pseudonyms for certain people is a mystery. It may be because they requested that their names be omitted.—N.F.M.

through one external crisis after another, they gave up making distinctions between foreign and domestic Communism, and for that matter between Communism and other forms of radicalism. A new era of political repression set in, and professional anti-Communists emerged as new men of power. With them emerged a new ethic in the United States. Talebearing and informing acquired the status of high virtues.

As early as 1946 some politicians running for Congress made the "leftist" political views of their opponents an issue. In southern California Richard M. Nixon, a little-known Republican candidate for a House seat, charged the incumbent, a widely respected liberal Democrat, with having "consorted with fellow travelers," with having been "a dupe of the Communist movement."

"I say this man is not fit to have your trust, to represent this district," Nixon said on hundreds of occasions. "He belongs to organizations that are headed by known Communists and their friends. Let me name some of them for you. . . . If you want him to continue to represent you, then by all means vote for him. But if you want to vote for America, for the principles that made this country what it is, then I say you should vote for me."

Nixon won the election that year, as did scores of others like him who served in the Republican Eightieth Congress. Some of them sat in the House Un-American Activities Committee, which in 1947 went on the first of its postwar rampages, impugning the "left-wing" groups it investigated, handing down indictments against refractory witnesses, generating publicity wherever it went.

In the summer of 1947 the White House Committee on Freedom and Security recommended that the President placate his anti-Communist congressional critics. "We have got to take the wind out of their sails," Seth Evans* said to the President. "These conservative fanatics want nothing more than an issue. We must give them no basis for attacking you, sir, as soft on Communism." Truman replied that the Attorney General, Tom Clark, had recently compiled a comprehensive list of subversive organizations. "Why don't you and the Committee look it over and tell me what you think of it," Truman said.

The next day Evans presented the list, which contained hundreds of names, to the five members of the committee. One

* Another pseudonym.—N.F.M.

of them, Reuben Hoffman, strongly opposed its promulgation. "How were these organizations selected?" Hoffman asked. "Who determines which of them is or is not subversive? And what about the innocent people who belong to them, who joined, say, the Cooperative League of America, not knowing it's a Communist—I mean, an alleged Communist—front? And what about due process? Were hearings held, experts called? In short, this list is patently unjust. I don't think the government should go into the business of telling the citizens what organizations they should or should not join. It'll play into the hand of the Un-American Committee and the rightist groups. We should be fighting this sort of thing, not condoning it."

"I agree with you, Reuben," Evans said. "But consider the President's position. After all, you wrote the memo last year. You should know better than anybody. The President's under siege. They're beginning to call him a pinko too. He has to do something. You know that Tom Clark wants to make membership in these organizations a criminal offense. Now I'm against that, and I'll fight it to the death. But we have to do something. I propose we approve the Attorney General's subversive list, provided it remains only a guide for the government and for private institutions, that it have no legal force or standing."

This proposal carried in the committee, and Truman accepted it. He then ordered—without the White House Committee's advice—the various departments and the civil service to rid the executive of "security risks," meaning those accused of belonging to the organizations on the Attorney General's list.

But try as it did, the administration found it harder and harder to convince the public that the Communist threat was primarily a foreign one. A series of sensational spy trials gave credibility to the claim by the extreme right that a Communist was a traitor by definition. In 1946 several high Canadian officials, including a member of parliament, were convicted of giving the Soviets valuable information on the atomic bomb.

Two years later the American public was stunned by the Alger Hiss affair.

Hiss had occupied an important position in the State Department before he was appointed head of the famous Carnegie Endowment for Peace, the coping stone of a lifetime of dis-

tinguished public service. He came from a good family, went to
the best schools (including Harvard, which graduated him with
highest honors), and moved in the best circles.

On a warm summer day in 1948, the House Un-American
Activities Committee, of which Richard Nixon was a member,
heard an incredible story about Hiss. One Whittaker Chambers,
a writer and magazine editor, testified that he had belonged to
Hiss's Washington spy cell in the 1930s. The members of the
committee, witch-hunters though they were, could not believe their
ears. The testimony seemed all the more implausible since it
came from a man who had had such a notoriously unstable life.
Chambers had suffered nervous breakdowns, and admitted to
having been an inveterate liar.

The committee was inclined to drop the whole fantastic matter,
but thanks mostly to Richard Nixon's urging it brought the two
men face to face. Hiss denied point-blank ever having known
his accuser. Later Chambers produced rolls of microfilm containing secret State Department documents which he claimed
Hiss had passed to him when they had both belonged to the
same cell, and which he had hidden in a disemboweled pumpkin
on his Maryland farm.

Hiss was tried for perjury (the statute of limitations precluded
his indictment as a spy) and convicted on the evidence of the
"pumpkin papers." It was established to the jury's satisfaction
that a typewriter which he (or his wife) had once owned had
typed the microfilmed pages.

The moral of the Hiss affair was clear. If a man like him could
be a spy, who might not be one? The radical right, its ranks
growing daily, went one step further: it was precisely such
men as Hiss who were most suspect.

The chief beneficiary of the case was Congressman Richard
Nixon, who received wide publicity and much commendation for
his role in the inquiry. Anti-Communists celebrated him as one of
their most promising crusaders. "Subversives of America beware,"
announced the *Christian Militant,* a right-wing weekly published
in Nixon's home district: "Dick Nixon is a comer. Some day he
will drive the Gadarene swine into the Potomac River."

Late in 1948, just after Hiss had been charged, Truman
gathered his top legal aides in the John Tyler Room. They were

Attorney General Tom Clark, Treasury Secretary John Snyder and Commerce Secretary Charles Sawyer, two of the President's closest friends, and Seth Evans, representing the White House Committee on Freedom and Security.

"My friends," Truman told them, "I'm getting a lot of flak on the Communist issue. Republicans are saying that the government is overrun with them or their sympathizers. You and I know that that's bunk, that they're trying to discredit us because they can't beat us legitimately. And I don't like all this indiscriminate labeling of people. The Hiss thing is hurting us. Now those Republican so-and-so's are saying that Hiss sold us down the river at Yalta. We've got to quiet down the public. I'm open to suggestions."

Evans spoke first. "Mr. President, I don't think there's anything further you can do without calling down the Yahoos on us. My own suggestion is that you try to explain the meaning of civil liberties to the people and that—"

Attorney General Clark broke in to say he disagreed. "You know, it's not only a tactic, Seth. The Communists here *are* a danger. They are committed to the destruction of our government and our way of life. I don't believe we should be defenseless against them."

"I'm with you there," Commerce Secretary Sawyer added.

"What would you suggest be done?" Evans asked Clark.

"Well, I'd jail the leading Communists. We have the laws to do it. It would all be done according to due process."

"On what grounds would you jail them?" Evans asked.

"I would jail them on the grounds that they've conspired to overthrow this government by force and violence."

"What do you mean by 'conspired,' Tom?"

"I mean they've organized cells, agitated in public, written inflammatory books and pamphlets, infiltrated and undermined private institutions. You know what I'm talking about, Seth."

"No, I don't, Tom. All you've shown is that they've taken advantage of the protection afforded by the Bill of Rights. They've peacefully assembled, spoken, and written. And I think the private institutions they've infiltrated should take care of themselves. What I'm asking is what they've *done,* what deeds they've committed, what illegalities they've perpetrated. And by 'they' I

mean specific persons. I can't imagine you'd write a bill of at-
tainder against all Communists."

Then Sawyer, who looked very uncomfortable during the
colloquy, intervened. "Look here, Mr. Evans, you're trying to
be a clever devil's advocate, a pettifogger, arguing fine points
of law while the barn's burning down. I say we've got to
prosecute the Communists as a public menace. Let the courts
decide the legal niceties."

Evans laughed and said nothing.

Truman, who seemed amused himself, turned to John Snyder
and asked him what he thought.

"Well, Mr. President," Snyder said in his high-pitched monotone, "I'm afraid I agree with Tom and Charlie. Not only are
they a public menace, I don't think the people will accept anything less than their prosecution. Then the Republicans won't be
able to accuse us of pussyfooting. We've got to take a hard line
against these people."

"O.K., that settles it," Truman declared, rising from the table.
"See what you can do about the Communists, Tom. I'm leaving
it in your hands. By the way, Seth, I thought you had the better
of the argument."

A month after this historic conference, eleven leading American Communists were prosecuted in New York City (their headquarters) for allegedly having violated a 1940 law that forbade
advocating or teaching the overthrow of the government by force
and violence.

The trial dragged on for about a year, as the Communist
lawyers attempted to turn the courtroom into a propaganda forum.
Never before had their clients had such an opportunity to disseminate their views. But their conviction, given the sweeping
provisions of the law, was a foregone conclusion. That they
were revolutionists was indisputable, and to convict them the
government needed only to produce the writings of well-known
Communists, from Karl Marx to Josef Stalin. The jury found
them guilty, and the judge sentenced them to five years in prison.

Before sentencing them the judge, Harold Medina, lectured
them in his private chambers on the blessings of a free, democratic, and lawful society.

"When we try men for breaking the law, we do so through

rigorous adherence to due process. Every defendant in a criminal case has the right to a lawyer and a jury of his peers. You have been given a fair trial in conformity to Article Six of the Federal Constitution. You men of the Communist Party, even though your loyalties may lie elsewhere, will appreciate the genius of a free and just system of law."

But the *Civil Liberties Digest,* a monthly bulletin for lawyers, criticized the Smith Act, the government, the jury, and the judge for their "concerted assault on the Bill of Rights. . . . Yes, the Communists teach and advocate revolution and form cells. What are we afraid of? The French, the Italians, the British, the Dutch, and the other Western countries which have larger Communist Parties than the United States do not forbid them to do these things. Why should we? We have the most exquisite pretensions in the world about civil liberties. We are also the most blatant hypocrites in the world. The Supreme Court, we trust, will strike down the convictions *and* the law."

The Supreme Court, however, voted to sustain the convictions and the law. Chief Justice Fred Vinson handed down the momentous decision for the majority.

"We have sedulously deliberated on the matter," he said, "and we have concluded that these men plotted to commit an unlawful act, an act all the more repugnant and intolerable since it would affect every American. The law does not object to preaching, or even organizing a revolutionary movement, so long as that movement eschews force and violence. The examples of Czechoslovakia, China, and Korea are fresh in our minds. The Republic would be remiss if it did not seek to protect itself against outrageous contingencies, among them internal enemies. We should not wait for our enemies to pounce on us before we arm ourselves. Let the convictions stand."

One of the dissenting opinions, presented by Justice Hugo Black, a crusty, uncompromising Southern liberal (and a very close friend of Seth Evans), showed the inconsistency between the Smith Act, under which the Communists were tried, and the First Amendment of the Constitution. "The First Amendment admits of no compromise. Its provisions are absolute and imprescriptible; it therefore flatly contradicts the Smith Act. Those who tamper with the First Amendment lay violent hands on the law of the land; they are the lawless ones."

And Justice William O. Douglas, the other dissenter, argued that Communist teachings did not constitute a "clear and present danger" to the United States. "If we are so weak and pigeon-livered that we can't abide a dose of revolutionary rhetoric, then we might as well give up our experiment in freedom."

The Supreme Court thus gave the administration a mandate to prosecute every highly placed Communist in sight. J. Edgar Hoover, chief of the Federal Bureau of Investigation, submitted to the political division of the Justice Department his personal dossier of five thousand people who, in his words, "can be convicted of subversion or treason or both." The FBI was placed in charge of the hundreds of "informants" who were kept on government payrolls as reserve witnesses in future cases. Thanks to these witnesses federal attorneys had no difficulty convicting anyone they tried.

Meanwhile, the forty-eight states passed sedition and subversion laws of their own. Not only the states, but counties and cities and private institutions as well, from labor unions to women's bridge clubs.

A general purge, an inquisition, swept the land. The hunt for "Communist sympathizers," "fellow travelers," "pinks," anyone whose past was "questionable," became a national pastime. "Witch-hunting," said one wag, "is as American as cherry pie." Seth Evans, resigning from the White House Committee on Freedom and Security, lamented: "Mr. President, what have we wrought, what have we wrought?"

Indeed, the worst was to come. More shocking even than the Hiss case were the great spy trials. In 1950, shortly after the Soviet Union announced that it had exploded an atomic bomb, a famous German-born scientist, Klaus Fuchs, was tried and found guilty in a British court of delivering top secret data to the Soviets. It was Fuchs's importance in developing the atomic bomb that made his case so profoundly unsettling. Later in the year a group of Americans were arrested for their part in the Fuchs conspiracy. Never had the American people witnessed anything so obscene as friends and relatives, brothers and sisters betrayed each other's complicity in the espionage ring. Those who gave state's evidence were usually given thirty-year prison terms. (Klaus Fuchs, who was more important than all the Americans combined, had received only fourteen years.)

The final episode in the drama was enacted early in 1951 with the trial and conviction of a married couple, Julius and Ethel Rosenberg. "You two," said Judge Irving Kauffman at the sentencing ceremony (attended by the Rosenberg's young children), "are convicted of the highest crimes known to man. You are the Judas Iscariots, the Benedict Arnolds, the Quislings of your country, your people. Your parents came to America in search of freedom and found it. Though poor, as many of us were, you were given the best education in the world, all of it free, and you became scientists. Look at what you have done. You have betrayed everything that was sacred to your parents and your nation. You passed atomic secrets to our enemy. Do you know what our enemy has done?"

Here the judge leaned over the bench and looked at them with burning eyes. His voice rose by several decibels. "Our enemy is waging war against us. Our boys are dying by the thousands in Korea. This war would not have started if Russia did not have the atom bomb, and Russia would not have had the atom bomb if you and your loathsome accomplices had not given Russia the secrets to make it. Do you realize the magnitude of your crime? Judas was responsible for the death of one man. You are responsible for the death of multitudes. I have no compunction, no remorse, in sending both of you to die in the electric chair. I regret the consequences to your children. May they know a different life."

Julius Rosenberg silently wept. He continued to weep as he and Ethel were led away to await their execution.

By the end of 1950 the country was in the mood for sweeping legislation. The Espionage Act of 1917 was still on the books, but it was too restricted in its application. To meet the needs of the moment Senator Patrick McGohey McCarran of Nevada and Representative Karl Mundt of South Dakota came up with a bill, the Internal Security Act. This act proposed to establish a board that would resister "Communist-front" organizations; that is, designate them as dangerous, subject them to constant surveillance, and stigmatize anyone belonging to them as "subversive."

The act also proposed to create "internment camps" for enemies of the people in periods of national emergency and banish or prohibit members of "Communist-front" organizations from working in defense industries (which employed millions of people).

In his testimony before McCarran's committee, J. Edgar Hoover commended the act as "a step forward in the fight against subversives. This will close the loophole through which they and their clandestine friends have been able to escape the law." He had one "proviso," however: "The act should make membership in these organizations a criminal offense. Subversives should not only be registered, they should be put away. Our men are ready to do the job."

Senator McCarran said he agreed with Hoover. "Only I want this bill enacted first. Then we'll build on it. Remember, there are a lot of Americans who are dupes and ignoramuses when it comes to the Communist menace. They have to be led to the truth by degrees, step by step."

"I'm completely with you there," said Hoover.

The Internal Security Act easily passed both houses of Congress. When President Truman received it for his signature, he asked his legal advisers to meet with him again. "You'll have to admit this damn thing goes too far," he told them. "Why we're back to the Alien and Sedition Acts, and we know how bad they were. The damned Federalists, the Republicans of the time, were out to get the Democrats, and the Alien and Sedition Acts did get some Democrats. No, I won't have it. Trying Communists is one thing. Registering people and setting up camps is another. Howard [Attorney General J. Howard McGrath], have your men work with Reuben Hoffman on a veto speech. I'm going to try to kill this thing before it becomes a monster and eats us all."

Hoffman's statement, modified and toned down in the veto message, was a passionate defense of civil liberties. It condemned the "pervasive hysteria and fear," the "immorality of guilt by association," the "irrational desire for total security" that underlay the act. "This legislation is clearly unconstitutional, and I would be violating my oath of office if I did not veto it. In reconsidering it, Congress should take a 'sober second look,' as Justice Hughes put it. It fails completely as a tactical measure.

What purpose shall we serve by driving these organizations underground, assuming even the worst about them? It will become
that much harder to track down subversives and spies. The
government has more than enough laws available to it. The
fallacy of the bill, in the final analysis, is that it promises total
security. There is no such thing. Once we desire total security
we shall find that the further we go in pursuing it, the further
we will be from possessing it. And so we will go still further,
until at last we are a police state. We will have gained nothing
and lost everything."

A week later, when they received the veto message, Senator
McCarran and Representative Mundt laughed heartily. "Why,"
said the senator, "we have more votes now than we had when
we first passed the bill. Let's show the President what the people
think of his sniveling defense of subversives. I personally think
he's going haywire."

Both houses overrode Truman's veto by substantially more than
the two-thirds margin required.

Communism had become an obsession with the American people.
The spy trials, the "loss" of China, the Soviet Union's possession
of the atom bomb, the grinding, relentless pressure of the Cold
War led more and more Americans to assume that the conspiracy
reached into the highest places of the government. They were
prepared to believe anything.

And so, when Joseph R. McCarthy, an obscure senator from
Wisconsin, asserted early in 1950 that there were 205 "card-
carrying Communists running loose in the State Department," the
public took him seriously. Ordinarily, a speech before a Lincoln
day gathering of Republican Party faithful in Wheeling, West
Virginia, would have gone unnoticed. But the newspapers picked
up Senator McCarthy's charge, and he was asked to elaborate
on it. Days later, at a dinner in Cairo, Illinois, for Republican
county leaders, he said, "There are 130 traitors making our
foreign policy today, now. I have their names and card numbers
right here [pulling some papers from a jacket pocket]. And I
have information on their activities—on how they have and are
at this moment selling our country down the river."

By now McCarthy was making headlines. In an open letter to
Secretary of State Acheson, printed of course in every newspaper

in the country, he demanded to know what the department was doing about its "traitors." "I think you owe the American people an explanation," McCarthy wrote. "You owe them candid answers to the following questions: Who are the Communists in your department? What damage have they already done to this nation? Why have you kept them on? What are you going to do about them?"

Truman read the letter in the morning paper and hurriedly called Acheson on the phone. "Dean, I don't want you or anyone in State to answer that S.O.B. Don't you go into the sewer with him. I'll see what I can do to make him put up or shut up."

Truman asked Senator Brian MacMahon of Connecticut, one of his trusted congressional leaders, to look into McCarthy's charges and also tell him something about McCarthy.

The next day Senator MacMahon informed the President that McCarthy had once been a judge in his rural Wisconsin community, had served in the Marines during the war, and had won election to the Senate in 1946 as an amiable man who had not been known to have strong convictions about anything outside of his career.

"Until that speech in Wheeling in February," MacMahon said, "he'd done nothing. He rarely spoke in the Senate, and when he did it was for the butter and cheese interests. Every year he gives each of us a Wisconsin cheddar. He's a nice enough guy, a bachelor, about forty-two, drinks a lot. There's nothing on him, though. We never knew him to be an anti-Communist, much less a fanatic. Then suddenly this thing. We'll see what we can do, Mr. President. Next week, we'll conduct a preliminary inquiry to determine whether our subcommittee should investigate his charges."

McCarthy grew increasingly audacious. In speech after speech he referred to the large number of card-carrying Communists in the State Department. Only the exact number kept changing, varying from speech to speech. Once it was down to fifty-seven, then forty, then back up to one hundred and thirty. Reporters and newspaper editorials pressed him to divulge their names, but he refused. "I'll choose the time and the place," he always said with a smile.

He played "the numbers game" to drive home his main

point: that ever since 1932, when the Democrats were voted into power, the Communists had been "exercising a tremendous influence in the government." "Remember," he would tell his audiences, "one of the first acts of the Democratic administration was to recognize Communist Russia. That administration helped Communist Russia in 1941 and throughout the war. It signed the Yalta agreement, which handed all of Eastern Europe over to the Communists. And what about the spies who gave away our secrets? What about China? The men who sympathized with the Chinese Reds are still in the State Department. George C. Marshall once called the Chinese Reds 'agrarian reformers.' Imagine that! Men like Marshall aided and abetted the Communist cause. I'm not saying Marshall was a traitor. But notice the pattern, which is clear as the morning light. The Communists have grabbed a third of the world while the Democrats have been in office."

Conservative Democrats hardly less than radicals and liberals condemned McCarthy for his "smear campaign." Even his friends insisted that he reveal to an anxious public the names of the "traitors" so that they could be ousted before doing more damage.

At last, in June 1950, he announced on the Senate floor that he would release the name of the man who "was in charge of the Communist spy apparatus in the State Department." Absent entirely from the speech was any mention of 40 or 57 or 130 or 205 "card-carrying" members of the Communist Party. His whole case, he admitted, rested on the guilt of this one person, this alleged superspy. Some people speculated that he would be a sensationally important official—perhaps, as a columnist for the *New York Sun-Courier* suggested, Dean Acheson himself.

But the mountain brought forth a mouse. Before a crowded Senate chamber McCarthy read the person's name. He was Professor Owen Lattimore of Johns Hopkins University, an authority on Asia, who had briefly served as a State Department consultant on his special area of competence. Very few people had ever heard of Owen Lattimore; even fewer had read his scholarly books on Outer Mongolia.

"Lattimore is our man," McCarthy asserted. "His cell devised the policies that lost us China, the greatest blow to the free world since the Communist takeover of Russia."

McCarthy's critics were more outraged than ever. They were now convinced that he had been lying all along, that he had been shamelessly deceiving the public for personal and political gain. "This man is an unspeakable demagogue," Connecticut's Senator William Benton declared.

McCarthy replied: "Bill Benton is a coward and a blackguard, a faithful worker in the Communist vineyards."

Such were the dialogues that customarily passed between McCarthy and his enemies.

As a matter of party policy, the Democrats were determined to discredit him. A Senate subcommittee did investigate his charges against the State Department, and its three-man majority—all Democrats—found no evidence of Communist influence in the State Department, and, moreover, cleared Owen Lattimore completely. The majority report went on to characterize McCarthy as "a reckless antagonist of civil liberties who has transgressed all the canons of fair play in dragging innocent people through the mud."

The report drove McCarthy to a paroxysm of fury. "The three men who signed this dirty sheet will be accountable to the American people for their misdeeds," he told the press. "I won't accuse them of being traitors, but isn't it obvious that they are doing the work of the Communist conspiracy? They are beneath contempt. They will be punished. I guarantee it."

McCarthy was angriest at the subcommittee chairman, Millard Tydings of Maryland. Tydings was the kind of conservative who brooked no assault on civil liberties. McCarthy publicly referred to Tydings as an "antique fool." "Tydings' number's up," he would say. "His tide's out."

It happened that Tydings ran for re-election in 1950. Few expected him to lose. He had represented Maryland for nearly thirty years; he had survived FDR's purge campaign of 1938; and he seemed to be as invulnerable as ever. Undaunted, McCarthy campaigned extensively for Tydings' opponent, who swore eternal fealty to McCarthy. McCarthy and his staff fought Tydings in many ways. The circulated fake photographs that showed him standing next to prominent Communists. They launched rumors linking him to subversives, atheists, homosexuals, and "women of ill repute." McCarthy used the same techniques in Connecticut, where Senator Benton also ran for re-election.

The results of the election were astonishing. Tydings and Benton were soundly beaten. Indeed, throughout the country the pro-McCarthy candidates did exceptionally well. Richard M. Nixon, running for the Senate seat in California, won a resounding victory after impugning the loyalty of his opponent, a well-known liberal lady.

The day after the election McCarthy spoke to the nation on radio. "The people have seen through the lies and smears," he said, "and they have announced that they will no longer tolerate coddling traitors and subversives. After twenty years their patience is exhausted. This is the beginning of our struggle to regain America."

McCarthy was now a power in the land. In the future politicians would think twice before criticizing him. The administration, too, avoided antagonizing him. It sought to placate him by enlarging the "loyalty" program in the executive department, dismissing from the State Department some of the old "China hands" who had predicted Chiang Kai-shek's defeat, and adding many new names to the Attorney General's list of "subversive" organizations. These concessions, however, only whetted McCarthy's appetite. In his New Year's message to America he assured his countrymen that they could look forward to a series of exciting investigations.

"I will look for subversives wherever they are. I will rout them out of their hiding places. No institution will be sacred. The universities, the press, unions, business, entertainment—these, like the government, have harbored Communists long enough. They will not find sanctuary as long as I live. I hereby declare war on the Communist conspiracy in this country, and I pledge my life, my honor, and my fortune to its destruction."

How Americans felt about Senator McCarthy and his crusade was apparent from a nationwide poll conducted early in 1951. According to its findings 59 per cent of the people approved of what he was doing; 30 per cent disapproved; the rest had no opinion. "I don't always like his methods," was the typical response of the majority, "but I agree with his objective, and I want to see him continue."

BOOK II

The Thaw

I

TRANSITIONS

LATE one evening in mid-January 1952 some of the leading Republicans in the United States secretly convened in the Georgetown, Washington, apartment of Senator Henry Cabot Lodge of Massachusetts. Among those present were seven governors, including Earl Warren of California and Thomas E. Dewey of New York, the chairmen of the boards of the three largest banks, two largest insurance companies, and four of the ten largest industrial corporations in the country, Senator Marcus Heminway of Nebraska and Representative Alex U. Wiefanz of Michigan, and the owners of three important "communications" empires, which accounted for a total of fifteen hundred newspapers, magazines, publishing houses, and radio and television stations.

"Not since the Estates General met on May 4, 1789," a Washington columnist wrote several months after the meeting, "had such a council of notables come together to discuss affairs of state."

"You all know why we're here, under these clandestine conditions," Lodge said, after calling his assembled guests to order. "Brad [Bradford Hillsman, his chief aide] has informed you of the general's interest in the presidency, provided no word of it be leaked out. 'If the public hears about it'—these are his exact words—'I'll have to deny it and repudiate your efforts to draw me into politics.'

"What General Eisenhower wants—and I have Brad's notes of their conversation before me—is a statement by, I quote, 'men prominent in the responsible wing of the Republican Party, favoring my candidacy and giving their reasons for it.'

"Gentlemen," Lodge continued, his eyes shining with enthusiasm, "I think our prayers have been answered. I think he's ready to come in with us. That's why you're here. But we must play our cards right. If we lose the general we're in trouble. I don't mean only the party. I mean the country. I don't want to lecture you—listening to me is not why you came. Only let's make sure we're agreed on where we stand. The Democrats have made a bloody mess of things. The Korean War is stalemated. Prices and wages are going up. Corruption is rampant, from the top down. Statesmanship has been reduced to cronyism and vulgar mediocrity. Worst of all, the country is divided. There's too much recrimination, too much contempt for due process and established institutions. We need leadership that will heal our wounds and restore a sense of unity, responsibility and fair play. There were a lot of Communists and fellow travelers in our government and elsewhere under twenty years of Democratic rule, and to that extend Joe McCarthy has been right, but you'll agree that the pendulum has swung too far over to the other side, and I think we should worry a little about civil liberties now.

"The problem, as you all know, is this. Is the Republican Party equipped to supply that leadership? The sad fact, I'm afraid, is that without the general it is not. Only the general can prevent Senator Taft's candidacy this summer. We all agree that the senator is a great Republican and a great man, and we admire his principles and his courage. I say that from the bottom of my heart. But you know as well as I do that he just can't beat a good Democratic candidate. If we nominate the senator—I know this from my own constituency—we'll drive too many of our liberals and moderates into the Democratic camp. Too many people think that Taft wants to turn the clock back. I don't think so, although I must admit his principles are often too pure and uncompromising for my jaded taste.

"In other words, gentlemen, Senator Taft would exacerbate the tensions in this country, even if he wins. We must have someone who is a moderate like us, like most Americans, someone who is unsullied by politics, and who is popular. It's as though Providence in His infinite solicitude for our nation had sent us, the people and the Grand Old Party, His own choice to fill all these requirements. We must not fail Providence."

When Lodge concluded, his twenty-one guests rose and ap-

plauded vigorously. Each later congratulated him for his eloquence. "Why, you'd make a great President yourself," one of
them said.

The statement drawn up by Lodge, Governor Dewey, and
Patrick Frankenthaler, president of New Haven Life, and signed
without demur by the others, was a condensed version of Lodge's
talk. It emphasized that the country desperately needed unity,
a "respite from politics," and a "cessation of the hatreds that
divide us." Also, it went on to say, the country needed "forward-
looking leadership" that would "maintain America's role in the
world" and not "retreat back into sullen isolationism." For those
and other reasons they as "committed Republicans," "solemnly"
asked Eisenhower "to grasp the reins of authority now fast
slipping from the hands of those who hold it. The well-being of
the American people depends on it."

The next day Bradford Hillsman brought the statement to
Eisenhower at his NATO headquarters just outside Paris.

"Tell Senator Lodge I'm favorably disposed," Eisenhower said
after he read it. "I agree with your analysis of things, but you
may be exaggerating my importance. Military men are popular in
America, as long as they stay in the military. But all right, I'll take
the plunge. You can count me in. Remember now, tell Lodge to
keep the whole thing under his hat until the time is ripe, which
may not be for some time."

"General," Hillsman replied, "you're a born politician. We'd be
darn foolish to say a word about your interest in the presidency.
We don't want you to be a target—not until you've sewn up the
nomination."

That nothing could stop Eisenhower had become clear by the
time the Republican presidential convention met at Chicago in
McCormack Hall, in July 1952. He had declared his willingness
to serve as President, "if that is what the American people wish,"
and had handily won every primary in which his name had been
entered.

But Senator Taft did not give up so easily. "It is a struggle for the
soul of our Party and our beloved country," Taft asserted on the
eve of the convention. For the past several years he had been
cultivating the support of the Party faithful from the conservative,
mainly rural and small-town states of the South and West. "I'm

not ashamed of the Babbitts," he once said in an interview, in his typically direct and forthright manner. "They're good Americans, solid as granite, and I'm proud to count them on my side."

Having locked up these conservative delegates, however, Taft found that he had, by a generous reckoning, no more than a third of the convention. The only question that remained was whether the convention could overcome the Party's ideological enmities preparatory to the campaign against the Democrats.

It was a disorderly, raucous convention, at least by the standards of decorum that Republicans took for granted. The Taft forces were angry and unappeasable. They had been so close to victory. Now, barring a miracle, they were doomed, and their leader, who was sixty-two, would never again offer himself as a candidate.

In the course of presenting a routine speech on the convention floor Senator Everett McKinley Dirksen of Illinois, a staunch Taft man, suddenly stopped and pointed at Thomas E. Dewey, who was then entering the hall. "This is the author of our malaise," Dirksen said, rising to the full measure of his vaunted eloquence. "You, sir, who have run twice and lost twice, you would take us down the ignoble road to defeat and ruin a third time. I call you a traitor, yes, a traitor to our Party and our Party's traditions. The people have repudiated you and everything you stand for because you have spinelessly imitated the Democrats. I say, let us rid ourselves of the castrating me-tooism that you symbolize."

But Dewey, imperturbable as an oak, smiled graciously, knowing that the day had been won, that Eisenhower would, in fact, receive the nomination on the first ballot [. . .]

Eisenhower had given little thought to whom his vice-presidential "running mate" should be, and he asked the party's National Committeeman, Matthew Wells of Washington, to consult with other leaders in drawing up a list of ten names from which the choice would be made.

All night the "Ad Hoc Conference to Select a Vice President" worked on the list. Among the names that appeared on it was Senator Richard M. Nixon's of California. Oddly enough, Nixon had not even been considered by the ad hoc committee. One of his closest friends, who was Matthew Wells's assistant, had prevailed upon Wells to place Nixon's name on the list, and Wells had done so. Both he and Wells were one day to be rewarded for their initiative—or for what a critic of Nixon was to term their "skulduggery."

That evening, while Eisenhower was pondering the list in his Hotel Excelsior suite—he had been told something about each of the men on it—Nixon paid him an unannounced visit. "I have learned, sir, that my name is being considered for the vice presidency," Nixon said deferentially. "I would like it removed."*

"Why?" Eisenhower said.

"Because, sir, I think my candidacy might embarrass you. I have acquired the reputation of being something of a crusader against Communism. Some have accused me of being ambitious. I have always thought of myself as a crusader for America, and I have taken up unpopular causes because I believed them right. If I have been elected to office by the people of California it has not been because of my alleged ambition. Nonetheless, sir, my name has been dragged through the mud, and I am determined to spare you any embarrassment."

Eisenhower, who had not met Nixon before, was impressed by this alert, forthright, and extremely mature young man of thirty-nine. He questioned Nixon at length, and learned—or came to assume—that Nixon's life was very much like his own: humble in origin, dedicated to public service, and rewarded solely for hard work and accomplishments.

"Senator," he said, "I hope you will take back your withdrawal notice. I'd like you to stay in the running."

Reluctantly, Nixon consented.

The following afternoon, Nixon was hurriedly called to Eisenhower's suite. "Would you accept the nomination if I offered it to you?" Eisenhower asked. Biting down hard on his jaws, his voice cracking perceptibly, Nixon said, yes, he would accept it "in all humility," and would try to be worthy of the office and "the exalted standards of conduct that you, sir, demand of your subordinates."

"Then by all means join my team," Eisenhower said, grinning

* How could Prescott have known what passed between Eisenhower and Nixon? Either one of them later reconstructed the conversation for him, or he invented it. I have mentioned this point already, but it is worth emphasizing.—N.F.M.

broadly and putting his arm around Nixon's shoulder. "You're the kind of young Republican this country needs."

The news of Nixon's selection was relayed to the Party leaders, who then decided on the pro forma procedure for nominating him later that evening. Grumbling could be heard here and there in the ranks, especially from the "liberals," many of whom regarded Nixon as "dangerous." Among these no one was more displeased than Governor Earl Warren. As head of the California delegation and one of the top Republicans in the country, he had not been consulted either about placing Nixon's name on the list or about choosing him as candidate. Warren had distrusted Nixon ever since he first made his mark as a congressman. Soon after Nixon's election to the Senate, one of Warren's assistants had been heard to say: "No, that young man's problem is not that he believes the end justifies the means. His problem is that he does not know what the right ends are."

Such objections aside, it was generally agreed that the Republican Party had "fielded" an unbeatable "ticket" for the November election.

The Democratic Party candidate, Adlai E. Stevenson, was hardly known to the American public. Ordinarily, this would have been no disadvantage. In fact, one of the rules of American politics has always been to choose presidential candidates who have the least number of enemies. But if a candidate has few enemies and is also very popular, as Eisenhower was, then obscurity loses its value. Stevenson came from one of the most distinguished Chicago families, long influential in Democratic Party affairs. He had served in the State Department for a while before his land-quence, wit, and urbanity graced Illinois politics like a breath of slide election as Governor of Illinois in 1948. Stevenson's elo-bracing air. Some Illinoisans were fond of saying, "From Lincoln to Stevenson there is none like Stevenson."

In July 1952, during a White House dinner for governors, President Truman bluntly informed Stevenson that he, Stevenson, was his choice as the Democratic Party's presidential candidate. "I'd sure like to see that Eisenhower beaten," Truman said, "and I'm confident you could do it, Governor, if you run a strong campaign and hit the Republicans where it hurts, in the goddamned gut." Stevenson demurred, claiming that the office "is beyond my powers now," and that, in any case he would have to reflect "long and hard" before making up his mind.

"Not too long," Truman admonished, "we've got to know soon. It might take some doing to put you over. But first you've got to want it, and want it hard."

After deep soul searching, and after writing three letters turning down the offer—none of which he mailed—and after a series of inconclusive conferences with Truman and other Democratic chieftains, he finally agreed to accept the nomination if it were "proffered" to him. He would under no circumstances "solicit" it. It was indeed "proffered" to him on his terms—"on a damned silver platter," as Truman put it.

In his acceptance speech Stevenson gave the impression that he would fight for the presidency much as a postulant seeks entry into the church. "In many ways," he explained, "the presidency of the United States is too great and too awesome for any man. But it must be filled, alas, and those who do so come to realize the infinite distance separating themselves from the office and the ideal it embodies." He went on to plead for "a new kind of campaign in American politics, one that will elevate the level of public discourse, talk sense to the people, strip away our illusions and conceits, and explore the issues to their depths." He deplored the "evil spirit of recrimination," the "pervasive mood of suspicion," the "fear of liberty and non-conformity" that "blight the moral landscape of America."

His speech was full of witty epigrams and quips. For example: "We all say, may the best man win. It only proves that the worst man does not always lose." "Who does not publicly profess to believe in the Ten Commandments and the Golden Rule? Who does not privately boast of having violated them?" "If Providence loved the Republicans, why did He make so few of them?" And so forth. It went without saying that Stevenson endeared himself to the intellectuals and better-educated strata of American society. They had never encountered a politician quite like him, and they eagerly hung on his every word.

The campaign hardly came up to Stevenson's expectations. The two candidates did not disagree over very much. No critical issues emerged. Eisenhower promised to continue the "Great Crusade" (the title of his book of memoirs) that he had led during the war, a crusade this time against "corruption" and "party spirit" and "factional distempers." He also promised to "go to Korea" to bring that "interminable conflict" to an end "with dispatch and with honor." Stevenson's strategy was to identify himself with the Democratic achievements of the past twenty years, yet dissociate himself from the Truman administration, whose policies and reputation for moral turpitude had made it so unpopular.

At the lower levels the campaign was exceedingly vicious. Almost every prominent Democrat of national standing was charged at one time or another with being a "traitor," or at the very least, a dupe of the Communists. Senator Joseph McCarthy surpassed himself. In speech after speech before enthusiastic crowds he referred to Stevenson as "the darling of the sissies and the Communist crowd." He displayed photographs showing Stevenson in the company of Alger Hiss, or vacationing at a New England hotel, "the rendez-vous point for a whole pack of traitors and spies."

Richard Nixon went around the country demanding to know "how many Communists, Communist sympathizers, and perverts still serve in the State Department and in other government agencies." "Come January 20th next," Nixon promised, "everybody working for the United States, for you, the taxpayer, will be investigated not once, not twice, but three times. We Republicans will not rest until this government, your government, is 99 and 44/100ths per cent pure."

Even Eisenhower succumbed to the contagion. The draft of one of his speeches contained a brief, laudatory reference to General George C. Marshall. Not that lauding Marshall, who had been Army Chief of Staff during the war and later Secretary of both the State and Defense departments, required much daring. Besides, Eisenhower owed Marshall a great deal. It was Marshall who plucked him from obscurity, a mere colonel in the infantry, and made him what he was, first the commander in chief of Allied armies in North Africa, then commander in chief of Allied armies in Western Europe. But when he delivered his speech Eisenhower said not a single word about Marshall. This was because, an hour before, Senators McCarthy and Albert Jenner of Indiana (known to the Washington press corps as "Caliban") had told him that if he said "kind things about Marshall" they would "blow the whistle on the man who sold China down the river to the Reds."

"Why, he may have made an error there," Eisenhower replied softly, "but it's ridiculous to say he was responsible for —"

"General, we are adamant about that," Jenner broke in. "I have some documents on Marshall that will shock you. They shocked me and the Senator here. They confirm our worst fears about that man. I'll have them sent to you first thing tomorrow."

For the sake of Party unity Eisenhower complied.

The newspapers received a copy of the omitted passage and gave prominent coverage to what developed into a minor cause célèbre of the campaign. "Politics doth make cowards of us all," commented the Buffalo *Sun-Eagle*.

Truman, who regarded Marshall as "the greatest American of our time," was angry. "I would never have suspected Eisenhower of treachery," he said to a group of reporters "off the record." "No, not in a million years. I'll never forgive him for it."

As for Jenner's document, it turned out to be an official State Department white paper, long since published, on Marshall's Chinese mission of 1946. "Throw it into the garbage," Eisenhower said on receiving it.

One day about a month before the election, the New York *Post* carried a sensational story that detailed "the questionable financial dealings" of Richard M. Nixon. According to the report, he had received loans and gifts from a group of Californians for whom he, as congressman, had done favors. The allegation was immediately picked up by newspapers throughout the country. Eisenhower was shocked. This, on the face of it, was precisely the kind of "corruption in government" that Eisenhower had been preaching against.

"Why, if he doesn't give us a darned good explanation for this," he declared to Matthew Wells and Henry Cabot Lodge, "I'm going to replace him as my running mate."

A mood of deep gloom suddenly descended on the Republican Party as the faithful saw their chances disappearing into limbo.

Nixon collapsed when he learned of Eisenhower's reaction. He staggered to a nearby couch where he lay for several hours, refusing—or unable—to talk to anyone, while his wife, Pat (who knew exactly what to do on these occasions) applied cold compresses to his forehead. Meanwhile, his aide was telling the press that Nixon would "explain everything" on television.

Two days later, before a nationwide audience estimated at seventy-five million, Nixon recounted the travails of a poor and struggling young congressman, heavily in debt, earning only enough to meet his family's minimal wants, and occasionally accepting an "innocent gift from some friends." As for political favors in return, there were none whatever. "It is a case," he said, "of guilt by association. I am accused, not directly but by an innuendo, simply because I knew these men. I did nothing for them while I served in Congress, and there is no evidence even to remotely suggest that I did."

The remarkable aspect of Nixon's talk was its brilliantly executed stage effects. Appearing with him in his typically middle-class living room were his wife, his two young daughters, Tricia and Julie, and his cocker spaniel, Checkers. Many in his audience must have wept when he said, his voice dropping down to a whisper: "My family and I have denied ourselves a life of luxury and sparkling success. You can see that for yourselves. Great wealth might have been mine had I pursued a legal career instead of dedicating myself to public service. Can it be said that I have used my offices to enrich myself? I have always believed in a life of personal sacrifice. That was how I was raised, and that is how I have conducted myself. Pat and Tricia and Julie, and, yes, Checkers too, have shared my sacrifices. And regardless of what happens to us, we will go on making our sacrifices for the good of our country."

Tricia and Julie were holding back their tears as he faded slowly from the screen.

Throughout his ordeal by television Nixon was racked by cruel head and shoulder pains. When he finished he dropped exhausted into the waiting arms of his aide. Just then the telephone rang. It was Eisenhower calling to say that he was "completely and absolutely" satisfied, and was, in fact, "more enthusiastic about Dick Nixon than ever."

Like a tonic, these words instantly cleared Nixon's head and shoulder pains, quickened his spirit and restored his energy and sense of command. He knew (as he later described it in his book, *My Six Crises*) that he "had passed the crucial test with flying colors." If anything, "the Checkers speech" redounded to his advantage. His name was now on everyone's lips. Overnight, he had become a national celebrity.

As expected, Eisenhower won the election handily, though Stevenson received more votes than any defeated candidate in American history. Oddly, Stevenson thought he would win, and, indeed, wanted increasingly to win as the campaign progressed. His defeat was a blow to himself and, even more, to his followers who had invested so much faith and hope in him. On election eve, when the Eisenhower trend had clearly emerged, Stevenson told his Party workers, "Let us share the consolations of our common destiny. There will be new dawnings, fresh tomorrows. Together we shall gather up the future."

Between his election and inauguration—a period of two and a half months—the President-Elect of the United States lays the basis of his administration. Eisenhower disclosed the kind of administration he preferred in a memorandum to Senator Lodge (defeated, surprisingly, by a very rich, very young Irish-American politician) who headed up a committee to suggest candidates for cabinet positions.

Eisenhower wrote: "I want the best men for the jobs. By best men I mean those who have had experience as leaders and who are above venal politics. I want men who could be relied on to take command of their departments and their cadres of subordinates and who, therefore, could carry out commands from above. I'll tell you what kind of men I *don't* want: greedy, grubby little politicians and bureaucrats who prey on the taxpayer and the hard-working, conscientious citizens of America. We've had too much of that kind already."

By the first of the year Eisenhower had chosen a cabinet of distinguished corporation executives, among them Charles E. Wilson, president of General Motors, as Secretary of Defense; Herbert Brownell, a senior partner in the New York law firm of Ireton, Winstanley and Lilburne, as Attorney General; and George Humphrey, president of Hanna Steel Company as Secretary of the Treasury. The cabinet also included the presidents of two other companies, two bankers, the second largest rancher in the country, and the largest automobile dealer in the West. The post of

Secretary of State, went to the well-known professional diplomat and corporation lawyer, John Foster Dulles.

"It is no derogation of this cabinet," *New York Traveler* columnist and bureau chief J. Scott Mover wrote, "to say that it bears comparison to nothing so much as Calvin Coolidge's cabinet of 1925. For President Eisenhower, too, it seems, the business of America is business. After twenty years of wars, conflicts, change, and dislocation, Americans undoubtedly desire a long season of peace and quiet and relaxed nerves, and this, from every indication, is what Mr. Eisenhower is prepared to give them."

2

TRANSITIONS (*cont'd*)

ON January 20, 1953, the day of Eisenhower's inaugural, Stalin summoned five of his closest subordinates for a meeting in his Kremlin apartment. Beria, Marshal Malinowski, Malenkov, Molotov, and Nikita Khrushchev, a Ukrainian whose star had risen rapidly in the last few years. Though personally less close to Stalin than the others, Khrushchev held a more responsible, or at any rate more powerful, position than they: he was Deputy Chairman of the Communist Party.

Stalin lay in his bed, his head propped up on pillows, his hands folded on his chest. Shrunk with age, he looked like a saint. His eyebrows and mustache were white as ash and his face was a tawny, waxen grey. His half-closed eyes were black and opaque. He talked in a low monotone. The others strained every nerve to hear him.

"Beria," he whispered, "tell them what you found out."

Beria nodded and pulled a paper from his pocket. "Here is the report from the Bureau on the doctors' conspiracy, which Comrade Stalin requested three weeks ago. At that time Doctors Levin, Kagan, and Abramovitch examined Comrade Stalin and announced that Comrade Stalin had a brain tumor. They recommended surgery. I quote the report: 'Doctors Levin, Kagan, and Abramovitch have been meeting regularly with other Jewish doctors serving the members of the Politburo. Some of these doctors, specifically Sapir, Ashkenazi, Oistrakh, Margolis, and Zilber, have been meeting clandestinely with worshipers of the Moscow Central Synagogue. The evidence points to a major conspiracy. The Bureau is still seeking out the other culprits involved in it. We shall report again in two weeks."

"My hunch was right," Stalin said sitting up and lighting a cigarette. "I've suspected them for a long time now, these assassins. How like the Jews. They infiltrate us, they worm their way into our confidence. They seem so sure of themselves, so domineering. They cure us of our petty illnesses. We depend on them. We fall into their hands. Then we're finished. They tell us we're seriously sick. Then they must operate on us, or treat us with their drugs. I've had the drug Kagan prescribed for me tested in the laboratory. It contains a poison which destroys the nerves when taken slowly.

"It's confirmed then, comrades. They are the agents of a plot to assassinate us and seize power. The Jews have moved against us and we must strike back. Beria, round up all the doctors and make them confess. Malinowski, place the troops on alert in every city, for the Jews are clever. They've prepared counterblows. Malenkov, Khrushchev, take measures to throw the Jews out of their offices. I want the state and party apparatuses to be cleansed of them. And when this is done I want every Jew in the country to wear a badge. Comrades, I want the pale restored."

Stalin lay back, closed his eyes, and smiled. "Back on Dzernadze Street we used to spit on Pfeffer the pedlar, pull his long coat. 'Christkiller,' we used to shout at him. Yes, Christkillers. Trotsky, Kamenev, Zinoviev, Radek, all Christkillers. Ha, but they did their penance, didn't they? No, not enough. They keep coming back like a nightmare. It's never enough. Hitler, that anti-Christ, he understood.

"'Sosa,' she used to say, 'when you can't swallow something, spit it out.' Mama, you're right again. I'm going to spit them out for good. But we were so happy when we didn't know them, no, nothing about them—it was before the seminary days—me and Ziza and Turk and Zvenzi. The songs we used to sing together. How does 'Heavenly Frost' go?

Send us your heavenly frost, O Lord our God,
The morning dew awaits us.
The earth lies clean and good.
Heavenly frost, O Lord our God, your answer to our prayers."

Stalin blinked his eyes as though waking from a dream.

"I won't hold you any longer, comrades. You know what to do. Beria, report back to me in a week."

While Stalin spoke his lieutenants cast quick, furtive glances at each other. And when they left, Beria said loudly, "Comrades, let us meet in my office in an hour to discuss the implementation of Comrade Stalin's order."

They got into their Zif limousines and went to their homes. They knew why Beria, whose voice rarely rose above a whisper, spoke so loudly in the corridor outside Stalin's apartment. Stalin's "palace guard," the special police assigned to guard him under the command of Colonel Gregory Vlasov, were, as usual, eying them intently.

The palace guard had grown over the years into a large, autonomous force. The saying went, "Beria watches everybody, but Vlasov watches Beria." The palace guard, in fact, was Stalin's ultimate security, its members having sworn a secret oath of "obedience unto death." For good measure, there was a palace guard within the palace guard consisting of those who were in communication with Stalin and no one else, not even Vlasov, whom Stalin did not entirely trust. In short, everyone suspected and feared everyone else. This was exactly what Stalin wanted. He liked to repeat an old Turkestani maxim that he had learned as a child: "You may occasionally turn your back on your enemies, never on your friends."

"Here is the only place where we can talk with a little freedom," Beria said, after Malenkov, Malinowski, Molotov, and Khrushchev had assembled in his office.

"We saw it all again. The Old Man is not himself. Everytime we see him he goes into another reverie and soliloquizes about the past. Last Tuesday he recited long passages from the Bible and laughed because he had outwitted his teachers at the seminary. The Jew problem is a figment of his warped imagination. Warped is an understatement, comrades. There is no doctors' conspiracy. We've known for a long time that some of them have been meeting members of the Synagogue—their own relatives. So what? As for the poison in the prescription—that's lunacy. Of course, it contains poison, though in such small quantities as to be harmless. It's standard for nervous conditions. I take it myself. I ordered the Bureau report prepared because Vlasov's men have been on my tail too. They tell him everything. You've had the same experience."

They nodded.

"What are we to do, comrades? I've put the doctors in jail. Some are being tortured, and they'll tell us what we want them to. I don't care about them, or about the Jews. As far as I'm concerned they can disappear tomorrow, or go to Palestine or America. But what then? Who will he go after next? What are we to do?"

They discussed the question from every side, but they came up with no answer.

"I will come out and say it, comrades," Khrushchev asserted. "Nothing is to be done until he dies. That's all there is to it. Our every move is known to Vlasov. My cook and chauffeur are Vlasov men. I'm being sent another secretary tomorrow. She'll be one too. Everywhere I go I'm watched. It's worse than '36, when I couldn't talk to anyone, not even my wife, for whole weeks at a time. I survived because I followed the Ukrainian proverb: 'Unburden yourself only to God. He does not gossip.'"

"You're right," Malenkov added, "so I propose that we carry out our orders, but, like Fabius Cunctator, procrastinate as much as possible. We will then have time to learn more of his plans. The Jews, obviously, are the first step. He's a sick man. He's not as efficient and alert as he used to be. He forgets details easily now. Let's hold back on the Jews."

The purge of Jews got under way in early February. From the start it was mired in one bureaucratic delay after another. Week after week Beria explained to Stalin how much progress was being made, fabricating statistics of Jews ousted from jobs, Jews imprisoned, Jews shipped off to work camps, Jews who committed suicide, Jews convicted of participating in the plot, etc.

The three million Jews of the Soviet Union, meanwhile, trembled for their lives. Rumors flew among them that camps would soon be set up, then gas chambers and crematoria. All of them, atheists and believers alike, those who belonged to the Party and those who did not, asked themselves, "Where is the Queen Esther who will save us from this Haman? Who will send the plagues that will lay this pharaoh low? Who will punish this Gog and Magog?"

Not since the Nazi invasion of 1941 were the synagogues so full.

One afternoon in March, Beria, Malenkov, Malinowski, and

Khrushchev were hurriedly asked to attend an "emergency conference" in Stalin's office. They found him sitting behind his great mahogany desk, wearing his wartime uniform. He looked unusually fit and clear-eyed. At his side, behind the desk, were Vlasov and a palace guard with his hands in his pockets.

"Maybe you know why I asked you to come," Stalin said distinctly, staring at each of them in turn. "Did you think you could get away with it? I always suspected you of plotting with the Jews, and I was right. At this time tomorrow you—"

Suddenly his eyes and mouth opened wide, he got up from his chair, swayed, and sank to the floor, moaning. Vlasov and the guard ran to him.

Khrushchev, running too, shouted: "Get them, hurry." Beria, Malenkov, and Malinowsky, who had been rooted to the floor like trees, quickly ran over.

As Stalin lay on the Persian-carpeted floor, moaning, the six men wrestled and fought in a great melee. The guard was easily subdued. Vlasov, however, put up a ferocious struggle and was vanquished only after Khrushchev leaped on his head with both feet and knocked him unconscious.

"We're in luck," Khrushchev said breathlessly, his eyes popping out of his head. "Nobody yet knows what's happened here. Beria, Malinowski, call your men. Bring them here right away. First we must take this building."

Within an hour Beria's police, joined by a battalion of infantrymen from the Kremlin barracks, had secured the building. Within three hours every major building in Moscow had similarly been occupied. It was all done effortlessly, arousing scant attention. The public knew nothing.

That evening Vlasov and his assistants were shot in the courtyard of the Moscow Penitentiary and buried in unmarked graves. A silent counterpurge took place throughout the Soviet Union. The "Vlasovites" were eliminated from the ranks of the Party, the secret police, the army, and the ministries of state.

"The social organism is now healthy," Beria announced to his colleagues. "The diseased cells have been removed."

Stalin lay in a coma at the Moscow University Clinic. The doctors (all non-Jewish) diagnosed his condition as a stroke brought on by "brain inflammation." The news stunned the

Soviet people, who had assumed that he was indestructible and who, after thirty years of his iron rule, could not imagine living without him.

"Our revered father and comrade and fellow worker has been struck down," *Pravda* wrote. "Messages of profound regret and sympathy are pouring in from all over the world, from children and workers and statesmen everywhere. Comrade J. Stalin is waging a titanic struggle for his life. Humanity, for whom he labored tirelessly, awaits the outcome."

Meanwhile, Beria, Malenkov, Molotov, Malinowski, and Khrushchev conferred without letup. They discussed three questions: What should they do if he recovered? What should they do if he remained in a coma a long time? What should they do if he died?

The first question answered itself. They had no choice. Should he live they would die. As for questions two and three, they agreed to set up a "provisional triumvirate" if the coma persisted and a permanent one if he died. They would decide its composition when the time came.

Late in the evening of the second day of Stalin's illness the doctors in attendance sent for them. "He has been opening his eyes and mumbling," one of the doctors said. "We were instructed to inform you the moment there was any change in his condition."

Beria, Malenkov, Malinowski, and Khrushchev were ushered into the half-lit room and gathered close to the grey porcelain figure lying in bed who now bore no resemblance to the man they once knew.

Blinking erratically, Stalin talked and chuckled under his breath. "Ah, you see, Sosa was right, wasn't he? My grades are good. Terdzadze's are better, yes, Mama, but he studies all the time . . . Yes, Father Isaurus, I wrote it. I only did what Christ would have done if He had walked among the workers. Go ahead, punish me . . . No, I don't trust Comrade Lev Davidovitch . . . Yes, Comrade Lenin, his grades are better. He studies too hard. He's devious . . . Don't storm the Winter Palace. No, don't. Don't trust him, don't trust him, comrades, St. Vladimir . . . Comrade Terdzovidovitchonstein is a thief. They're all thieves. They all study too hard. That's why they get good grades . . . Yes, Mama, I—"

Stalin stopped talking and blinking and closed his eyes. His breathing grew more and more irregular. His visitors, who had been bending over him, came to the foot of the bed. "I think we've heard his last words in this world," Malenkov said.

"He may rule over us in the next," Beria added.

"You're humor is grim," Malenkov replied. "It's enough to make one pray for redemption."

An hour later the doctors pronounced Stalin dead.

For two days and nights Stalin's body lay in state in the Great Hall of the Palace of the Russias. Hundreds of thousands of people passed in review, paying homage to the man who had brought them so much hope and suffering, joy and death, who had led them, for better or worse, in their moments of high destiny. Buildings in every Soviet city were draped in black. The radio performed *Te deums* from Schubert, Beethoven, Franck, Brahms, Borodin, and Milhaud, interspersed with commentaries on the achievements of this "father of peoples."

Speaking for the Politburo, Khrushchev delivered a poignant eulogy on Stalin's wisdom, magnanimity, and capacity for leadership. "With his death we have lost the best and greatest part of ourselves."

The Jews of the Soviet Union did not join in the mourning. They quietly greeted the news of his death as a jubilee. "Let us rejoice," the Grand Rabbi of Moscow whispered to his son as he raised a goblet of sweet wine to his lips, "the angel of death has delivered us."

The plan that had been decided on during Stalin's illness went immediately into effect. Beria, Malenkov, and Molotov, "the Grand Triumvirate," jointly ruled the Soviet Union, and a new principle, "collective leadership," was advanced to justify the new arrangement. The world wondered why these three men had been chosen. It also wondered where the real power resided. Few believed that "collective leadership" could work.

"The triumvirate governing the Soviet Union after Stalin's death will prove as durable as the one that governed the Roman empire after Caesar's," Andrew Bequest, a highly respected "Kremlinologist" noted in the *Glasgow Sentinel*. "Who is going to be the Soviet Augustus Caesar? And will he inaugurate another age of the Antonines? It is too much to be hoped for. In any case, I think we have seen the last of the Stalins."

In late March 1953, two weeks after the triumvirate had been installed, Beria, Malenkov, Malinowski, Molotov, and Khrushchev went down to Stalin's splendid dacha in the Crimea, overlooking the Black Sea. During a midnight repast of sturgeon, vodka, and black bread, Beria rose and declared that his proposals were ready. "Comrades, we all agree on one thing: it's time for a re-examination. Eisenhower and Churchill* have called for new approaches, for an era of peace. Are they sincere? Can they be trusted? We won't ever know, comrades, until we've tested them. What tests? Let's look at the main areas of tension.

"First and least important, Korea. I say least important because the war there involves no fundamental conflict. No one has anything to gain or lose there. Second, the atomic bomb. Soon we and the Americans will have hydrogen bombs. Ragozin tells me one hydrogen bomb can liquidate Moscow. Scientists don't have to inform us that such weapons make no distinction between capitalists and Communists. Yes, comrades, we will win the next war, if it comes. But we may end up envying the dead. Third, Germany, the most intractable problem. I don't have to remind you of it. The revanchists are arming to the teeth. The American fools think they can control Adenauer and bend him and the old Nazis in the government to their will. In Georgia we say, 'Play with the devil and the devil plays with you.'

"I come to the point, comrades. We must scale down the Cold War. Maybe Eisenhower and Churchill want to scale it down also. Let us seize the initiative. I propose that we undertake the following major policy changes. First, we will persuade comrades Mao and Kim to sign an armistice in Korea along present lines of discussion at Panmunjom. What if they resist such a solution? We will see. Second, we will try to reach an agreement with the West on control of the atomic bomb and other weapons of mass destruction. We can concede a little to each other. Why not? We can let them inspect provided they destroy their stockpiles or turn them over to a neutral. And third, we must stop the Germans from rearming. Will the Americans give the Germans atomic weapons? Then we will have to march

* Who had been re-elected Prime Minister in 1951.—N.F.M.

in. To avoid that possibility I propose—and don't be alarmed by my saying this, comrades—that we give up Ulbricht and the GDR [German Democratic Republic] in exchange for a neutral, disarmed, unified Germany, just as were prepared to do back in May 1949.

"Why do I put forward these proposals? Because I'm convinced, comrades, that a relaxation of tensions would benefit us. We must get on with the job of building Communism, giving our masses the fruits of their labor. Even if we have to yield up something valuable, a détente would be to our advantage. Thank you, comrades. I have finished."

While Beria spoke Molotov had been drinking more than his usual amount of vodka. He had been staring into space, his back stiff as iron, his face a mottled red.

"I must register my disapproval of Comrade Beria's remarks," Molotov said, speaking very rapidly. "Do you think the West will concede us anything without demanding a pound of our flesh? With all due respects to you, comrade, I am constrained to call your proposals naïve. The United States and Britain will interpret our generosity as weakness, our initiative in seeking a détente as pusillanimity. They will become ever more aggressive, more militaristic, more imperialistic. The consequence of your proposals, should we act on them, will be—and I must be candid—to increase the probability of conflict and war. Yes, they are clever. They will 'string us along,' as the Americans say, leading us to think that progress is being made on the armaments and German issues. Then, enveloped in our own illusions, we put down our guard more and more. Meanwhile, their preparations for further aggrandizement continue."

Molotov seemed more composed now, and he spoke more slowly and deliberately.

"I propose that we tell the West the following: First, that we will do no more than *discuss* inspection of atomic facilities after all stockpiles have been destroyed. Second, that we abandon the fiction that Germany can ever be neutralized, recognize the German Democratic Republic's autonomy, and strengthen Ulbricht's hand. And third, that we strive to keep the Korean War going at the present benign level. For that war, comrades, serves our interest very well. Many, many American troops are tied up there, at huge expense to the United States, thereby aggravating its contradictions.

"Comrades, why should we solve the West's problems? The troops now in Korea may eventually find their way to Europe. As for our own people, I would be the first to advocate improving their condition—once the threat to their lives is removed. Remember, they mustn't be lulled to sleep by false expectations. I recall something V. I. Lenin said to us just before the Revolution, when we were all hiding in the cellar of Asnov's house. 'If and when we take power,' he said, 'we Bolsheviks will be like doctors who insist on curing their patients before allowing them to indulge their pleasures!' Comrades, we must not give up our role as doctors."

Malenkov seemed to be smiling. There was no way of knowing if he actually was, since his round face never expressed emotion. (This was a quality that Stalin reputedly liked in him. "I detest men who carry their emotions on their sleeve," Stalin was once heard to say. "And you, Malenkov, don't even have any in your heart.")

Malenkov got up, lifted high his vodka glass, and offered a toast. "Comrade Molotov, your eloquence was magisterial. It deserves to be celebrated."

The others, Molotov excepted, laughed and drank up.

Malenkov continued, "It may surprise you, but I'm not going to say very much here. Besides my head is beginning to swim and I would like to take a bath. I find it strange that Comrade Molotov has so little faith in the people of the Soviet Union. Does he think they will become voluptuaries if tensions relax, if they can buy more goods, if they don't have to worry about war quite so much as they did? I quote Lenin: 'Trust the masses. Go to them as a humble student, not as a stern master.'

"Let me ask Comrade Molotov one other question. Does he have so little faith in our army? Let us for the sake of argument imagine the worst. The Americans have sent more divisions into Germany because the Korean War has ended. The West German army is increased too. Will they defeat our men in the field, if it comes to that? Can they take us on after we have mobilized our masses? They know they cannot defeat us. Therefore, they may, after all, accede to the neutralization of Germany, which will at least set up a buffer zone between us. It's certainly worth a try. I favor Comrade Beria's proposals."

Malinowski, who looked more porcine than usual when he drank, said that he, too, favored them. Only, as commander of the armed forces, he wanted the Soviet Union to serve notice "to any potential aggressors that they will be decisively rebuffed, for the Soviet Union possesses a full arsenal of the most up-to-date weapons, including atomic arms of every description."

They all nodded in perfunctory agreement.

Finally, Khrushchev rose to speak. He was obviously high, for he had a wide grin on his face. When he drank too much he would often play the part of a clown or buffoon. But as everyone who knew him came to realize, there was more to his buffoonery than met the eye.

"We Ukrainians have a saying: 'When the arguments flow heavy the issue has been decided.' Comrades, all of you were exceptional. You are born debaters. Excellent. I'd like to drink to the exquisite entertainment we have witnessed. I'm not being disrespectful. You know that. My sainted mother taught me: 'He who feels respect most shows it least.' I wish only to state here that I agree wholeheartedly with all of you and favor putting Comrade Beria's proposals into effect. Let us throw them the bait. When they snap we will haul them in. Another toast."

Before long the West began noticing the telltale signs of change. At state receptions in Moscow and in other capitals Soviet diplomats dropped hints that their "minds were not closed"— the stock phrase—on a host of issues that divided the blocs. *Pravda* quoted Lenin on the desirability of peace between nations "with opposing social systems." Soviet UN delegates conspicuously toned down their Cold War rhetoric, avoiding, for the first time in years, any reference to the American President as "the tool of the ruling classes," etc.

Of singular significance were the speeches delivered by Soviet leaders, particularly those by Malenkov, whom most Western authorities believed was Stalin's successor. To be sure, Malenkov went through the usual ritual, condemning the United States for its "belligerent and provocative policies," and warning that it faced "a crushing rebuff" should it "embark on aggressive adventures." But Malenkov also stated what the West had not heard since the Second World War, that "all peoples today desire peace, whatever their ideological differences," that "hydrogen bombs do not distinguish one ideology from another, and Socialists do not wish to inherit a world of rubble and radioactivity," and that "it is time for the Soviet Union to turn its attention from capital goods industries to consumer goods industries," the task of Communism being "to raise living standards beyond the wildest dreams of the capitalist exploiters, in accordance with the immutable doctrine of Marxism-Leninism."

Western Kremlinologists found it worthy of note that Malenkov omitted saying "Marxism-Leninism-Stalinism." "There is a pattern developing," one Professor Adam Homburg wrote in the May 1953 number of *Foreign Policy Review,* "which bears close scrutiny. We may be on the verge of an important break in the international log jam."

Behind the scenes, meanwhile, Soviet leaders were busy implementing their policy decisions. Mao Tse-tung and Kim Il Sung secretly flew to Moscow and were whisked from the airport to Beria's office, where the Politburo awaited them.

"There is no reason, comrades, why the fighting should go on," Beria said mildly. "Nothing more, it seems to us, is to be gained in Korea. One more hill, one less hill, what does it matter? The Americans are not going to repatriate the prisoners they hold, and there is no way you can force them to. The Soviet Union maintains that you should agree to an armistice with the United States simply on the basis of the status quo."

The Soviet statesmen expected Mao and Kim to object strenuously, and they had prepared a series of tough moves, including a threat to withdraw Soviet arms from the Chinese and North Korean forces. Both Mao and Kim, however, were tired of the costly war and welcomed the chance to end it despite the fact that most of the twenty-five thousand North Korean prisoners in UN hands would not go back home.

"All right," Mao said, "but suppose the Americans resort to trickery and deceit, suppose they attack Manchuria, suppose they bring in atomic weapons—what would the Soviet Union do?"

"I think I can answer that," Khrushchev shouted. "We'll answer back in kind. We'll send in our own volunteers to Korea.

They won't get away with it. The Americans will know where we stand."

"If this is your promise, comrades," Kim Il Sung said, "then we, Comrade Mao and myself, will sign the armistice."

After Mao and Kim had gone, Beria asked Khrushchev if he trusted "our Asian comrades."

"No," Khrushchev replied, "but since they do not trust us what choice do they have? They want peace, too, and they're afraid the Americans might escalate the conflict. An old Ukrainian proverb goes: 'When fear and doubt copulate wisdom is born.' The Korean War will end."

At the extremities of the Communist "World Island" the Soviet Union was setting the forces of change in motion. Walter Ulbricht furtively arrived in Moscow the day after Mao and Kim departed, and, like them, appeared before the Politburo. "Comrade Ulbricht," Beria said softly, in his most blatantly pedagogic manner, "what do you think of new initiatives by our side to solve the German question?"

"Yes, comrades, I recently heard you had something of the sort in mind. I welcome a new initiative."

Ulbricht spoke these words grimly, laboriously, as though they had been forced out of him. Bald-headed and goateed, he resembled Lenin at a distance. (Stalin once remarked: "Imagine Lenin as a prison warden, and you have Ulbricht.")

Beria continued, "The Politburo has decided that it would be well if in the next few weeks you could broaden your coalition to include more members of the Socialist Party."

"Why, comrade, do you want us to do this?" Ulbricht asked.

"Because, comrade, we have reason to believe that the West may jettison Adenauer and the revanchists and remove their troops if you broaden the base of your government and Soviet troops are similarly withdrawn from the German Democratic Republic. Eventually—and this is our hope—there will no longer be any foreign troops on German soil, and your government and the West Germans can negotiate a treaty of unity."

Ulbricht rose. "Comrades, we welcome the new initiative. We think your suggestions excellent, and will carry it out at once."

When Ulbricht left, Beria said, "He is a fox. We'll have to watch him closely. If it were up to me—I speak only for myself, comrades—I would not be displeased if he met with an accident."

The others objected. "We must wait," Malenkov said. "Let's not discuss accidents now."

"By the time we discuss it, it might be too late," Beria said, smiling slightly. "Beware the fox who escapes his trap."

3

ROLLBACK

AS Secretary of State, John Foster Dulles occupied the most important cabinet position in the Eisenhower administration. In some respects his authority was comparable to Eisenhower's. That was because Eisenhower himself wanted it that way. When he appointed Dulles after the election Eisenhower made it clear that he expected "State" to be Dulles's responsibility.

"I'm not one of those Presidents who thinks he's got to run everything," he told Dulles at the time. "FDR, I remember, had his finger in every darned pot. Cordell Hull, a great man, was nothing but his errand boy. Now, Foster, you know there's no one whose judgment I appreciate more than yours. I'd be a damned fool if I tried to interfere with you. And you can count on my backing one hundred per cent."

Though a Republican, Dulles had been one of the architects of American foreign policy since the war. He had been called in as an adviser or consultant on most of the important State Department decisions, and was credited with at least one major achievement, the framing of the peace treaty with Japan. His career marked the apogee of a long and illustrious family tradition. For generations the Fosters and Dulleses (the main branches of the family tree) were prominent in business and law, in missionary work and foreign policy, combining all in a diapason of imperial statesmanship. He was one of the most successful corporation lawyers in the country. (He was senior partner in the firm of Stuart, Stafford, Halifax, and Jeffrey.) As an elder in the First Marble Presbyterian Church of New York, he was active in Protestant affairs and kept abreast of events in church theology and politics. His favorite reading was Knox's *Sermons,*

The Lives of the Protestant Saints, the writings of Cotton Mather,
and Milton's *Paradise Lost.* Looming up from his desk in large
bold letters was a quote from John Bunyan: "For the Righteous
the Devil conjureth up every cunning Snare and Delusion. Beware;
Strait is the Gate."

Early in February 1953, Dulles lectured the National Security
Council, Eisenhower attending, on the topic, "Directions of United
States Policy toward World Communism." As its title suggested, it
was intended to be a broad definition of American principles
governing foreign policy decisions in the years ahead. Dulles
spoke extemporaneously, as was his custom, from notes hastily
jotted down a few moments before.

"Some of you may recall a talk given three and a half years
ago, just after China fell, by my esteemed predecessor, on the
somber theories of the geopoliticians. He accepted those theories
and said that whoever controls the World Island—the Siberian-
Chinese land mass—stands an excellent chance of dominating
the world. It was, you may remember, a rather pessimistic report,
though Mr. Acheson put a brave face on it. Well, I have a more
optimistic report.

"In the first place, too much is made of those grandiose
geopolitical concepts. We're not dealing with Tamerlane or Attila
or Genghis Khan. We're dealing with an empire of hundreds of
millions of people kept down by satanic force, restless, unhappy,
desiring above all the freedom that is their birthright too. For,
Mr. President, gentlemen, the World Island, if you please, is
vulnerable.

"I am not referring here to military assault. That is not my
theme. I am referring to its inner weaknesses. Consider what
lies behind the iron curtain. First, there are the satellite countries,
yoked to a monstrous tyranny. The people of East Germany,
Poland, Hungary, Czechoslovakia, Romania, Albania, and Bulgaria would assert their independence without a second's hesita-
tion. That we take for granted. Less well understood, perhaps, is
the hatred felt by the various nationalities *within* the Soviet Union
for their oppressors. After all, the population of Great Russia is
about half that of the Soviet Union as a whole. The people of
the Baltic countries, the Ukraine, White Russia, the Georgians,
the Muslims of Central Asia, the other subjugated minorities—

Jews, Tartars, Christians, and the like—they would declare their independence as well, if they could. The Soviet Union, in short, presides over an empire like the one established by the Mongol hordes. It bears within itself the seeds of its dissolution.

"Now the Republican Party in its last platform implicitly acknowledged the possibility of dissolution when it vowed to support the captive peoples behind the iron curtain in their quest for freedom. I helped draw up that particular plank, and I subscribe to it fully. I'm convinced—and I speak here as a realist, without illusions about the nature of politics—I'm convinced that the free world will win out in its struggle against this besetting evil of the human race. It will win without going to war. And it will win much sooner than is commonly thought. Too often pessimism becomes a self-fulfilling prophecy. If we believe that Communism is the wave of the future, then we tend to yield to it as though it, in fact, were. This spiritual submission to the furies of Communism, you will agree, was the chief problem of the previous administration. The objective of that administration, unfortunately, went no further than to hold back the wave, at best contain it. In my opinion, Communism is the wave of the past. I see it receding steadily in the days and years ahead. We may see its disappearance as a threat to freedom and Christianity in our lifetime.

"But rolling back Communism will be preordained only if we make it so. We can be the prophets of the new day, fulfilling not our own prophecies but those enjoined on us by merciful Providence. And so I propose three methods, employed simultaneously, by which the United States and the free world can force a rollback of Communism. We have the spiritual capacity to accomplish it. We need only the will.

"First, there is negotiation. The United States is not averse to negotiating differences with the Soviet Union, provided we negotiate from strength, overwhelming strength, the strength of the just, and negotiate to secure *our* ends. In fact, our abiding hope is that the Soviet Union will voluntarily make good the wrongs it has committed since 1945, to go back no further. But we know from experience that Communists do nothing voluntarily, or rather volunteer to do something only when confronted with a more forbidding alternative. The Soviet Union, for example, voluntarily got out of Iran, voluntarily ended the Berlin blockade, voluntarily refrained from devouring Yugoslavia. Need I cite more examples?

"Second, there are military alliances. We have seen how successful the Truman Doctrine and NATO have been. They have stopped the Communists dead in their tracks. I propose we extend the alliance system to cover the whole circumference of the World Island, so-called. The State Department is now drafting a series of ironclad pacts with those countries of the free world that have reason to fear Communist aggression and subversion.

"This raises the question of the neutral nations. They perceive no difference between, or refuse to identify with, either side in the struggle. If and when India and Indonesia and Egypt and the others come to realize where their true interests lie they will be welcomed into the structure of free world alliances. I think it's only a matter of time before they see the light.

"Third and last, there are the other techniques. I say other techniques because I'm not free at the moment to spell them out in detail or with any specificity. It's enough to say that several departments of the administration are drawing up a master plan to counter the less overt forms of subversion and aggression— less overt but at least as dangerous. We must be prepared to utilize without compunction what I would call the arcane strategies against our foe. We must build up our counterespionage activities. We must infiltrate the ranks of our opponents. So as to win friends and influence people [here Dulles smiled] we must employ much more extensive, much more sophisticated propaganda devices. We must enlist every private group that has international affiliations and commands international trust—business, labor, religious organizations, students, intellectuals, and so forth—in the holy crusade against Communism. We must, in a word, enormously expand our Central Intelligence apparatus and invest it with new and creative responsibilities.

"And so, Mr. President, gentlemen, I close on a note of hope and good cheer. We shall seize the initiative and press forward our advantage, forcing the enemy to surrender his ill-begotten treasures. I'm confident we will witness the peaceful transformation of the Communist empire into a collectivity of free and independent peoples and nations. To bring this about is the mission we Americans have covenanted with Providence. We here in this room are privileged to be the leaders of such a people."

Three months after Dulles delivered his lecture he conferred at length with President Eisenhower on the "overtures" for a settlement that were coming from the Soviet Union.

"Mr. President, an interesting situation has suddenly arisen. It rather surprises me. I didn't expect the Russians to feel the pressure of discontent so soon. To judge from our informants there the peoples of the Soviet Union and the satellites are growing more and more restless, and the Communists are worried. That's why they're seeking some kind of accommodation with us. They say—and this is all quite informal, in the nature, really, of hints dropped here and there—they're willing to concede on inspections to get a treaty on atomic arms, and they're willing to concede on free elections in a unified Germany to get a treaty guaranteeing German neutrality."

Eisenhower asked Dulles how he evaluated these "overtures."

"Well, Mr. President, in the first place, I'd be exceedingly wary, for the Soviets may be using these concessions as sweeteners to get something in return, for example Soviet hegemony over Eastern Europe."

"Of course," the President said emphatically, "that would be clearly unacceptable."

"Or," Dulles continued, "maybe the Russians have got to concede, maybe they've got to draw in their reins because they lack the strength or resolve to keep up the competition with us. The other day Malenkov remarked that the Soviet economy must switch over to consumer goods to satisfy the needs of the people. Keeping a large army, producing atomic and hydrogen bombs, why, these are expensive undertakings. How long will their people accept the Spartan regimen they're subjected to? Personally, Mr. President, I don't believe the Russians are able to sustain the load. That's why I'm against lightening the load. Or, to change the figure, pulling their chestnuts out of the fire."

"But, Foster, this is a curious thing. Won't that drive them to rash behavior? After all, if they think they're going down, why, they might go down fighting, taking us down with them. During the war the Germans fought harder'n hell just because they knew they'd been beaten. Look at the battle of Berlin. Zhukov lost two hundred thousand of his crack troops there. Yet the Germans knew the war'd been lost a long time ago."

"I see your point, Mr. President, but I think we can discount such actions on their part. We have an enormous atomic superiority over them, and they know full well they would be destroyed like Sodom and Gomorrah if they tried to, say, invade Western Europe. The Russians have always been cautious in provoking direct conflict. And whenever it appeared a conflict might develop they've drawn back. They want no war, sir. But if we were to disarm ourselves—that is, agree to give up our stockpile of atomic arms and castrate NATO, which, as you know, is their objective in seeking the neutralization of Germany —then and only then would they be tempted to move against us. By keeping up the pressure, Mr. President, we ensure the peace. I subscribe to Jonathan Edwards' great advice: 'He who would reach the Lord must first enter the Devil's sanctuary.'"

Eisenhower smiled. "Go ahead, Foster, and handle those overtures as you think best, and report back to me if anything new develops."

"One more thing, Mr. President," Dulles added, "we're fairly certain now that the Chinese and North Koreans will come to terms at Panmunjom, though we don't know exactly when. That issue, sir, is settled, I think."

Eisenhower nodded his head vigorously. "That's good news, because I was getting goddamned mad at the procrastinations there. You're right about keeping up the pressure. They realized, I think, that my patience was wearing thin. I doubt I would have let those talks continue past summer. Let's hope we have an armistice, signed, sealed, and delivered before then."

The armistice was, in fact, signed at Panmunjom in late June 1953, three years after the fighting had begun, and after more than a million people died, including thirty-eight thousand Americans. Though the agreement had come after two years of negotiation, Eisenhower, who had been in office only five months, received the credit for it from a grateful American public.

Following his conference with Eisenhower, Dulles flew to Bonn, the capital of the German Federal Republic, to discuss the German question with Chancellor Konrad Adenauer. All day the two men talked in Adenauer's oak-paneled office, which was

full of his family pictures—he had forty children and grandchildren—and other memorabilia of a rich Rhineland life.

"Der Alte," or the old man, as he was affectionately called,
was approaching eighty, yet his vigor would have daunted a man
fifty years younger. Tall and trim, he stood straight as an arrow.
He exercised commanding authority over the government and
the Christian Democratic Party, the party devoted to the interests of business and the goal of "a united, democratic,
Christian Europe."

"Mr. Secretary," Adenauer said, "you know what the Russians
are up to. To us it is clear as spring water. They are going to
offer up the East German puppet state as a sacrificial lamb in
order to obtain a unified Germany to their liking, a Germany
that will be neutral in the struggle between freedom and Communism, civilization and barbarism. Most Germans, certainly the
Christian Democratic Party, as you are well aware, resolutely
oppose any arrangement that will prevent Germany's affiliation
with Western civilization, ratify the Oder-Neisse line as Germany's
permanent border, and cut us off from the protection of NATO,
thus leaving us to Russia's tender mercies.

"I might add a fourth, *entre nous*. A unified Germany under
any conditions might place a left-wing or Socialist coalition in
power. A third of West Germany's electorate votes Socialist. We
reckon that three quarters of East Germany is Socialist too.
Combine the two and you have a Socialist majority. That would
be a disaster, Mr. Secretary. It would set back indefinitely the
task of educating the people to democracy and freedom that the
Christian Democratic Party has been carrying on for five years.
We cannot let that happen. I therefore urge you, Mr. Secretary,
not to succumb to Soviet blandishments. We had a saying in the
good old days: 'When the Bear dances it is time to pick up your
gun.' "

Dulles laughed. "We certainly won't put down the gun, even if
the Bear does somersaults. You're perfectly right, Herr Chancellor; your analysis of the issue coincides precisely with ours. I
told the President last week pretty much what you have just told
me, and he agreed that we must uphold the ideals of Western
civilization at all costs. The governments of the United States,

Great Britain, and France are awaiting definite word from the Soviet Union on its intentions.

"Herr Chancellor, my government has decided that German unification is possible only under the conditions you have specified—that the new Germany be linked to the West, that it retrieve the lost territories, that it respect the free institutions established under previous democratically elected government. It is highly improbable, you will agree, that the Soviets will give so much away. Not unless something is happening behind the iron curtain of which we are ignorant."

"No matter," Adenauer replied. "They will not change very much, whoever rules over them. The policy we Germans favor is simple and unambiguous: to maintain the status quo so that we can develop our way of life without interference or interruption. May I quote Schiller?

> *You who are free!*
> *Be yourself every moment of your life.*
> *That's the meaning of liberty."*

The West's response to Soviet overtures—or rather its refusal to make one—played neatly into Walter Ulbricht's hands. On his way back from Moscow he had told his protégé, Willi Stoff, that he was not "fooled for one moment." "I have long ago given up false hopes. Beria knew that I knew he was lying. Obviously he didn't care because they're planning to throw us over. The Democratic Republic is expendable. Why? I don't know yet. Maybe there's to be a deal with the Americans. Maybe we're to be sacrificed for a disarmaments deal. But I don't think the deal's been made. If it had been he wouldn't have lied to me. He would have thrown me out on my ass, maybe worse. Some joke, eh? After all I've given to the movement, after all I've suffered.

"But enough excuses. I've one card left, and I'm going to play it when the time's right. Remember what Novalis said: 'If life has dealt thee no cards to play hie thee to a monastery and say thy beads.' "

Ulbricht had rightly perceived what was taking place behind his back. Soviet authorities in East Germany were encouraging the anti-Ulbricht faction in the government to begin "a campaign of criticism" preparatory to taking power. This faction favored closer ties with the "unificationists" of West Germany and with those Socialists who desired a new and restructured Germany, one free of ancient dogmatic controversies and independent of both sides in the Cold War. The leaders of the anti-Ulbricht faction were led to believe that the triumphant moment was at hand, and some of them were even sounding out the head of the West German Socialist Party, Erich Ollenauer, to determine "a possible basis of accord and common effort."

It was just then, in mid-June, 1953, that Ulbricht played his hand. His regime ordered the work quota, already oppressive beyond endurance, increased by 50 per cent.

"The satanic mills of nineteenth-century Manchester and Pittsburgh were not as bad as our factories have become," said Kurt Meyer, the Minister of Education and a prominent "unificationist." "If our workers are not commodities—how can they be in a Socialist society?—neither are they men."

Mass discontent in East Germany, fed by factory insurgents, grew worse by the day. Ulbricht, meanwhile, was incommunicado. He was nowhere to be found. The regime, in fact, seemed to have absconded. His opponents realized what his strategy was: to create a crisis that would, in the end, force the Soviets to send in troops.

At last one of the factories, the Stalin Werke of East Berlin, exploded in revolt. The workers put down their tools and marched toward the Ministry of Justice to present their demands for a lower work quota and for other reforms, notably the right to establish their own councils and union delegates. No one stood in their way. The march was the signal for a full-scale work stoppage, as East Berliners poured into the streets to join the swelling band of insurgents.

General Maxim Urenko, the Soviet commandant, attempted to reach the Premier, the President, Party boss Ulbricht. To no avail. He finally spoke to Kurt Meyer, who had been imploring the crowd to return to their factories and homes. "Your demands will be met," Meyer kept pleading with them, "but you must first go back. You're playing into our enemies' hands."

"There is no government here," Urenko complained. "It's vanished. Who's giving orders? Who's in charge?"

"It's all part of Ulbricht's plot. He planned this whole thing."

"I don't care about that," Urenko replied. "I have my duties. Can you, or anyone, disperse the crowd? If you can't, my men will come in. I don't want bloodshed. It's up to you."

But the crowd would not disperse. And as its numbers increased so did its anger. Crowds were also beginning to form in Halle, Dresden, Leipzig, and other industrial centers, and reports were circulated of unrest in Prague, Warsaw, and Budapest.

Urenko, meanwhile, had spoken to Malinowski and Khrushchev. They had declared that the uprising had to be "smashed" at all costs. "Don't hesitate for a single second. Destroy this cancer," Khrushchev shouted into the phone.

Before carrying out his order, Urenko spoke again to Meyer. "It's hopeless, General," Meyer said in despair, "bring in your troops."

Within an hour Soviet tanks and armored carriers were rumbling through the streets of East Berlin and every other large city in East Germany. Accompanying them were loudspeakers warning that groups of three or more would be instantly fired upon. The uprising was crushed. What there remained of the government of the German Democratic Republic was to be found at Soviet Army Headquarters.

During the two and a half days of the rebellion, the five-man Soviet Presidium—Beria, Malenkov, Bulganin, Molotov, and Kaganovitch—along with Khrushchev and Malinowski, met around the clock at the War Ministry deep in the bowels of the Kremlin. The Presidium was split into two, or more exactly, three factions: "the tough ones": Molotov and Kaganovitch (Stalin's burly, reticent brother-in-law, the only prominent Jew in the Soviet hierarchy); "the tender ones": Beria and Malenkov; and "the fence-sitter": Marshal Nikolai A. Bulganin, a wily military commissar who had survived the Kremlin wars by waiting until the last moment and then siding with the "right" group. Since Stalin's death he was thought to be "leaning toward" Khrushchev.

Molotov was bitterly sarcastic. "I'm afraid events have not added to Comrade Beria's luster as a statesman. He will have to admit that foreign policy decisions are a trifle more complex than running a secret police bureau."

"I object to Comrade Molotov's impertinence," Malenkov asserted, his eyes shining under his heavy, watery lids. "If he has a point to make let him make it. Shall we dredge up each other's mistakes? I'm sure Comrade Molotov would prefer we did not."

"Yes, I will stick to the point," Molotov returned. "We are now observing the fruits of our decision to accommodate the West. Our enemies have suddenly come out of the cracks in the wall. We have read Ulbricht's statement of an hour ago telling us what we should have anticipated all along. Encourage the anti-Soviet elements and they will try to deliver the German Democratic Republic over to the West. That, comrades, is what the uprising is all about. It is a fascist-inspired counterrevolution. What is more, it is stirring up the fascists in the other peoples' democracies. We are confronted with an ugly situation and we must show no mercy, not a scintilla of it.

"Now I come to the nub of the point. Comrades Beria and Malenkov were, and perhaps still are, hopeful that the United States would seek a détente with us. They are right, of course. Only it is a détente that would leave us impotent, a détente based on the rollback principle enunciated by Dulles and other American politicians. They talk of liberating the captive peoples by inciting rebellion among the peoples of the Socialist bloc. There you have it. Far from discarding the German revanchists, the United States has adopted their approach. It wants to re-create the fascism of prewar days. It wants to ring the Soviet Union with enemies again! The uprising is part of an organized and co-ordinated plot, comrades.

"I wish I did not have to say it, comrades, but did I not foretell the disaster that threatens to befall us? I repeat the words of St. Basil of the Don: 'Suffer, ye prophets, for rendering the truth unto thy brethren.' My advice is simple. No further talk of negotiation with the West. Crack down on the troublemakers everywhere. Restore Ulbricht to full power. Treat the Adenauer regime as an enemy. Let the Americans come to us as supplicants."

Throughout, Beria smiled in his slightly ironic way and stared off into the distance.

It was Malenkov who spoke for "the tender ones." "We Russians have a proverb that applies here: 'Don't be too quick to judge, especially where you have a stake.' Comrade Molotov,

who wants to be honored as our Cassandra, would have us
believe that the issue is settled, and, so far as he is concerned,
nothing more is to be said. But much more is to be said.
Now let *me* point out several things.

"First, we know that Ulbricht engineered the crisis and committed deliberately provocative acts. Comrade Molotov would
reward him for it. I would shoot him for it. Second, there are
no fascist plots. Such plots are figments of Comrade Molotov's
febrile imagination. Let us admit it, comrades, discontent exists
in the peoples' democracies, and yes, even among dedicated
Communists. Comrades Rakosi, Pauker, Berman, Gottwald, and,
oh yes, Ulbricht too, have not always acted as exemplary servants of the proletariat. And third, are we so certain that Dulles
means what he says when he boasts and postures about liberating
captive peoples, and so forth? May it not be for domestic consumption? These are plenty of American lunatics, and the Republican Party won many votes for their promises to take a
strong stand against us. Grigenko, in his analysis of American
politics, does not believe Dulles is sincere. I quote from Grigenko's report: 'Dulles is a member of the ruling class who
poses as a Peter the Hermit. But he is a realist, not a fanatic.'

"In short, comrades, I maintain that we stick to our policy
of rapprochement, being always flexible, of course. At the same
time, we must, needless to say, crush incipient uprisings and
demonstrate our military power as a warning to lunatic reactionaries and revanchists."

"We can argue here day and night, comrades," Bulganin said
after proposing an adjournment of the conference. "Nothing will
have been gained. We are talking in a vacuum. We will not
decide anything until the issue has become clearer. Before we
act let's wait to see what happens."

"I agree wholeheartedly," Khrushchev said. "As we Ukrainians
put it, 'Blessed are those who hurry. Redeemed are those who
wait.' "

In the weeks following the Berlin "June Days" Dulles repeatedly emphasized America's commitment to the rollback
principle. "The concepts of freedom and despotism," he declared
in a major statement before the National Press Club, "cannot
be contained or pigeonholed or kept behind curtains, whether

made of iron or bamboo or fluff. Freedom either advances or retreats. The world will not remain half slave and half free. It will go one way or the other. The captive peoples of Eastern Europe know that they can look to free men for sustenance and encouragement in the troublous days ahead."

Statements such as these, combined with the West's insistence on incorporating East Germany into the West German state, convinced the Soviet leaders, Beria and Malenkov included, that "the tough ones" were correct after all and that the Cold War should be pursued with unabated determination.

The screws of repression were accordingly tightened again, both in the Soviet Union and in the peoples' democracies. Ulbricht won back his power, and the unificationists were purged or took refuge in West Germany. Soviet leaders no longer dwelled on the horrors of war, the desirability of consumption, leisure, and the good life, and the need for "coexistence between different social systems." Rather, they stressed the heroic themes of ideological conquest, self-abnegation, and, should "the imperialists and warmongers attack," war to the death.

On the morning of July 10, 1953, the Presidium held a routine meeting in the Building of Nationalities. When the members took their seats, Malenkov asked their permission to deliver "a few remarks of general interest." Suddenly he wheeled toward Beria and pointed his finger at him. "Lavrenti Beria, I accuse you of high treason against the Soviet state and the Communist Party of the USSR."

Before Malenkov finished, Beria rose and ran toward the door, knocking over his chair. He would have made the door if Bulganin, who sat next to him, had not managed to hold him long enough for Khrushchev and Kaganovitch to come over. They flung him to the ground, breaking his glasses and tearing his suit in the struggle.

"You fools," Beria shouted hoarsely from the floor. "My men have instructions to come in and arrest all of you. Muravchek is in my office now. He knows exactly what to do. This is senseless. You're finished. Each and all of you."

"We'll see about that," Khrushchev shouted back. "Maybe we know something you don't know. Call Muravchek right now and tell him to try nothing unless he wants to commit suicide.

At this very moment, Mr. Beria, the army has your headquarters surrounded. Troops are outside this door too. Your men
won't do a fucking thing. Too smart for your own good,
weren't you? Get up and do as you're told. If anything goes
wrong, gospodin, you die."

Khrushchev had pulled out a large Bunin automatic from his
pocket.

Beria did as he was told. Smiling ironically as ever, he called
Muravchek. Minutes later soldiers in battle dress hauled him
away to the Lubyanka Prison.

The tables, obviously, had been turned on Beria. He had
lost out in the game of Kremlin intrigue. Even before Stalin's
death Beria's secret police had been "permeating" the middle-
level bureau chiefs of the army and the Party—Malinowski's
and Khrushchev's appanages, respectively. With Vlasov's destruction, the permeation increased.

For their part, Khrushchev and Malinowski enlisted the support of everyone on the Presidium. Secretly, relentlessly, they
conspired to bring Beria down. Meanwhile they protected
themselves with a special corps of crack army officers and men.
The abortive Berlin rising and the general failure of the policy
of détente Beria had sponsored gave them their opportunity.
Their intention was to charge him with the sole responsibility
for the failure, then initiate a purge. But Beria learned of the
plan and carefully worked out a scheme to arrest all of them
at a meeting of the Presidium for July 10. On July 8, however,
one of Khrushchev's counteragents (a chauffeur for Muravchek's
chief lieutenant) discovered what Beria was up to and "blew
the whistle."

Pravda reported Beria's "impeachment" as a traitor. The story,
which appeared below the soccer results, told of his "complicity"
in "anti-state" and "anti-Party" activities going back to 1916.
It hinted that he had been in touch with the "fascist enemies"
of the Soviet Union and, more recently, with "the capitalist
warmongers." Though the article said he would be tried for
his "high crimes," no trial was held. In fact, nothing further
was heard of Beria until late December, when *Pravda* announced
that he had been shot at dawn—"a fitting end to one of the
most infamous traitors of all time."

Overnight Beria had ceased to exist as an historical personage. His name was removed from every Soviet encyclopedia and reference work. To fill the enormous vacuum articles on the Bering Sea grew rather long, receiving, in the Great Soviet Encyclopedia, twice as much space as all the oceans of the world combined.

Though he remained in the background, his face often absent in pictures of the front rank of Soviet statesmen, Khrushchev had definitely established his primacy in the Kremlin hierarchy. Like Stalin before him, he used the Party machinery for his ascent. Beria's "henchmen" in the secret police were replaced by men loyal to Khrushchev, many of them Ukrainians like himself. The army, too, came under stricter Party control. Meanwhile, Khrushchev kept up the pretense of "collective leadership," as Malenkov and Molotov and Malinowski appeared to represent and speak for the Soviet Union. In reality, Khrushchev was the decisive voice, with Bulganin acting as his mouthpiece.

Years later, explaining why he waited so long before "surfacing," he cited a Ukrainian maxim: "'Until he sees his prey, the wise hunter will silently hide in the bush, his trigger cocked, ready to shoot at any time.'"

4

ROLLBACK (*cont'd*)

IN late July 1953, the National Security Council convened in the Ulysses S. Grant Room of the White House to hear Secretary of State Dulles present a full-length review of American foreign policy. Attending, besides the President, was Dulles's brother, Allen, head of the Central Intelligence Agency, the Joint Chiefs of Staff, the Secretary of Defense Charles E. Wilson and his assistants, the secretaries of the Army, Navy, and Air Force.

"Mr. President, gentlemen," Dulles said, holding a pointer and standing in front of a large map of the world, "we're gathered here because the President thought the time propitious for a major review of the international situation. The Korean War, our primary concern for three years, is over, allowing us to concentrate our attention elsewhere in the world. I'm fairly confident that, so long as we maintain our vigilance, we can expect no further trouble from the Chinese and North Koreans, at least not for a while. What I propose to do here is go over the other trouble spots and suggest ways of dealing with them. Your own suggestions, gentlemen, will enable the President to frame our policies judiciously and well."

"Now let me add a word here to what Foster has just said," Eisenhower broke in. "My mind is completely open to your views, gentlemen. This is a free give-and-take discussion between men whose judgments I trust, men of sobriety and good will. Foster will define the issues for us."

Dulles thanked the President and continued. "First and foremost is the problem in Iran. You know the strategic and economic importance of Iran. Russia, its neighbor, as you see on the map, would like nothing better than to get hold of the

Iranian oil fields, not so much because Russia needs the oil herself as because she wants to deprive Western Europe of it. Now the situation is serious. Premier Mossadegh is a fanatical nationalist who won't compromise an inch in paying the British for the oil fields he's seized. Mossadegh is not a Communist, but he definitely has the support of the Tudeh, or Communist Party of Iran, and, of course, the Soviet Union, which is ready to lend him money and technicians. So far he's refused to accept Soviet aid.

"His attitude, however, seems to be shifting ominously. Let me read a portion of Ambassador Henderson's latest report, received hours ago. I quote:

"'I met Mossadegh yesterday and told him that the United States would like to see a settlement that would satisfy both Iran and Britain. He began to shout and flail his arms at me. "Britain wants only her privileges back," he said. "She wants to control our country again and buy out our politicians. And you back her to the hilt." Then he went into one of his crying fits and, through his tears, pleaded with our government, which was born of "an independence movement," to understand his position. Iran, he stated, needed one hundred million dollars immediately.

"'Suddenly he stopped crying and looked at me malevolently. He said, "You realize that if the United States does not supply the loan my government needs, other countries will. Take heed." My own analysis is that Mossadegh is not bluffing. He will go to the Soviet Union unless we make one of two choices. Either we give him the loan, thereby securing his victory, sanctioning the nationalization of the oil fields, and rebuffing Great Britain, our closest ally; or we help the Shah throw him out of office. If the latter succeeds, all will be well. The Shah is firmly committed to the West. If the latter fails, if Mossadegh wins out, then we will have a first-rate catastrophe on our hands. The risk is very great. But I believe it is worth running.'

"That," Dulles resumed, "was Loy Henderson's excellent account, and I agree with him unequivocally. I'll return to Iran in a moment.

"Next I turn to Guatemala, which, as you will note, lies directly below Mexico and preciously close to the Panama Canal.

We have word that the government of Jacobo Arbenz Guzmán is also drawing closer and closer to the Communist side. Some Communists have entered the government. Arbenz is a notorious demagogue, whipping up the masses with promises of land reform, and he's already expropriated some valuable United Fruit Company land.

"Mr. President, gentlemen, if the Communists take over in Guatemala, as they appear to be doing, then we'll have a Communist enclave right in our hemisphere, only a stone's throw from the Canal, at the median point of the Central American bridge—you see it here on the map—between the two continents. I'll return to Guatemala later.

"While I'm on the subject of Latin American problems I should mention Cheddi Jagan's Communist-inspired movement in British Guiana. But the British are attending to that quite nicely, and I'm assured by the Foreign Office that Jagan will never take power, no matter what his percentage of the votes.

"As for the other trouble spots, the diagnosis is mixed. The Hukbalahap Communists in the Philippines are definitely losing. The people now see them for what they are, cheap demagogues. Their day is past, I'm pleased to say, thanks to President Ramón Magsaysay.

"Conditions have also improved nicely in Malaya. The British are gaining the upper hand. They are flushing the guerrillas out of their hiding places. The capture of their leader is a big blow for freedom, and I think the end is in sight, though it may be a few years before it's officially over.

"Conditions in Indochina, I fear, are not so good. The Communist guerrillas there, the Vietminh, are as tenacious as they are evil. The more men the French send in the more resistance they meet. The Vietminh have begun organizing armies and conducting mass assaults on French bases. I'll come back to Indochina also in a few moments.

"Before I proceed further, I'd like to read you part of a report drafted late last year by one of our undersecretaries for political affairs on the meaning of the various insurgent movements in the world. I'm a great believer in the adversary approach to issues, and so I think we should listen to this young man's report. It represents the liberal answer to the problems I've been discussing. I quote:

"'We should not allow our Cold War animus to cloud our thinking. We should not surrender the long-term interests of the United States in a rapidly changing world to short-term narrowly conceived strategies. In Guatemala and Iran reform governments have come to power. Both are leftist in orientation and distinctly nationalist. What they both seek above all is to rid their countries of the incubus of foreign imperialism. They also seek to distribute the wealth, that is, the land, somewhat more equitably. The concentration of wealth in Iran and Guatemala is grotesque: in both countries ninety-five per cent of the land is held by about two per cent of the people. The landlords grind the faces of the peasants into the soil.

"'In the Philippines, Malaya, and Indochina we find insurgent movements rather than governments striving to achieve similar ends. It would be a mistake in each instance to assume that sympathizing with them necessarily means siding with the Soviet Union. Our policy, in fact, should be to separate radical reform from Cold War obsessions. It is the landlords who identify reform with Communism, who conceal their predacity and power behind a show of friendship for the United States. I strongly believe that our government should avoid supporting the privileged interests lest we become the architects of a new Holy Alliance in a world of cataclysmic change. We should furthermore endeavor to persuade Great Britain and France to recognize the right of the Malayans, Guianans, and Indochinese to handle their own affairs. We should forbear from aiding our colonial allies in putting down insurgent movements—movements that must, in the fullness of time, succeed.

"'These views, let it be repeated, are set forth as candidly as they are in the belief that they correspond to the *enduring* interests of the United States.'"

Dulles looked up. "You will admit, Mr. President, gentlemen, that those were candid words indeed, and well expressed. I appreciate their cogency though I disagree with them entirely. To act as the author suggests would be disastrous, utterly disastrous. The United States is not opposed to reform movements, even, on occasion, those that may expropriate private property without due process. After all, we have given substantial assistance to Bolivia's revolutionary government. We know that if it should fall something much worse is apt to replace it.

"No, the issue is Communism versus anti-Communism, and on that issue this administration—here I think I reflect your sentiments, Mr. President—draws the line. In Iran, Guatemala, Guiana, Malaya, and Indochina, the Soviet Union or Communist China will gain immeasurably if the insurgents, or the revolutionary regimes, succeed in their nefarious purposes. I'm not against reform. Within limits I welcome it. But Communism is a horse of a different color. The good Timothy said it perfectly: 'Lay your sword to the false prophets, for they would turn brother against brother, son against father, debtor against creditor.'"

"Engine Charley" Wilson, the Secretary of Defense, spoke briefly. He said he "substantially approved" of Dulles's "presentation and analysis." Only, he had one "qualification." He did not think the United States should support any government, even one professing to be non-Communist, that nationalized foreign properties.

Wilson was famous for his blunt speech, a quality Eisenhower liked in him. "What the hell, Mr. Secretary, what is a Communist anyway? I don't see the damned difference between someone who takes my property from me and calls himself a nationalist, a Hottentot, or whatnot, and someone who calls himself a Communist. Mr. Secretary, I think we should lay it down pretty sternly to bandits and outlaws, whatever color clothes they wear."

Dulles peremptorily dismissed Wilson's "qualification." Dulles asserted that the United States must live in a world that "contains various shades of grey" along with "the white and black of freedom and despotism." Among "our staunchest allies," he pointed out, were the numerous "Socialist governments of Europe." "No regime better suits American interests than the Communist regime of Marshal Tito, which we've kept alive now for five years. And lest we forget," Dulles added with a laugh, "the American revolutionists confiscated the Tory estates and paid only a fraction of the indemnity."

Next Admiral Arthur William Radford spoke. He was Chairman of the Joint Chiefs of Staff and reputed to be the toughest anti-Communist since James Forrestal was Secretary of Defense six years before. No one contested Radford's brilliance or competence, only his judgment. During the Korean War he had on several occasions publicly sided with General Douglas MacArthur. Some of Radford's critics referred to him as "Let's Get It Over with Radford," or "The John Wayne of the Admiralty." He talked very deliberately, in a low-voiced monotone, moving his eyes slightly through narrow slits. Usually he wore dark-tinted glasses.

"I have a qualification, too, Mr. Secretary," he declared. "The complexity of your presentation mystifies me. Malaya, Guiana, Indochina, Iran, why it's like counting the branches of a tree when what we're after is its root. I mean Russia and China. They are the root of the problem, and it's to them we should address ourselves. We're all cognizant of the reasons for these crises here and there—we can go on enumerating them all day. It's not the Filipinos, Vietminh, and so forth—they're only the tools, agents, instruments. If the Russians and Chinese hadn't given them the orders to rise up they wouldn't have risen up. I'd like you to tell us, Mr. Secretary, how we should deal with the root of the problems you yourself have defined so expertly."

Dulles answered that the problems were, indeed, complex, that they consisted of roots and branches and leaves, that "the United States could not go around brandishing ultimatums to the Russians and Chinese," and that since the Eisenhower administration "the United States has made it abundantly clear it will tolerate no more Koreas; that aggressors in the future can expect massive retaliation."

But Radford persisted: "I think this government should inform the Soviet Union and Red China that it will hold them responsible if the insurgency or troublemaking continues beyond a certain point. They should be told in plain American language that our patience is not unlimited."

Eisenhower intervened: "On general principles, Admiral, I agree with you. But, darn it, you know from experience that you're never in absolute command of your subordinates, especially if they're at remote outposts. I don't think the Russians or the Chinese can tell the Huks or Gooks or Spooks or what have you to stop insurging after the darned thing has gotten under way. Why it's like army headquarters calling a battalion to retreat during a battle. Why I remember—no, never mind. Please go on, Foster."

"At this juncture, Mr. President, I would like to turn the floor over to the other Mr. Dulles, a man with whom I enjoy a passing acquaintance."

The other Mr. Dulles, Allen, looked and acted like a small-town college professor or banker. He judiciously smoked a pipe, wore an affectionate mustache, spoke softly and listened well. Yet this man had been a super-spy since the war. As chief of Central Intelligence he was responsible for thousands of secret agents working in every country in the world, including the United States. It was often said that next to the Secretary of State he had the most say over American foreign policy.

"Mr. President, gentlemen, I shall report on what the Central Intelligence Agency is now doing, or is prepared to do, in those countries to which the Secretary alluded. In Iran, our agents are readying themselves for a critical turn of events. They are working closely with the Shah, with ex-Premier Zahedi, and with the leading members of the parliamentary opposition. In Guatemala, too, preparations are under way, though we don't know exactly when the situation will break there. Two of our best men, MacManus and O'Brien, are getting up an army in Honduras—with the co-operation, I should add, of the Honduran government—and they have recruited some pretty good American pilots. In the Philippines, I'm pleased to say, we have infiltrated the Huk ranks. Two priests and two nuns who have been ministering to lepers in Mindanao and who now treat the Huks are our operatives, and very good ones to boot. I shall close on an optimistic note. I think, Mr. President, you can look forward to important news from Iran within the next couple of weeks."

Thanking his brother, Secretary of State Dulles resumed.

"I'll only say in conclusion that we've drawn up an aggressive— not a bellicose, but an aggressive—plan of action to meet the Communist threat. It's already been approved of by the President, at least in outline, and it remains to be implemented. By this time next year, if everything proceeds on schedule, the

United States will have formed military pacts with most of the nations bordering the Communist empire—the World Island again—and with those nations that in any way feel threatened by it. A gigantic, I will venture to say stupendous, net will have been thrown around that empire, preventing it from expanding any farther. Japan, which constitutes an integral part of that periphery, will be brought into more active partnership in the concert of free nations. In a month hence I will present to this Council and to the Congress a detailed account of the military pacts I have in mind."

Eisenhower thanked Dulles for "leading a tremendously fruitful discussion," and dismissed the Council.

Allen Dulles knew whereof he spoke when he referred to "a critical turn of events" in Iran. At the very moment the National Security Council was meeting in the U. S. Grant Room, Ambassador Loy Henderson and CIA agent Glenn Prall, one of Allen Dulles's lieutenants, were advising Shah Pahlevi on how he might overthrow Mohammed Mossadegh. They decided that the Shah should publicly assert his "constitutional authority" over the army. Should Mossadegh fail to challenge that authority, the Shah would consolidate his control by purging the army of nationalists and other Mossadegh sympathizers.

"Short of sending in American troops," Henderson told the young Shah, "the United States will do everything in its power to help you and the Iranian people."

The following day the Shah announced that by the powers entrusted to him under the constitution he was taking "active command of the armed forces of Iran." But Mossadegh, crafty as ever, declared the Shah's command to be "purely ceremonial" under the constitution.

The issue went to parliament (the Masjumi), which divided irreparably into pro-Mossadegh and pro-Shah factions, the latter comprised mainly of large landholders. Armed with extraordinary powers of his own, Mossadegh called for a referendum on the constitutional question and dissolved the parliament.

While the tug of war was going on, the CIA and the American military mission in Teheran were busy. Henderson and Prall had in effect set up anti-Mossadegh headquarters in the American embassy. Every day scores of CIA agents were flown into Teheran for deployment in the "crunch."

They did not have to wait long. The Shah, his every move planned by Henderson and Prall, dismissed Mossadegh—again in accordance with the constitution—and appointed General Fozlollah Zahedi as his Prime Minister.

Mossadegh cried when he learned of his dismissal. Then he laughed. "I hereby dismiss Shah Pahlevi," he informed his cabinet, which was sitting around the clock. "I will also dismiss the Americans."

The Shah had expected his dismissal notice to provoke a general rebellion by his "devoted subjects." Nothing of the sort occurred. Mossadegh, it seemed, had the situation firmly in hand. The Shah and his personal entourage fled Iran in the middle of the night. Zahedi and his men escaped to the mountains where they found refuge among primitive tribes. To celebrate their triumph Mossadegh and his cabinet held a miniature feast in his bedroom (fatigue having confined the old man to his bed). Mossadegh proposed a toast of wine from the royal vineyards. "Soon Iran will be free to have her own destiny, a nation among nations. We have prevailed because we have stood with the people against the selfish few, with the future against the past."

The celebration was premature. On the night of the feast Henderson and Prall led a score of CIA agents and a hundred or so anti-Mossadegh army officers on a rampage through the streets of Teheran. They knocked down statues, broke windows, painted slogans, and scattered leaflets announcing the victory of the Tudeh Party, the establishment of a "workers' and peasants' republic," and "the unconquerable solidarity of Iran and the USSR." The next day General Mehdi Anzooz read a statement that had been drawn up by Henderson and Prall. In the name of "the Iranian people" it denounced Mossadegh's "usurpation" as the prelude to the "communization" of the country, the destruction of religion, family, and property—"all that is sacred to the people of Iran. . . . Patriotism requires us to act. We cannot wait another moment."

"Now we'll storm the Winter Palace," Prall said with a smile. In a series of lightning moves the officers who had rioted the night before captured the buildings that housed the Prime Min-

ister and cabinet, the Ministry of Justice, and the radio station,
and sealed all routes from the city. Mossadegh and his followers—
the cabinet, members of parliament, civil servants, dissident officers, among others—were picked up and promptly thrown in jail.

Hours later the Shah returned and assumed full powers, the
constitution now being his to interpret and apply as he wished.
Prime Minister Fozlollah Zahedi told the people over Radio Iran
that the nation had just "cured itself of a malignant disease,
and, Allah willing, is on its way to complete recuperation."

What he meant was that Iran would settle its differences with
the West. Minutes after the coup, the United States loaned the
new government forty-five million dollars and promised that more,
much more, would be forthcoming. "The amount is for you to
determine, sire," Ambassador Henderson told the Shah, who
beamed with pleasure.

After arduous negotiation, the dispute that had brought about
the crisis—the proper compensation for the nationalized Anglo-
Iranian Oil Company—was resolved to everyone's satisfaction.
The oil fields were denationalized and turned over to a consortium
of eight international companies, five of them American (three
of these actually belonged to one firm, Standard Oil of New
Jersey), whose revenues were to compensate Anglo-Iranian for
its losses.

"It was a perilously close call," John Foster Dulles admitted to
Eisenhower when the agreement was concluded. "Iran had escaped from the valley of the shadow of death."

After Iran, the United States was able to give its full attention
to Guatemala. To coordinate intelligence operations there President Eisenhower, at Allen Dulles's request, appointed John E.
Puerifoy as its ambassador. Puerifoy had distinguished himself as
a tough fighter in the Greek civil war. On any given day this
diplomat might have been seen heading a charge against the
guerrillas in mountainous Thrace, his pearl-handled revolvers
smoking in his hands. Another day he might have been seen holding forth brilliantly at an embassy cocktail party in Athens,
charming the foreign dignitaries (and their wives). Like a movie
star he graced every role in which he was cast (which was why
his subordinates in Greece irreverently called him "Captain Courageous," "Jack Armstrong," "Tall in the Saddle," etc.). Puerifoy's

mission in Guatemala was to "effect the removal" of the current regime headed by Jacobo Arbenz Guzmán "unobtrusively"—i.e., without openly involving the United States.

Puerifoy's strategy, worked out in close consultation with Washington, was simultaneously to undermine the Arbenz government and organize an "emigré" army in neighboring Honduras. His two CIA assistants, Ivan MacManus and Sean O'Brien, were placed in charge of that army, whose nominal chief was a conservative Guatemalan army officer, Carlos Castillo Armas. Armas's group in Honduras, the "Anti-Communist Front," was a ragtail, motley outfit, consisting of assorted mercenaries recruited from all over Central America by the CIA. In Guatemala City, meanwhile, Puerifoy was holding clandestine meetings with anti-government officers.

The Arbenz government knew what was taking place and complained repeatedly before international bodies—the United Nations, the Inter-American Conference, the Organization of American States—about the impending invasion. To no avail. In fact, by a vote of seventeen to one the Tenth Inter-American Conference condemned "Communist interests" in the Western Hemisphere. The Arbenz regime was in a quandary. It knew that its only chance of survival was to arm the peasants, to whom it was distributing the land. Yet if it did so, it would alienate those professional army officers who were nationalists, not radicals. They would fight for Guatemala. They would not tolerate a people's army.

In the late spring of 1954 the Arbenz government decided to arm the peasants. But it could not procure arms from the United States, the traditional source of military hardware for Guatemala (and for every country in Latin America). It therefore undertook to procure them from Eastern Europe, Poland in particular.

When Puerifoy wired Dulles that a Polish ship was unloading weapons in one of the port towns, Eisenhower himself responded. "A very dangerous situation exists down there," Eisenhower said sternly at a press conference. "We don't want to see the Communists gain a foothold in this hemisphere. The Monroe Doctrine, the Roosevelt Corollary, and the Platt Amendment, as you know, are still in force. We're not going to shirk our obligations."

Eisenhower's remarks were the signal for the "crunch" to

begin. With MacManus and O'Brien at his side Castillo Armas led the invasion into Guatemala. From Honduras and Guatemala radios blared forth the news that a mighty army was entering the country on several fronts and was rapidly pushing into the interior. Actually, the irregulars quickly bogged down in the jungle thickets near the frontier. Much more effective were the bombings of Guatemala City and elsewhere by CIA-piloted planes. At the same time Puerifoy was able to recruit a sizable number of disgruntled officers. He explained to them that the United States had no intention to intervene or bring other countries into the conflict (there being little love lost between Guatemala and its neighbors), and that the United States favored an agreement between them, the officers, and Castillo Armas for "the good of Guatemala, Latin America, and Western Christianity." The agreement was effected.

Unable to field an army in time the Arbenz government melted away. Arbenz himself fled to the Mexican embassy. Armas rode into Guatemala City a conquering hero. Sitting alongside him in the jeep were MacManus and O'Brien. In the front seat sat Puerifoy, his shirt open, his pearl-handled guns jammed into his pants. A State Department officer on the scene wrote: "it was the final touch in a perfect Hollywood scenario." Puerifoy's mission, at any rate, was accomplished.

During the next several months the "counterrevolution" ran its course, as thousands of "Communists"—that is, Arbenz sympathizers—were imprisoned and the agrarian reforms were jettisoned. Later in the year, having seized the presidency of Guatemala, Castillo Armas laid down "the cardinal principles" of his regime: "respect for property, respect for foreign investors, respect for all constituted authority, paternal, religious, and political."

In a ceremony on the White House lawn President Eisenhower congratulated Puerifoy "for doing so much to repair the long and abiding friendship between the people of Guatemala and the people of the United States." And at Fordham University in New York City, Cardinal Spellman honored Castillo Armas as a "knight errant for Christianity and freedom." [. . .]

The CIA operations in Iran and Guatemala formed only a part of the grand strategy to "roll back" Communism. The most essential part, because the most durable, consisted of the military alliances that Secretary Dulles forged in 1954.

In March of that year the United States and Japan signed a Mutual Defense Assistance Agreement whose aim was to build up a Japanese "defensive" army and establish a close working arrangement between the fighting forces of the two countries. In September, the United States, Great Britain, France, Australia, New Zealand, Pakistan, the Philippines, and Thailand launched the Southeast Asia Treaty Organization (SEATO). Under its provisions all members were to come to the aid of each in the event of attack. SEATO was obviously directed against Communist China. Implicitly, however, it could be applied against native insurgent movements. A month later, Great Britain, Turkey, Iran, Iraq, and Pakistan signed treaties committing themselves to each other's defense. This alliance, the so-called Baghdad Pact (because its headquarters were located in Baghdad), was intended to protect "the northern tier" of the Middle East from Soviet assault. Though the United States refrained from formally joining the Baghdad Pact it was the brainchild of Dulles himself, and he took special pride in its existence.

"NATO, SEATO, Baghdad, bases in Tripoli, Morocco, Spain, in every one of our allied nations," Dulles wrote the President in his year-end report on the state of the State Department, "are among the brightest jewels of our foreign policy. Communist China and the Soviet Union will henceforward no longer be constrained merely by our words or by their conjectures of our possible response. Now they know exactly where they dare not tread. They are engirdled by a chain of steel. The number of links, moreover, will increase in the years ahead, and the chain will grow immeasurably stronger. But I will not carry the simile any further. Sufficient unto the day."

5

INDOCHINA

ONE day in mid-February 1954, President Eisenhower and Secretary Dulles met in the White House Library for a routine review of recent foreign developments. The President had asked for "an informational briefing, preferably short," on the situation in French Indochina. The Vietminh insurgents there had been scoring minor victories against the French army, and the subject of American aid was coming up more and more frequently in press conferences and in National Security Council meetings. And so Eisenhower requested a more thorough "briefing" on the history and causes of the Indochinese conflict than he had so far received. Dulles accordingly brought with him an expert on Southeast Asia, a professor at a large Midwestern university (he will be called Leonard Vale here), who had spent some time in the region as a consultant for the army and the Central Intelligence Agency. At the moment he was a member of the State Department's Asian Policy Planning Division.

"Mr. President," Vale began, "the Indochinese conflict goes back a long way. The Vietminh revolutionary movement got under way in the 1920s, then expanded in the '30s."

"What kind of movement was it?" Eisenhower asked.

"It had Communists, nationalists, and radicals of every stripe in its ranks. It favored worth-while objectives: breaking up the French-owned plantations and distributing the land to the peasants, independence of the Indochinese states, political democracy, and the like. They disagreed among themselves on everything but getting the French out of their country."

"What about Ho Chi Minh, Mr. Vale?"

"Ho is a Communist, I have no doubt of it—some of my colleagues don't think so—but he's very shrewd. He never presses his ideology too far. He's no blind dogmatist. He represents himself primarily as a nationalist, a Vietnamese patriot. And he has a very able group of lieutenants, notably General Nguyen Giap, the commander of the Vietminh, who's a brilliant tactician, a master of guerrilla warfare, as the French are discovering to their cost. We mustn't underestimate these men, sir. Someday Americans may be fighting them."

"Heaven forbid," Eisenhower said, grimacing. "Continue, Mr. Vale."

"During the Second World War Ho and the Vietminh fought the Japanese occupying army."

"You mean they fought with the Allies?"

"Well yes, sir, for two reasons. First, because, being Communists, Ho and his men—like the Chinese Reds—believed that the main task was to beat back the fascists. And second, because the French had promised—and the United States had vigorously supported that promise—to relinquish Indochina when the war ended. For a while the French seemed determined to make good their promise. Elections were held and Ho's party won a majority. Bao Dai, the nominal ruler of the country, a French puppet, retired to the Riviera to spend his remaining days at the gaming tables and with his mistresses. But then, without warning, the French commander in Hanoi, acting under De Gaulle's orders, threw out Ho and brought Bao Dai back from lotus land.

"As soon as they could regroup themselves the Vietminh began to conduct guerrilla warfare, their great source of strength being the peasant hamlets, where they work during the day and from which they sally forth at night.

"This is literally an underground army, for they burrow tunnels deep in the ground and connect them up like so many subterranean highways. The French were able to contain the Vietminh pretty well until 1949, when China fell to the Communists. Since then the Vietminh have received arms and technical assistance and, above all, sanctuary from China."

"Well, I must say," the President said, frowning, "from your account, Mr. Vale, the Vietminh have a damned good case, don't they? Incidentally, why did the French go back on their word back in '46?"

"I don't quite know for certain, Mr. President. It may have been De Gaulle's hope to restore France's tarnished glory. It may have been pressure from the military, from the colonial establishment, from the plantation owners. The funny thing, Mr. President, is that the French Communists did not object too strongly at the time. But neither did they take Mao Tse-tung very seriously. Stalin, as you know—"

Dulles interrupted Vale to thank him for his "splendid summary," which "helps place the issue in perspective." Eisenhower agreed warmly, rose and showed Vale to the door.

"I should like to emphasize the gravity of the Indochinese crisis, Mr. President," Dulles said after Vale had left. "The French botched up the situation terribly. They could have gotten somebody other than that corrupt hedonist, Bao Dai, to take over in 1946. They gave the Vietnamese people some choice: Bao or Ho.

"But all that's water over the dam. Mr. President, we can't let the French lose. For if they lose the free world loses, too. Vietnam is at the very center of the great Southeast Asian peninsula. If Vietnam falls to the Communists the rest of Indochina, Laos and Cambodia will fall, then Thailand, then Malaya, and beyond these are Singapore, Indonesia, the Philippines. It would be an unmitigated calamity."

"Yes, that's for sure," Eisenhower asserted. "How much aid are we giving the French?"

"We're supplying most of their arms. I would go so far as to say that we're at this moment practically underwriting the cost of the war. This year's estimate is approximately one hundred fifty million. However, as Mr. Vale informed us, the guerrillas are getting stronger and bolder. I suggest, sir, that you call a meeting of the National Security Council to discuss the situation and perhaps recommend some policy changes."

Eisenhower agreed, without specifying when the Council would meet.

Only three weeks later, however, at Dulles's urging, Eisenhower called the Council together to take up the Indochinese "conundrum." The French army had suffered some further defeats, and at the "impregnable" mountain base of Dien Bien Phu a large garrison was surrounded by powerful Vietminh forces. The French government was pleading for more American military and economic aid to its hard-pressed colonial army.

"We are holding the ramparts for the free world," Foreign Minister Georges Jupien told Dulles during an emergency visit to Washington. "In this international struggle France should not be required to bear the burden alone, especially when one considers that behind the guerrillas stand two mastodons, China and Russia. We ask for no American troops, only American material assistance."

The United States had to take a position one way or the other on Indochina, and Dulles convinced Eisenhower that he could no longer put off a decision. Hence the Security Council meeting.

Present in the Franklin Pierce Room of the White House, besides the President, the Dulles brothers, the secretaries of Defense and Treasury and their assistants, and various experts (including Leonard Vale), was Vice President Nixon, just back from a long and highly publicized speaking tour throughout the country (in which he again excoriated the Democrats for having been "soft on Communism," and praised the administration for having fired so many "security risks" from the government).

"Gentlemen, this is a grave moment," Eisenhower said, frowning deeply. "You're all aware of what we're up against. The French want us to do more for them. Well, what are we to do for them, and therefore for ourselves? This is the most important decision this government is going to make since the Korean War began in 1950. I've asked you here to help me make up my mind. Foster, why don't you get it started. What do you think?"

"Mr. President, I can state it succinctly. The French will lose unless we act quickly. The only way to defeat the guerrillas, in my view, is to send in our planes against them, and if that doesn't suffice, atomic weapons. I've explained why Indochina, more exactly Vietnam, is so vital to the free world and to the interests of the United States. Foreign Minister Jupien is right, of course. The French army is holding the ramparts, and if Indochina were to succumb to the Communists the bell would toll for us, for all liberty-loving men, for all Christians. Mr. President, the decision to involve the United States in the Indochinese conflict would be a difficult one to make. I realize that. But future generations will honor you for it."

"I second the Secretary's salient remarks," said Admiral Radford, who again wore his tinted glasses. "Only," he continued, speaking in his slow, measured tone, "I would proceed a step further. Indochina should be bombed, to kingdom come if necessary. But none of us believes that the guerrillas are the problem. We know that the problem is in Moscow and Peking. They started this imbroglio. They should be forced to stop it. France can't force them to stop it. We're the only one who can. Mr. President, I respectfully recommend that you dispatch an ultimatum to Moscow and Peking demanding the cessation of hostilities in Indochina and the dissolution of the bandit army. I sound tough, I know. But by all that's holy and just on this planet how are we going to have peace and justice if we act like gentlemen toward those bastards? Sorry for the language."

Nixon spoke next. "I wish to express my agreement with Secretary Dulles and Admiral Radford. Intervention is, I believe, imperative. Before we do so, however, I suggest that we send not an ultimatum to Russia and China but a clear announcement of our intention to go into Indochina. This would accomplish what Secretary Dulles and Admiral Radford both desire, yet avoid a nuclear showdown."

"Well," Radford replied, "maybe we should have a showdown now. It'll come sooner or later. This is as good a time as any, and probably better. Reality is brutal. We've got to face it down."

"But, Admiral," Dulles said matter of factly, "it would be rather foolish of us to blow up each other's cities over Indochina, important as it is. If Germany were threatened it would be another thing."

"Exactly," Nixon said, "I think we can get Russia and China to end the war by the simple expedient of threatening intervention. If they don't end it, then we should intervene."

General Everett Houghton, Commandant of the Marine Corps, raised an objection. "I oppose U.S. intervention in Indochina," he stated in his pronounced west Texas drawl. "That place is an endless swamp, a jungle, a desolation. Why, once we're sucked in we'd never get out. I'm sure of it. We'd begin to send in technical personnel, then we'd have to protect them with troops, then more troops. I appreciate the strategic importance of Vietnam, and I don't want to see it fall to the Communists. But I'm a military man, and in my opinion we should let those little colored people fight among themselves."

"I'm no military man," Secretary of Defense Wilson added, "but I agree with the general. I think the people of this country might become madder'n hell if we got stuck there in Indochina. In the last thirteen years we've fought two pretty costly wars. The Republican Party is, and has been, the party of peace and prosperity. The Democrats will really hang this one on us if we get in. And what about the price? If you think we're spending a hell of a lot now helping the French, and going that much further into debt to do so, how much more will we spend when we're in the thing. The public is already raising hell about high prices. Listen, if the damned Communists are such a danger— and don't get me wrong, I'm alive to their danger—why don't the Indians, Siamese, Burmese, and what not go in there to protect their freedoms? It's their continent. Why should we do it for them? Mr. President, the question, as far as I'm concerned, is this: Is Indochina worth saving, assuming we can save it? Personally, I don't think so."

Dulles retorted with obvious emotion. "I'm afraid General Houghton and Mr. Wilson misunderstand my position. I'm against sending in troops. What I propose is the bombing of the Vietminh in concert with French troops. I've spoken to Generals Roseland and Piersall and they maintain that saturation bombing attacks would enable French troops to strike back hard at the guerrillas, hard and successfully. As for the cost of a stepped-up war, how do we measure it against the cost of future wars? We've learned, I trust, what happens when you appease an aggressor, particularly one armed with a fighting faith, atheistic and demagogic and evil as that faith is. Stopping the Communists before they take Indochina would save us from *really* getting into an Asian land war.

"Now, General—beg pardon, I mean Mr. Wilson—you wonder why the other countries with a stake in the region don't get involved, why it's we who get involved. The reason is that we're the leader of the free world, like it or not. If some nations prefer to hide their heads in the sand, or opt out because of cowardice, should we do it too? That's not the mission Providence has assigned us. Why else have we become a great power? Surely not to lord it over others, nor aggrandize the wealth and territory of other peoples. To us has fallen the task of protecting the freedom and civilization that has developed on this earth and that Communism endeavors to destroy. The struggle we're engaged in is the struggle of competing missions, one destructive, the other creative. If we abandon that struggle we abandon the best part of ourselves."

A long pause followed these impassioned words. Clearing his throat, Nixon said, "Congratulations, Mr. Secretary, you have said the last word on the subject, as far as I am concerned."

Eisenhower had been listening to the debate attentively. When it appeared nothing further would be added he adjourned the meeting. "I'm going to think over everything you've said here, consult a few others, and come back to you with my decision in a week or so."

He went at once to his Gettysburg, Pennsylvania, farm, where he could think in peace among the softly undulating green hills, and among his cattle, horses, and sows. To allay suspicion, to make it appear a routine vacation, he took no one with him but his family, his press secretary, Peter Peggotty, and a few members of the White House staff. He held his conversations by long distance telephone.

First he asked the congressional leaders of both parties if the United States should intervene in Indochina. Senate Majority Leader William F. Knowland of California favored "all-out intervention." His views closely paralleled Radford's. House Majority Leader Joe Martin of Massachusetts was "skeptical" of the whole thing. "Indochina isn't worth the life of a single American boy or a single taxpayer's dollar." The Democratic leaders of the House and Senate, Sam Rayburn and Lyndon Johnson, both of Texas (Eisenhower was especially fond of them, often inviting them to the White House for a drink of branch water and bourbon in the early evening), thought the United States should be "extremely circumspect," as Rayburn put it.

Johnson compared Indochina to a "great big manure pile" from which "we'd never be able to extricate ourselves." Johnson also pointed out that "getting bogged down there would be more unpopular with the people than Korea. You'd have a lot of trouble putting it over, Mr. President. We learned never to fight the Indians on their stamping grounds, and that's what we'd be doing over there. But whatever you decide, you can count on Democratic support."

Eisenhower next conferred with four of the top generals in the country: Matthew Ridgway, Omar Bradley, Alfred Gruenther, and, of course, Douglas MacArthur. All but MacArthur advised against American involvement in an Asian land war. Bradley summed it up pithily: "It would be the wrong war, at the wrong time, in the wrong place, against the wrong enemy." Ridgway argued that the French should not have been there in the first place and that "we would be making a dreadful mistake if we became France's colonial surrogate. The United States should not be identified with the cause of colonialism."

MacArthur, however, declared that the Communists understood nothing but force. "Responsible nations, like responsible men," MacArthur said, from his eighteen-room suite at the Waldorf Towers, "restrain themselves by an inner moral sense. That is what we mean, Mr. President, by a civilized code of ethics. Communists do not observe, but rather hold in profound contempt, the canons of civilized ethics. They altogether lack the inner moral sense. They inflict violence and are circumscribed by violence. Had we defeated them in Korea this dastardly business in Indochina would not have arisen. Our pusillanimity has encouraged them to press forward on another front. Well, Mr. President, we have got to do in Indochina, then, what we failed to do in Korea. I believe it imperative to bomb their sanctuaries as well as their supply depots in China. I regret having to convey to you this melancholy piece of advice."

Finally, Eisenhower consulted the heads of government of the leading NATO nations. Prime Minister Churchill said that the "United States should not incarcerate herself in Indochina," though everything should be done to help the French "short of sending in your planes, ships, and, worst of all, your men." "I must say in candor, Mr. President, it would be folly of the first magnitude."

French Prime Minister Proteus Laniel approved of American intervention. Yet he raised a possibility Eisenhower had not considered, namely that it "might invite Chinese, perhaps Soviet intervention in turn. We would then have an international conflict in Indochina, or Southeast Asia—a conflict, Mr. President, that, in the nature of things, would be borne mainly by the United States."

And West German Foreign Minister Heinz von Essingen (Adenauer was seriously ill) cautioned against "too strong an Asian orientation. Remember, Mr. President, as you know better than anyone, the decisive battleground for Western civilization is Western Europe."

Within a week Eisenhower had made up his mind, and he called the National Security Council together (again in the Franklin Pierce Room) to inform it of his decision.

The United States, he asserted emphatically—he had already told Dulles and Radford privately—would not, while he was President, "send American men, planes, or ships to fight a land war in Asia." At the same time, he said, he was authorizing the State and Defense departments to step up American assistance to "the valiant French army in Indochina. . . . Laniel is confident that with more planes, helicopters, and heavy weapons, the guerrillas can be stopped in their tracks and decimated."

While he spoke Eisenhower conspicuously avoided looking at Vice President Nixon, who was sitting directly in front of him. The reason for the snub was that, two days before, Nixon had delivered a speech before the National Press Club in which he strongly hinted at American intervention in Indochina. Much was made of Nixon's remarks, which were regarded as an official administration statement, and as such, "a trial balloon" to measure public opinion. When he learned the contents of the speech Eisenhower was "hopping mad." "I don't like anybody trying to force my hand," he said to Peter Peggotty. "It's a good thing for him that it got such a bad reaction."

Later, a letter from the President reached the cabinet secretaries and other high level functionaries in the administration, "advising" them against "issuing public statements that convey the impression of reflecting the views of the administration on matters of public policy."

The President's Indochina decision had deep ramifications. For some months the great powers—the United States excepted—had been informally discussing the possibility of holding a conference to resolve the Indochina problem. The last obstacle disappeared when it became definite that the United States would not intervene in the war. Accordingly, in early April 1954, the most impressive conference since the Second World War opened in Geneva. Attending were the foreign ministers of Great Britain, France, the Soviet Union, Communist China, the French-recognized governments of the three constituent states of Indochina—Vietnam, Laos, and Cambodia—and the representatives of the Viteminh guerrillas. The American delegate was Undersecretary of State Hiram Beadle Smith, who was more an observer than a participant. His main function was to act behind the scenes as "a brake" against the tendency to give away too much to the Communists.

Apparently no such brake was needed, for the conference bogged down at once over the French refusal to recognize the Vietminh as the spokesmen for the Vietnamese people. They were willing to concede only—and this over the strenuous objection of the "official," or French-sponsored, Vietnamese delegates—that the Vietminh might obtain a few innocuous cabinet posts in the existing government. "As I've suggested," Dulles told the President after the second fruitless week of the conference, "there is nothing to discuss. To the Communists, negotiation is merely another form of warfare."

That same day the French surrendered their redoubt at Dien Bien Phu. Ten thousand men of the French Foreign Legion— most of them Africans, Vietnamese, and Germans—were taken prisoner in the greatest Vietminh victory of the eight-year conflict.

The effect on France was electrifying. The army asked for many more men, including conscripts (who had so far been spared). The Laniel government fell, however, before it could respond to the request. The Assembly, which had been in an uproar for days, installed Pierre Mendès-France as Prime Minister. A radical reformer, Mendès-France had been critical of the Indochinese war for years. In speech after speech he had called attention to the "polarization" of French society, to the "obsession" the war had created in the "national consciousness," preventing "the important work of reform from ever getting done," and "to the parlous cost, increasing every day, that the French taxpayer has to pay."

Shortly after taking office, Mendès-France, acting as his own Foreign Minister, went to Geneva "to move the conference off dead center." He did precisely that. He immediately laid it down to the "official" Vietnamese delegation that it could no longer exercise veto power over France. "Now," he said politely to Tuang Hoc Xuy, the head of the delegation (and Bao Dai's nephew), "the tail will no longer wag the dog."

The conference suddenly assumed a business-like quality. The rhetoric and name-calling ceased. Thanks to the combined efforts of three extremely experienced diplomats—Britain's Foreign Secretary, Anthony Eden; China's Foreign Minister, Chou En-lai; and the Soviet Union's Vyacheslav Molotov—a formula was worked out that proved satisfactory to everyone at the conference except the Americans and the Vietnamese representatives.

The French army was to leave Indochina. Laos and Cambodia were to become independent and neutral. Vietnam was to be divided temporarily into two parts along the 18th parallel: the Vietminh North (with its capital at Hanoi) and the pro-French South (with its capital at Saigon), the people of each having the right to move to the other. The Geneva agreement also provided that "free elections under international supervision" were to be held throughout Vietnam in 1956 to set up "a single government for a united country."

It was in the course of the conference that Dulles and Mendès-France had their celebrated exchange over the telephone.

Smith had presented Dulles with an outline of the projected agreement. Dulles was angry. He even intended to fly to Geneva to "have it out" with Mendès-France, but was dissuaded by Smith, who pointed out that such a visit would have "a deleterious effect on the conference and, hence, on our relations with France and Great Britain." Dulles thereupon insisted on talking to Mendès-France personally, by telephone, and this was arranged.

"You have surprised us," Dulles said. "The United States was convinced, having been told time and again by the French government, that the Indochinese war was being fought for the sake, not of France alone, but of Western civilization. Now, sir, you propose to abandon the struggle and allow the Communists to have their own state, one half of Vietnam—the more populous half at that—thereby enabling them to take over, piecemeal to be sure, the rest of Indochina, and much else besides. This is handing it to them on a platter. Suppose Ho Chi Minh wins the 1956 election, as he probably will, since no amount of international supervision can properly oversee an election in which Communists take part—what then? No, we're shocked, Mr. Prime Minister. This is a regrettable acquiescence in outlawry."

"I understand your feelings, Mr. Secretary," Mendès-France replied in perfect English, "but I don't think you understand ours. Nor, I must tell you, do you fully comprehend the situation. I, therefore, am surprised, too, for I would have expected you of all persons to take the whole context into account before rendering a judgment. Now, we differ over the meaning of Western civilization. Not only do you and I differ. We Europeans, we Frenchmen, indeed, differ among ourselves. Many of us do not think we honor Western civilization by carrying on a war to maintain colonial and imperial privileges against a popular native movement. You would not say England was fighting for Western civilization when she tried to put down your war of independence."

"But," Dulles interrupted, "there was no Communist world threat at the time, no great power who would exploit American independence for its own predatory ends."

"Come, come, Mr. Secretary. Why did France and Spain and the Netherlands and Russia support the Americans in 1776? They wanted to weaken Britain. Perhaps they saw their opportunity to take over the American colonies. As for Communism, what did the European ruling classes consider American republicanism if not a threat to civilization? Certainly they would help the Americans become independent. Then they would crush the American ideal of republican equality.

"But we are getting away from the point. The essential issue, Mr. Secretary, is that the war is destroying France, ripping us apart, draining us of our morale, our wealth, our vital energies. France is a sick society. To avoid dying she must end the Indochinese war. That is the long and the short of it. The French people have imposed a mandate on me. Under the circumstances, I have conceded less than I might have. Half of Vietnam is pro-Western. The other two states are neutral and non-Communist. Yes, Mr. Secretary, I love Western civilization. That is why I have decided that *France* must be saved."

The Indochinese armistice was signed in July 1954. Several months later Eisenhower appointed retired General J. Horton Hollings ambassador to South Vietnam. Dulles had recommended a "knowledgeable military man" for the post, and few officers were more highly respected than Hollings. Before his departure for Saigon he received a lengthy briefing from Dulles.

"You're well aware, General, or I should say, Ambassador, that you're about to embark on an extraordinarily important assignment. The French are pulling out of Vietnam in accordance with the silly timetable worked out in Geneva. But we won't leave the South Vietnamese defenseless against their external and internal enemies. We have good reason to think that Prime Minister Ngo Diem will be able to pull his country together if he gets enough help. How can we best help him? What assistance, military, economic, and any other, can we furnish him and his government? If anyone can answer that question, General, it's you."

"Thank you," Hollings said, "but won't it all be for nought if he loses the election in '56? Why pass on a lot of supplies when they might end up in the hands of the Communists?"

"Precisely, General. Hence we're not anticipating any change that might be brought about by the '56 election. In fact, we're assuming the election won't be held. I'll be damned if we're going to give away South Vietnam to the Communists because of the deal at Geneva. We didn't sign that travesty and we're not obliged to submit to its conditions."

"May I ask you this, Mr. Secretary? Suppose the North accuses the United States and the Diem government of perfidy, and suppose it attacks. They have a damned good army of seasoned soldiers up there, the best in Southeast Asia."

"That's where your talents come in, General. I want you to see to it that a viable South Vietnamese army is established, trained, and equipped by us. An army so good the North won't dare attack or undermine the government. The President, you know, does not favor sending American troops to the Asian mainland, and you and I agree with that precept. We therefore must make the South Vietnamese the equal of the North Vietnamese."

"I will do my best, Mr. Secretary."

Under Hollings' direction a large American staff of officers, non-coms, CIA personnel, and civilian technicians began to mold an army in South Vietnam. The cadre of that army was drawn mainly from Vietnamese who fought with the French. Many of them, moreover, were Catholics who had emigrated from the North after the armistice went into effect. The overwhelming majority of South Vietnamese people, however, were Buddhists and anti-French. They looked upon Ho Chi Minh as their deliverer. [. . .]*

* Prescott wrote a note to himself at this point in his manuscript. It reads: "resume here later, new facts, etc." He evidently intended to go back to this crucial part of his *History* in the light of subsequent developments.—N.F.M.

6

PEACEFUL COEXISTENCE

IN January 1955, Nikita S. Khrushchev, Secretary of the Communist Party of the Soviet Union, sent out a call to three hundred of the Party's leading functionaries to attend a two-day "symposium" late the next month at Kremlin headquarters. A "symposium" was the government's method of apprising the Party hierarchy, and through the hierarchy the millions of Party workers in every farm, town, and city in the Soviet Union, of a new policy that was about to be launched. Traditionally, the secretary, or his representative would define the policy, and the delegates to the "symposium" would form discussion groups to work out the techniques for informing the rank and file at the local level.

"Comrades," Khrushchev's voice rang out over the amplified loudspeaker system of the Central Assembly Hall to the delegates who had managed to come to Moscow despite the massive snow that had fallen over most of the country, "we are on the threshold of a new epoch. We are gathered here to announce this fact to our people and to Communists and the proletariat everywhere.

"For the past thirty-seven years the Soviet Union has been preoccupied with three fundamental tasks. First, the consolidation of the Revolution. Second, the creation of a Socialist society. Third, the defense of the homeland. These tasks could not, of course, be separated. To fulfill the goals of the Revolution it was necessary to build up industry. And to protect the Socialist society it was necessary to build a great workers' army. We have accomplished these three tasks.

"Now the Communist movement grows and multiplies daily in every corner of the earth. Industrial production in the Soviet

Union increases at a rate three to four times that of the United States. Our armed forces, having destroyed the Hitlerite aggressors, are now second to none. Our enemies know our capabilities. They know we possess the most advanced rockets and the most powerful hydrogen bombs. They know they cannot save themselves by attempting to destroy us. Nor do we have to give the capitalists a push. Capitalism is doomed by its own contradictions. Someday, we will lock arms in comradely embrace with the oppressed workers of the West.

"We must think, then, of the fourth task that confronts us. Lenin said: 'Socialists must be prepared to suffer today in the certainty that tomorrow is theirs.' Comrades of the Communist Party of the USSR, tomorrow is here! It is upon us. We have arrived at the critical moment of transition from Socialism to Communism, the moment for which, in Lenin's words, 'mankind has yearned from the time of its birth.' To us, who made and inherited the Revolution, is given the historic task of clearing the path for that transition. The factories and farms of the Soviet Union are now on the verge of producing an abundance of wealth and leisure such as the world has only dared to dream of. But while others were content to dream, Marx and Engels and Lenin taught that behind the dream lay the truth—for those who would act, for those who were, or are, Communists. Yes, our reality is a hopelessly wild fantasy to the capitalists and their cynical allies, clients, and lackeys, some of whom—and you know who they are—call themselves Socialists.

"It will not be long, comrades, before every Soviet citizen will work at his chosen occupation for as long as he likes, consumes what he desires, and spends his leisure time at libraries, parks, museums, galleries, the theater, the cinema, concerts. Under Communism we shall even have the right to do nothing, to be lazy. Yes, that too. 'To rest is to do God's work,' as a Ukrainian proverb tells us. Here, then, is what the transition from Socialism to Communism will mean. A quantity of commodities, from the simplest to the most complex, from food and clothing to cars and television sets, far greater than the United States at its most prosperous can ever produce. Once we have reached that point of quantity—when we can truly affirm, 'From each according to his ability to each according to his needs'—

we will effortlessly make the leap to quality—a Communist way of life in which every person will be joyous and free, in which the kingdom of necessity will at last have been conquered. That is the message, comrades, you will carry to the people.

"But before we can shift from capital goods production to consumer goods production we must have peace and the assurance of peace. Though we can smash any aggressor who attacks us we prefer that no aggression take place. Because we are and will remain impregnably strong we can seek reasonable relations with the capitalist states, relations based on reality. The Soviet Union is convinced that, being realists, the capitalist states do not seek war, of whose consequences they are fully aware. Why, therefore, may not our social system and theirs, we and they, co-exist on this planet peacefully? By all means, let us compete. Capitalists boast of their competitiveness. Well, let us give them a taste of their own medicine. Let us see which social system demonstrates its superiority. The Soviet Union wants to normalize relations with all non-fascist states that are willing to obey the rules of international law. We welcome contacts between their people and ours, provided they do not send us hooligans and troublemakers, spies and subversives. We welcome trade and cultural exchanges.

"To sum up, comrades. During the transition period from Socialism to Communism the Soviet Union will pursue a policy of peaceful co-existence and normalization of relations. And so, without catastrophes, without wars, we will obtain Communism, and the rest of the world will beat a path to our door in search of the magic potion of happiness. And yes, we will give them the formula. Become Marxists-Leninists, become Communists, we will tell them, and you too will know what true happiness is. That is what we will tell mankind."

During the "symposium" Khrushchev also informed the Party apparatus that the "draconian" days were over, that rule by terror would no longer be tolerated. The "dictatorship of the proletariat," the absolute authority of the Party, would continue as ever, but not in the despotic form that the Soviet people had experienced without letup since the 1920s.

And indeed, step by step in the course of the year he reduced the "work norms" and raised pensions, emphasized the principle of "Socialist legality" in future dealings with "criminals," closed down many more labor camps and rehabilitated some of the victims of purges going back to the early '30s, granted a modicum of freedom to intellectuals, and quietly effaced some of the most blatant reminders of Stalin's legacy, such as the statues of him in every public square in every city and town and hamlet in the country. (Conspicuously, Stalin's body was removed from Lenin's tomb—temporarily, according to *Pravda,* permanently, according to rumors circulating in Moscow.)

"Are we witnessing the beginning of a thaw in the Cold War?" Robert Oliphant, a diplomatic correspondent for Reuters News Agency asked. "Can we detect some cracks in the ice?" The term "thaw," later popularized by Soviet writers (in particular Ilya Ehrenbourg, who wrote a book by that title), entered into the vocabulary of the times.

Among the manifestations of the thaw was the series of visits that Khrushchev and Nikolai Bulganin—who had replaced Malenkov as Premier—made to various neutral and Western countries. Nothing pointed up the contrasts between the new epoch and the old more clearly than their "peregrinations," Stalin having never left the Soviet Union in peacetime. Khrushchev and Bulganin seemed to enjoy exposing themselves to public view. The public seemed to enjoy them in turn. They were both short and stout and avuncular-looking. One could hardly call them sinister. "Krush and Bulge, the great comedy duo, now playing in these parts," read a cartoon caption in *Smack,* an English journal of humor. Raymond Byquest of the *Edinburgh Bugler* compared them—in appearance—to "teddy bears." "Children might love them," Byquest wrote, "but adults beware."

Khrushchev provided excellent newspaper copy. (Bulganin spoke little, being content to smile, nod his head, and remain in the background.) With free abandon Khrushchev offered his opinions, judgments, and Ukrainian adages on any subject that came within his purview. His critical remarks, though often insulting, were refreshingly candid just the same. When he visited a model factory in Lancashire he said it reminded him of a "prison, well lit, airy, pretty, but still a prison." During a tour of the Tate Museum, with its rich profusion of Matisses, Redons,

Soutines, Lipschitzes, Epsteins, Grosses, and Modiglianis, he was quoted as saying, "It's all a cacophony, a jumble of insane images and objects. Who can like them but corrupt capitalists and decadent aristocrats?"

After a conference with Labour Party leaders he remarked: "These Socialists, so-called, bring to mind a Ukrainian saying: 'It isn't a wolf who wears sheep's clothing; it's a sheep.' The Labour Party leaders are what they seem—sheep." To an Indian delegation who had shown him the Taj Mahal, he exclaimed: "Very beautiful. But where do you think it came from? From the backs of the peasants who slaved for the vanity of a prince. They could have done with a little more food and a little less beauty."

Their trip to Yugoslavia was their most important. Seven years before, Stalin had cast Tito out of the Communist pantheon as a renegade and traitor. Since then Yugoslavia had drawn closer and closer to the West. The Communist regime was slowly "humanized," as artists and intellectuals acquired the freedom to experiment and as bureaucratic and police controls in general diminished. But Yugoslavia was still a one-party dictatorship, ruled by a self-perpetuating oligarchy of "Marxists-Leninists." That was precisely why "Titoism" was such a dangerous heresy within the Communist world. The example of its independence threatened at every moment to break the monolithic unity imposed by the Soviet Union. All the more remarkable, then, that Khrushchev and Bulganin should fly to Belgrade to visit "the notorious apostate," as Khrushchev himself had once referred to Tito.

Some Western correspondents exaggerated in calling it "a latter-day Canossa." They did not come to Tito to lay themselves at his feet and beg his forgiveness. They sought to bring him back to the Communist camp.

"Listen, comrade," Khrushchev stated in the course of their eight-hour meeting on Tito's enormous yacht (the gift of Greek shipping mogul Thersites Onassiarch), "the West gives you credits and arms. The Soviet Union will give you that too, and we will double the amount. We make no conditions, only that you rejoin your comrades. Come home to where you belong."

Tito smiled broadly, his white teeth glistening in the Adriatic sun. "My oracle has warned me. Beware of Russians bearing gifts."

Khrushchev replied jocularly: "Bulganin is a Russian. I'm a Ukrainian. You can trust me."

"I do trust you," Tito said. "But do you think I would be wise to place all my eggs in one basket now? In any case, my people would be very unhappy if I made an about-face. They would ask me, 'After all that has happened could you go back to the old servitude?' "

"It would not be servitude," Khrushchev asserted. "That's the point, comrade. It would be a new relationship."

"I know, I know," Tito said, "but how will I convince the people? What possible guarantee could you give me that we would keep our independence? What I will agree to is this. Let us gradually have normal relations between our countries. We will accept credit from you. Meanwhile, we will continue our friendly relations with the West, remaining, as always, neutral in the Cold War. I think the cause of peace is better served by my neutrality—as by Nehru's and Sukarno's and U Nu's and Nasser's—than by our siding with either of the great powers."

"Yes, but you're a Communist," Khrushchev said, after a moment's pause. "They aren't. Do you think the capitalists are doing you all these wonderful favors for nothing? 'Only the dead receive gratuities,' my old father used to say. How long will you go on serving their interest? This may not be your intention. Objectively, it's what you're doing, comrade."

"I resent that accusation," Tito said slowly, his face growing red. "I'm not going to exchange insults with you. Anyway, I'm not as good at it as you are."

"Thank you for the compliment. Forgive me. Let the remark pass."

"You know why the Americans have supported me since '48," Tito continued. "Because they wanted me to stay alive. I'm under no illusions. I'm valuable to them as long as you're my enemy. I don't want you to be my enemy, and I would rather the Americans didn't help me for these reasons. It's up to you, comrades. If we can live together, if you don't condemn us as heretics and don't turn our neighbors against us, the

Americans won't be so generous. Capitalists are not always so stupid. If they were, we Communists wouldn't have such a hard job."

"We've had our differences, and we still have them," Khrushchev said. "But I like you. We can talk as men. We shouldn't be enemies any longer. We're willing to discuss your proposals. They sound reasonable to me. Let me say this, however. I don't think your people should go around the world like Christian missionaries, boasting of the new Communist faith, boasting also of how you tweaked Stalin's nose. You should make them shut up. The Ukrainians have a piece of advice for boasters: 'Watch what you say. It's hard to boast with a hole in your tongue.'"

"The Ukrainians are a wise people," Tito said, smiling again. "We Serbians also have a saying: 'Better to boast about yourself than fawn on others.'"

"The Serbians are a wise people, too, and so are the Russians, right, Nikolai Andreyovitch?" Khrushchev asked with a loud laugh, thumping Bulganin in the ribs. "It's time for lunch."

Before he left for his "peregrinations," Khrushchev had raised the issue of Austria before a meeting of the Soviet Politburo. "Let's get rid of that excrescence," he said. "Austria's a bother, nothing more. If the West asks nothing of us why shouldn't we and they pull out of there and give it back to the Austrians—if they stay neutral?"

Molotov, Kaganovitch, and Michael Suslov, a "theoretician," who usually supplied arguments for the "tough ones," maintained that the status quo was preferable. "Suppose Austria was freed and became neutral and then drifted over to the West?" Suslov asked. "What would we do? Invade? Launch a third world war? Better keep the country divided, I say. Better that we keep a third of it than give all of it to the West."

"False fears," said Bulganin. "Austria is not Germany. How many people does it have—six million, eight million? The size of Moscow. Do you think they'll want to antagonize us? Austria is surrounded by Communist states. We can take the chance, though it's no chance at all."

Dulles discussed the Soviet offer with other senior State Department officials. "My inclination is to reject it," he said. "The

Russians have something up their infernal sleeves. Let's imagine Austria became free, independent, and neutral. How long would it remain so? I think it would go the way of Czechoslovakia. Keeping our troops in Austria is the only solid protection we have. To me it's obvious. The Soviets want to get our troops out of there. Then nothing can stop them."

"But sir," said Serge Coudert, chairman of the Central European Policy Planning Division, "I feel that the Soviets, in tendering the offer, anticipated our fears. There is no reason, for example, why free elections could not be written into an Austrian peace treaty, thus precluding a Communist coup. Besides, the Soviets very likely have no intention of bringing Austria into the Communist sphere. Nor do they care what kind of regime it has so long as it is not anti-Soviet, anti-Communist. If neutrality works, Mr. Secretary, it will rescue some three million Austrians from Soviet occupation. I think the risk worth taking."

Dulles relented enough to present a "lawyer's brief," as he put it, on both sides of the issue to President Eisenhower. Eisenhower quicky concluded that the United States should "go ahead and sign a treaty if it's a good one."

And so, in late June 1955, Austria became whole and self-determining again. The treaty, signed by the Big Four, forbade her from joining any military alliance and promised that her independence and territorial integrity would be respected. It was the first major agreement between the Soviet Union and the United States since the Second World War.

"We Ukrainians have a saying," Khrushchev told American ambassador Charles Bohlen at a party in the Soviet Foreign Ministry, " 'The harder the first step, the easier the others.' With God's help this agreement will be the first of many."

The Austrian Treaty was not the only sign of the thaw in international relations. Earlier in the year Prime Minister Churchill electrified the world by announcing that he would seek a meeting of the Big Four to "resolve the outstanding problems of our stricken times." In doing so, Churchill evoked images of the glorious days of the war, when he and Stalin and Roosevelt, giants of a bygone era, would come together and decide the fate of the world.

For a while Eisenhower seemed unsympathetic to the idea of

a Big Four conference. Dulles had been advising him that it would be "premature" and would turn into "a propaganda forum for the Communists." "It would be better if we, our allies, and the Russians first try to work out some of our problems at the ministerial level. Then, I think, a summit conference might get somewhere."

A number of Eisenhower's other advisers, however, recommended that he seize the opportunity lest it slip by. In a memorandum to the President, Harold Stassen, head of the administration's disarmament agency, pointed out that "the world yearns for a commitment in behalf of peace by the great powers. True, nothing concrete may come of a summit meeting. But the climate of opinion would change for the better. Concrete results would flow from the general change of attitudes and motivations."

Dulles dismissed the memorandum contemptuously. "Stassen was, is, and always will be, a muddlehead," he confided to Beadle Smith. "Like so many do-gooders around here his realities arise from his hopes. I'm afraid the President, bless him, has a streak of that quality in himself."

In fact, Eisenhower had made up his mind by mid-May 1955 that he would like to see the Soviet leaders face to face. "Nothing is lost in talking these matters out," he told Dulles, who listened grimly. "Our people, all humanity, are tired of the conflicts, the fears, the unrelieved arms race. Damn it, they don't understand why we can't all come to terms. Bulganin is right. We have different social systems, but we can coexist peacefully. We don't have to be bosom buddies."

"Yes, Mr. President," Dulles said quietly, "provided we keep our powder dry and let them know unequivocally how far they can go."

"Why of course, Foster. Now suppose they abide by those limits. Suppose they want to reduce their arms expenditures. Suppose they moderate their design for world conquest. They know damned well they can't win a war."

"True, but then they try other tactics—subversion, guerrilla warfare, playing on legitimate problems of poor peoples. They're as cunning as the Serpent, and like the Serpent they never stop, they never rest."

"But, Foster, I don't see how we can get out of it. We have to live on this planet together. Either we live or die together on it. That's the main problem. The others are secondary."

That evening, speaking before the Republican Dames' dinner in Washington, Eisenhower let it be known that he would consent to a summit conference. "I will do anything, meet with anyone, go anywhere, act in any way, serve in any capacity if it furthers the pursuit of peace in the slightest."

Privately, Dulles thought Eisenhower had "demeaned" himself. "His speech writers see him as a John the Baptist, to go no further. Well, the fat is in the fire. The charade is on."

After some preliminary controversy over where they should meet—Cannes, Innsbruck, Uppsala, Reykjavik—the Big Four agreed on Geneva, where the monumental Palace of Nations was placed at their disposal.

The conference began on July 18th and lasted five days during which time the two sides aired their views and presented their proposals and counterproposals. Four main subjects came up for discussion: Germany, European security, disarmament, and "cultural contacts."

It was apparent from the opening speeches that they were as far apart as ever. The Soviets wanted Germany, and, indeed, the whole of Europe, East and West, neutralized and "disengaged," as Bulganin phrased it. The West insisted that Germany once unified, be allowed to join whatever military organization it preferred (meaning NATO, of course), and that the two alliances, NATO and the Warsaw Pact, discuss "matters of mutual interest." The Soviets asked for categorical prohibitions against the manufacture of atomic and hydrogen weapons and for precise limits on the size of armed forces (e.g., no more than 1,500,000 each for the United States, the Soviet Union, and Communist China, nor more than 750,000 each for Great Britain and France—a perfect balance).

In an impassioned speech, Eisenhower called for an exchange of "military blueprints," which would specify the exact size and composition of the armed forces of every country, along with a system of "aerial inspection" of bases and installations. When Eisenhower concluded, Khrushchev sprang to his feet (though it was not the Soviet Union's turn to speak) and asked: "Does that include the bases the United States keeps all over the world and especially on the borders of the Soviet Union?" Eisenhower said nothing.

Finally, Bulganin suggested that "the best representatives of our respective cultures visit and enrich each other under arrangements worked out by our foreign ministers." At Dulles's urging the West in response proposed that each side be free to broadcast and send newspapers, magazines, books, works of art, and the like to the other without censorship.

The Geneva summit conference was no success if by success is meant the settlement of differences, the framing of treaties, etc. What emerged from the conference, rather, was a heightened feeling of trust, a sense that problems might be approached in a new way. Eisenhower was satisfied that Khrushchev and Bulganin were "honorable" men with whom one might in the future "go to the bargaining table without fear of being stripped bare."

For their part, the Soviet leaders were impressed by Eisenhower. At one point in the conference, following a statement by Bulganin on how the Soviet Union had suffered in the last war, Eisenhower declared: "I solemnly swear by everything that is sacred to me that the United States will never participate in an aggressive war. War is repugnant to me and the American people. War is unmitigated hell, now more than ever. We want peace and happiness. I would give everything, my life, my treasure, my good name, yes, everything, for the sake of peace."

The Soviet delegation was visibly moved. Molotov nodded his head approvingly. Bulganin rose to say: "We believe you, Mr. President. We know you are sincere, and we feel the same as you do."

Some of the Soviet diplomats who attended the conference afterwards compared Eisenhower to Prince Myshkin as a "type." "Only," they went on, "he, more than Myshkin, is a victim of circumstances. What can he do?"

On the last day of the conference each of the leaders present vowed to work "in the spirit of Geneva" (which soon became an international catchphrase), and expressed the hope that more summits would be held. "Perhaps," said French Premier Arnulph

Fourier, "such conferences will take place every year, or every two years, and humanity will celebrate them as days of jubilee."

Dulles, who had not stopped doodling for five days, was heard to mutter: "Sounding brass and tinkling bells. To no avail, to no avail."

As tensions lessened, as the thaw worked its effects, so, correspondingly, did a sense of moderation and sobriety return to the American people. This new sense was reflected in the spectacular demise of Senator Joseph R. McCarthy, though "McCarthyism"—a term that entered the lexicon of American politics—lingered on.

In 1953, the first year of Eisenhower's presidency, McCarthy stood at the apogee of his powers. He had come into his own. As head of a Senate subcommittee on "internal security" he cut a wide swath across American society, investigating whomever and whatever he pleased. No institution was sacrosanct. Indeed, his contempt for the traditional canons of respectability accounted for much of his popularity. He accused Harvard University, for example, of being "a seedbed of treason for over twenty years," *The New York Times* of being a "nesting ground of subversives and misfits," Columbia Broadcasting Company of being a "repository of ideological filth, of harboring effete snobs who want to run America into the ground," etc.

His technique of investigation never varied. First, he would announce to the press that he was going to such and such a city to "expose the Communists" who worked for such and such an organization. Before summoning the witnesses he would reveal their names and the nature of their alleged malfeasance (usually gossip, hearsay, unverified charges of every description). Waving a slip of paper before the cameras he would asseverate, in his tremulous nasal voice, "Here I have the names of twenty-five spies presently employed by ————." Then he would bully and hector the witnesses, repeating the charges he had already made. By this time, of course, they had been convicted before the very partial bar of public opinion, and they had no way, since he was immune from prosecution, of clearing their names.

Meanwhile, he enjoyed the support of the administration, which promptly tried refractory witnesses, and fired some employees and hired others at his behest. At the State Department

Dulles completed the job Acheson had begun of getting rid of practically all the old "China hands"—that is, those who had expressed reservations about Chiang Kai-shek—as well as others whose "loyalty"—meaning their political judgment—McCarthy had questioned. "Clear it with Joe" was the refrain heard in the corridors of government in those exigent days.

The administration bent over backwards to appease McCarthy, but he was not to be appeased. For what he sought was nothing less than the government's submission to his will. He was affronted when Eisenhower appointed Charles Bohlen ambassador to the Soviet Union. "This man is a notorious fellow traveler," McCarthy said on the Senate floor. "Will we send him to Communist headquarters to receive his orders directly from his masters?"

By the end of 1953 he was referring to "twenty-one years of treason." "This government," he said in a Thanksgiving Day speech in Appleton, Wisconsin, his home town, "is still chock full of Communists and subversives and the administration is still dragging its feet. I say here and now that I'm going to investigate people in high places, let the chips fall where they may."

True to his word, he opened a series of well-publicized inquiries into "subversion in the Army," specifically the "all important" Signal Corps laboratories in Fort Asquith, New Jersey. McCarthy maintained that an army dentist at the fort (one Norman Schwantz), though "a known subversive," had been promoted from captain to major. His whole case rested on the question: "Who promoted Major Schwantz?" His committee called the Secretary of the Army, Robert Stevens, and a succession of generals, including the commandant of the fort. McCarthy gave all of them a tongue lashing and implied that they too were somehow involved in the Major Schwantz plot.

Early in 1954 McCarthy threatened to widen his investigation of the Army. "We're getting to see how this government works," he declared at one of his hearings. "The Communist conspiracy goes very deep, how deep I dare not say at the moment because we're still investigating. I don't want the innocent damned along with the guilty. But I'm shocked beyond words."

The next day Eisenhower conferred in the White House Round Room with Attorney General Herbert Brownell, Republican Party

Chairman Leonard Hall, Secretary of Defense Wilson, and Vice President Nixon.

"The problem is this, gentlemen," Eisenhower said sternly. "We've got to do something about that son of a bitch, McCarthy—I'm going to be frank as hell here. I'm getting reports daily about how he's demoralizing this government. He's making a laughing-stock of us abroad. He's treated Stevens like a thug, a Communist. He's pushed three of our top generals around as though they were serving time in a stockade. I'm not going to have it. I'm fed up to the gills with him. We've got to fight back. Well, what do you think?"

Wilson thought that "the President should publicly denounce him and forbid administrative personnel from testifying before him."

Nixon agreed that McCarthy had sometimes been "too excessive, too zealous," but did not think the President should divide the party. "Remember," Nixon pointed out, "there are millions of silent Americans who sympathize with him. We shouldn't turn Republican against Republican." He then suggested that perhaps McCarthy could be deflected onto some "prominent Democrats" or some "questionable labor union leaders."

"I don't buy that," Eisenhower said peremptorily.

"Neither do I," Brownell added. "Besides, he *has* to attack the government. The Democrats are out of power. They're no longer a good target. He's after the big fry—us. I have a suggestion. Let's try to discredit him in a way that would hurt him most—not ideologically or politically, but personally. He's vulnerable, you know. I think we can lay something heavy on him. He's been trying to procure some trivial favors from the Army on behalf of one of his staff members, an intimate buddy of Roy Cohn's named David Schine, who was recently drafted. Cohn's been calling up the people at Fort Dix to get Private Schine off various duties, KP and the like."

"Why the nerve of the son of a bitch," Eisenhower blurted out.

"Yes, and Cohn's even threatened the officers there, claiming that he has 'dirt' on them. Incredible, isn't it? Well, I think the Army can blow this up into quite a thing."

Hall said he agreed completely with Brownell. "The only way

you can get Joe, it seems to me, is by hitting him hard, with all you've got, wherever he's weakest."

Eisenhower reflected for a moment. "All right, we'll do it. Dick, I want you to organize this thing. Herb, Charley, you'll give Dick all the assistance he needs. I want McCarthy brought down a notch or two. He's a reckless liability now. If it comes down to it then by gosh let the people choose between him and me."

Accordingly, Nixon and two government attorneys, William Rogers of the Justice Department and Emil Touhy of Defense, worked out the strategy of attack. It was to be launched by the Army, not by any administration official. The public would be told that McCarthy had been soliciting "favors" for one of his staff members, and it was for this reason—and here the public would "make the leap of inference," in Nixon's words—that he was accusing the Army of covering up subversion.

"This will hit him hard," Nixon said. "I hate to do it. But maybe it'll force him to be a little more careful about whom he chooses as a target."

Overnight the Army-McCarthy controversy exploded into a major cause célèbre. Publicly, McCarthy denounced the "Pentagon brass" and the "Defense Department bureaucrats" for "trying to divert attention from their own misdeeds by smearing me, by assassinating the character of my staff members, and by wittingly or unwittingly acting in the interests of the Communist conspiracy."

The Army, meanwhile, "leaked" more and more details of how Roy Cohn had alternately pleaded with, cajoled, and threatened military officials, from the Secretary of the Army to Schine's company commander and platoon leader, so that Schine might have overnight and weekend passes.

In April 1954 the parent Internal Security Committee appointed a special panel of seven Senators, four Republicans and three Democrats, to inquire into every aspect of the controversy and render a verdict. For months the panel interrogated a host of witnesses, including all the principals, granting the latter the right to interrogate each other. The entire proceedings were televised.

While, as expected, the panel vindicated neither side's claims, failing on the one hand to sustain McCarthy's charge that Army was covering up subversion or on the other the Army's charge that

McCarthy was guilty of favoritism, nonetheless the hearings achieved the administration's purposes. They destroyed McCarthy as a political force. Before the pitiless cameras he presented the spectacle of a malicious and foul-mouthed bully. Cohn emerged as his sullen and devious cohort. It was as though both of them deliberately acted out the parts that their enemies had assigned them. McCarthy's popularity, and therefore his effectiveness, dropped markedly after the hearings.

Several months later his fortunes took another turn for the worse when the Senate voted overwhelmingly to condemn him for his "contempt" of a special committee that had been looking into his campaign behavior.

At the end of the year Attorney General Brownell could confidently inform the President: "Sir, I don't think Joe will give us much trouble now. No one's listening to him any more. He's been struck down by his own hubris."

"Yes," Eisenhower added, "but with an assist from us."

In the final analysis, circumstances, not his personal defects, defeated McCarthy. He rose to notoriety on the fears generated by the Cold War. When those fears were allayed, when peace began to be good politics, McCarthy lost his leverage on public opinion. And the more strenuously he opposed Eisenhower, whose popularity as a man of peace continued to grow, the more he isolated himself. His accusations simply went unpublicized. He had lost his audience.

The rise and fall of McCarthy bore a paradox. He easily routed the liberal Democrats. It was at the hands of moderate and conservative Republicans that he met his Waterloo. [. . .]*

* Prescott wrote an aside to himself here which reads: "name names, say something about American conservatism, etc, etc."—N.F.M.

7

ANCIENT LEGACIES

DURING one of the sessions of the Geneva Big Four conference Khrushchev suddenly left the Assembly Hall of the Palace of Nations to meet his secretary and aide, Semyon Smerdyakov, who had just flown in from Moscow.

"While you've been gone," Smerdyakov said, breathlessly, "Molotov, Shepilov, Malenkov, and Kaganovitch have been plotting. They're sending their men into the provinces on 'official business.' You know what business they're up to. I've come as quickly as possible."

Khrushchev nodded. "The apples are ripening, though it's not yet autumn. I expected this, Semyon. Don't worry. I know what's going on. Our comrades aren't as clever as they think. But I'm glad you're here anyway."

That evening at the Soviet villa outside Geneva Khrushchev, Smerdyakov, and Bulganin discussed the political events back home. "Don't you think we should smash them right now," Bulganin asked. "The Army is ready, the police are ready. Why wait?"

"That's not the question," Khrushchev replied. "The question is not when we liquidate, but how. There are many ways to chase wolves in the forest. We must liquidate in such a way as to prevent another Stalin from taking over the Party. To chase the wolves Stalin brought in a tiger. You look a little surprised, comrades. What's the matter, Nikolai Andreyovitch?"

"Nothing. But I thought Stalin was unique. The circumstances, the situation—can these be repeated?"

"And how does Stalin enter in?" Smerdyakov asked.

"I appreciate sharp questioning," Khrushchev said sarcastically.

" 'A good cook makes the fat fry,' my sainted mother used to say. Yes, Stalin was unique. But remember, Nikolai Andreyovitch, another despot will be unique in his own way. Who knows? Kublai Khan was different from Genghis. And yes, Semyon dear, Stalin does enter in. He's our holy ghost: invisible but present. The comrades who are plotting behind our backs—little do they know we can see better from the rear than from the front—think they, or one of them, will take up where Stalin left off. He's their inspiration, their pole star.

"Do you see what I'm saying? They don't complain about changing the names of cities, removing statues, removing poems in children's books. The memory of Stalin even can be expunged. They don't care about that. It's the precedent that remains behind. Our birds of prey want to build their nest on top of that precedent. They follow the cult of personality, and they wish to perpetuate the cult of personality."

"The cult of personality," Smerdyakov said approvingly. "A perfect phrase. It strikes the nail on the head."

"In other words, comrades," Khrushchev continued, "we haven't gone far enough. We must bring the whole matter—the cult of personality problem—to the surface. The masses must be made conscious of it. Till now we've taken pygmy steps. We must take a leap, for, as Lenin said, 'The abyss awaits us whichever way we turn.'

"Here is what I propose. Little by little we'll reveal Stalin's crimes, his madness, his incompetence—in time, everything. This, we'll say, is what the Soviet Union can expect if it succumbs again to the cult of personality. This is the lesson to be drawn from Stalin.

"I ask you, what is our goal, comrades? First, to consolidate the rule of the Party and guarantee Socialist legality. Second, to cast Molotov, Malenkov, Shepilov, Kaganovitch, the whole bunch, into the camp of the personality cult. Once we do that we can decide how to punish them.

"We have to bring some order into our affairs, damn it, or we'll never be secure. Are you secure, Nikolai Andreyovitch? How can you be? Every time we hear a fart we'll have a purge. It's us today. Who'll it be tomorrow? Like Stalin we'll send spies to every hamlet and home to listen for farts. Our enemies will listen for ours. The blood will never stop flowing. We must grasp the beast of fear by the throat. Stalinism, the cult of personality, that is the beast. Destroy it and we'll have security. We can rule in peace and not have to look over our shoulders every second of our days and sleepless nights. Remember the old days?"

"How will you grasp the beast by the throat?" Bulganin asked.

"I don't know yet. I think we should move slowly and systematically: articles, Party symposia, meetings. Not at once. Meanwhile we'll watch our enemies like eagles. Let them make a mistake and we'll lift them up with our mighty talons and bear them off to the deserts of Central Asia where they'll live on roots and thistles. As for camps and trials and killings—let's not have any more of that."

The anti-Stalin campaign was accelerated almost from the moment the Soviet delegation returned home from Geneva in early August 1955. Letters were published in *Pravda* recounting the cruelties experienced in work camps. Other letters affirmed the doctrine of Socialist legality over the "arbitrariness and capriciousness of willful leaders." (*Pravda* reported that a worker from Pinsk had proposed to his local union that a statue of Stalin in the city's main park "be stored in a warehouse until a better site for it can be found." The union shouted its approval. The Pinsk Soviet agreed, and the statue disappeared.) It was whispered about that Stalin had personally indulged in grotesquely evil acts: sadism, sodomy, tortures of every description. Intellectuals were permitted to write "in a bittersweet vein," as the Writers' Union expressed it.

At the same time, a "countercampaign" was begun by those wishing to save Stalin's reputation. *Pravda* also printed excerpts from a speech by a Komsomol member in Novosibirsk attacking "those who slander our achievements of the past and the wisdom of our heroic leaders." Similar sentiments were recorded in *Red Star,* the army newspaper. And Mikhail Sholokhov, the renowned novelist, called for the "garroting" of the "anti-Party vermin who stain the honor of our country" and "would hand the Revolution over to our enemies."

By the fall it was obvious even to outsiders that the Party hierarchy was rent into warring factions. "From all indications," Herbert Inquest wrote in the London *Telegraph and Despatch,*

"the Politburo is split three ways: at one extreme stands Khrushchev, who favors a return to Stalinist repression; at the other
stands Malenkov, who favors further liberalization; in the middle
is Molotov, the apostle of the status quo. The outcome may depend on the Army."

In October Khrushchev decided he had to "leap ahead" sooner
than he had anticipated. "Our comrades are more resourceful
than I thought," he told Smerdyakov. "They're not doing anything,
but they're fighting us every step of the way. They're well-en-
trenched, and it may be hard to root them out. 'Old weeds are
hard to pull.' We have to act now. Tell Podduyev [the chief
censor] to clean out the press, a complete purge. *Pravda, Trud,
Red Star, Tass*—all of them gone over with a fine comb. Tell
Bogdanov [Assistant Secretary of the Communist Party] to announce a meeting next year of the Party Congress."

"A Party Congress, Nikita Sergeyovitch?"

"Yes, a Party Congress. I'm going to lay it down there, Semyon.
As a child I learned a Tatar maxim: 'The truth is as painful as
the wound of a sword.' I'm going to give a speech to the Congress
that will be as painful as the wound of a sword. It will raise their
hair, make them wince. I'll spare none of the details, not even
the details of my humiliation.

"Do you know what Stalin did? He once forced me to dance
before the entire Politburo—poor bastards, most of them were
shot a little later. Once, he made me eat a dozen potato pancakes
at midnight—my national dish, he said. Once I had to stand on a
table and read Lermontov to him and his guests for hours. That
was his idea of fun. He called me his jester and fool.

"Once, I dared protest to him. He threatened to send me back
to the mines. I remember his words as clearly as yesterday.
'Nikita Sergeyovitch, how would you like to mine coal again in
the Ukraine? It can be arranged. Hard work might do your
waist some good.' When he spoke this way there was one thing
to do: lower your head and await the verdict. We were at the
mercy of a tyrant, a madman. He was ten times worse than Tamur.

"But enough, Semyon, you'll help me draft the speech. No
one else will know about it."

From all over the world Communist delegates converged on
Moscow for the Twentieth Party Congress of February 15–25,

1956, the first since Stalin's death, the second in eighteen years. Herbert Inquest wrote: "This is the new leadership's Congress. It was called together to ratify and legitimate the policies that have been undertaken in the past three years. We therefore should expect no surprises. The Congress will hear and of course unanimously validate everything that the Soviet Union has accomplished in foreign and domestic affairs. In short, an exercise in braggadocio and tedium."

The first ten days of the Congress bore out Inquest's prediction. The fifteen hundred or so delegates who assembled in the St. Barnabas Hall of the Great Kremlin Palace heard and wildly applauded accounts of Soviet trade and industrial statistics, Soviet scientific triumphs, Soviet military prowess, etc. These matters were disposed of perfunctorily.

Interest picked up during the speech by Anastas Mikoyan, the Assistant Premier, known to many as "the Armenian Magician" because he had survived every purge since the early 1930s. He was now considered Khrushchev's closest confidant. Mikoyan spoke of the need to "liquidate the last vestiges of the cult of personality." The delegates were puzzled by his allusion to "the errors of the past, whose legacies still afflict us." They understood the implication in these remarks. They wondered what meaning to draw from them.

Their question was answered on the last night of the Congress. Only the Soviet delegates were present for the final closed session. A thrill of excitement ran through the hall as Party Secretary Khrushchev entered and acknowledged the thunderous ovation.

For the next six hours, well into the morning, Khrushchev spoke, interrupted only occasionally by applause; the delegates were too enthralled, too stunned to break into the speech. His passion did not flag for a single second as he presented the full chronicle of Stalin's crimes, brutalities, and perversities over a thirty-year period—that is, all but nine years of the Soviet Union's history. He told of how Stalin had aroused the fears and hatred of Lenin; how Stalin had exterminated his revolutionary comrades; how he had ordered them beaten and tortured to elicit false confessions; how he had sent millions to die in slave labor camps; how he had nearly destroyed the army by his insane purge of generals; how he had nearly ruined Soviet agriculture by having millions of kulaks killed; how he had refused to believe, even after he had been told again and again, that the Nazis would invade the Soviet Union, thereby failing to prepare the country for the holocaust; how he had imagined himself a supreme military genius, conducting the war single-handedly; how he had demanded absolute reverence from the Soviet masses; how his paranoia deepened with age; how he had isolated the Communist bloc from the rest of the world; and how he had planned another tremendous purge just before his death.

"Most of us seated in this hall," Khrushchev asserted, "would have ended up as corpses, buried anonymously in open graves."

Though the speech was secret its sensational contents were soon known throughout the Soviet Union. The Communist Party apparatus carefully distributed bits and pieces of it to every factory, farm, village, and parent-teacher school meeting. It was done in a quiet, organized way. At a meeting, say, of a local trade union the leader, a Party-functionary would discuss some of "the issues" raised at the Congress. After reading passages of Khrushchev's speech, he would ask the rank and file to tell their impressions of Stalin, their unhappy experience. Then he would deliver a series of homilies on the dangers inherent in the cult of personality. This method also gave the local Party functionaries some idea of who needed "further guidance and education."

"We must smash the icons," wrote N. I. Shepilov, *Pravda*'s editor, "and we must smash the iconodules too." He meant the stubborn defenders of Stalin who, here and there, actually rebelled against the anti-Stalin campaign. In the spring of 1956 reports circulated of clashes in Georgia, where a number of "Beria's henchmen" were shot. Bulganin, speaking to a congress of collective farmers, called for "Party discipline" against "gangster elements" who "pine for the old days."

All in all, Krushchev's offensive was a brilliant success. Their forces muted and dispersed, his enemies in the Politburo ceased to conspire against him. This only emboldened him to mount a fresh attack. Molotov quietly "resigned" as Foreign Minister to spend, he was quoted as saying, "my remaining days in the quiet of my home and family, serving where and when my country needs me." Kaganovitch left his post as Minister of Transport and disappeared from view. Meanwhile, thousands of local officials in the party and the state bureaucracy were sent packing. Significantly, none of the victims of this minor purge was shot or imprisoned. [. . .]*

By late spring the rest of the world also knew that Khrushchev had given a "secret speech" at the Twentieth Party Congress. One or another manuscript version of it could be obtained in Warsaw, Budapest, and Belgrade. The Soviet Union attributed these underground copies to Western agents and local "opportunists and slanderers." Then, one day in June, the United States Department of State released what it claimed was the official text of the speech, and it was, of course, printed, fully or partly, in every major Western newspaper. This time no repudiation came from the Soviet Union, a tacit admission of its authenticity.

The effect on the Communist movement in the West was seismic. The feelings of seasoned old Communists when they read the speech was perhaps best expressed by Paul Zigorin, a leading "theoretician" of the powerful French Party. He wrote in *Hors de combat,* an independent left journal: "If Khrushchev is right then we Communists, even more than our class enemies, have been victimized and duped by 'history.' We assumed that Comrade Stalin had been correct down the line, despite occasional excesses committed in his name—provoked in any case, we thought, by the fascists.

"Now we are told by his successor, himself one of Stalin's protégés, that everything said against him, all the lies and propaganda of the bourgeois press, were not only true; they merely scratched the surface. What then have we given our lives for? Ah cruel irony! We thought we were the advanced guard of history. History, it turns out, has made fools of us.

"Or rather, we have made fools of ourselves. We surrendered our lives not to a movement that failed—a noble wager!—but to the most profound negation of our hopes—the most contemptible folly!

"We Communists have arrived at the *Nullpunct.*"

Later in the month the Presidium of the Italian Communist Party—the largest, most successful Communist Party in the West

* Prescott has cryptically written here: "consult SS's message of 1/9/64."

—held an emergency meeting to take up the Twentieth Congress speech. After an acrimonious, eighteen-hour session the delegates voted to address the following questions to Khrushchev:

"(1) Why did you wait so long to speak out? (2) Why did you go along with Stalin all those years? (3) Did you yourself not commit many of the crimes of which you accuse Stalin? (4) Why did you fail to mention anti-Semitism, though it is well established that Jews were often singled out for persecution? (5) Why was it necessary for Communists to learn the contents of your speech through American intelligence sources? (6) What guarantee can you give that another Stalin will not emerge? (7) What measures will you take to increase the freedom of Soviet citizens?"

Palmiero Togliatti, the Italian Party's shrewd leader, commended the Presidium for its "candor" and "honesty" in drawing up such "penetrating" questions. He then proceeded to water them down appreciably. He did say, however, that the time had come—and he would soon offer it as a statement of policy—for each of the Communist Parties to pursue its own independent course. "Comrade Khrushchev's speech has cut loose the leading strings once and for all; there are no centers any more; we are equal."

The Italian and French Communist Parties easily weathered the crisis because they were so large and so solidly institutionalized. Elsewhere in the West the Communist Parties lost whatever credibility they still had. Members who had held on despite the Great Purge, despite the Hitler-Stalin Pact of 1940, despite everything, now found that they could hang on no more and they left the party and renounced the past—the better part of their lives. Paul Zigorin had spoken for all of them.

These crises in the Communist movement were like so many ripples in the infinite sea [. . .]*

---

* Prescott does not break off here, but the thought is obviously incomplete. He probably intended to add something later.—N.F.M.

8

HEGEMONY

IN early March 1956, one week to the day after he spoke to the Twentieth Party Congress, Khrushchev conferred in his lavishly furnished office with Boleslaw Bierut and Matyas Rakosi, the Communist Party bosses of Poland and Hungary. Both men had been deeply devoted to Stalin, whose orders over the years they had unfailingly executed. Bierut, quiet-spoken and lack-luster, had risen up the Polish Communist hierarchy by hard work and strict obedience to command. "He rowed through life with silent oars" —so it was said of him.

Rakosi on the other hand was a bluff and bellicose man. "The mailed fist of Budapest," as he was known, carried out orders too, but with a flair: he seemed to enjoy being cruel. It was Rakosi who coined the phrase "salami tactics" to describe his method of taking power. "We Balkan Communists do not want violence," he explained to *New York Traveler* correspondent Darius Berger. "What we try to do is take possession of the government effortlessly, by stages, one slice at a time. First we enter into a broad coalition, then we increase our representation in such departments as police and internal security, finally we push out our enemies altogether and retire them to private life. No one gets hurt that way and it works out for the best."

Bierut and Rakosi were called to Moscow because the situation in their countries was "deteriorating." The people were growing "restive." According to reports from Soviet ambassadors to those countries, the Party structures were breaking down as local functionaries more and more voiced popular demands for higher pay, fewer restrictions, greater national independence, the release of political prisoners, and the like. The question of Poland and Hungary, and of the peoples' democracies in general, could no longer be put off.

"Comrades," Khrushchev said sternly, "you're going to have to handle these problems yourselves. If you get into trouble don't count on our intervening for you. We don't want to send our bayonets. Berlin was enough. My advice to you is this. Get tough with these rebels, but also throw them some bread. Give them what they want, as long as you keep order and carry out your obligations to us. That's my advice."

"Yes," Rakosi said, "I agree with you, Comrade Secretary. We must give them something. But what? How much? I know my people. Those Magyar fanatics will ask for more, then more, always more. I believe in the carrot and the stick—provided I have a big enough stick. And I don't have one unless I can count on the Soviet Union. With the Soviet Union I am everything. Without her, nothing."

"Should I place tanks and artillery at your disposal, comrade?" Khrushchev asked sarcastically. "How many divisions and squadrons would you like?"

"Comrade Khrushchev, I implore you, understand the dangers we face," Bierut said mildly. "The insurgents in Poland are Titoists. I'm prepared to make concessions to these national Communists, as they style themselves. I'm willing to bring some of them into the Politburo, the Committee, the government. What will happen? I know my people, too. They will go beyond Titoism and demand a restoration of the old regime. The church will come back, the farmers will want their land, the workers their so-called rights, the bourgeoisie their property, and so on and on. Everything will fall apart."

"Listen," Khrushchev replied, "I'm not asking subservience from you. Stalin's dead, I hope for good. You can be on your own a little more now. What's wrong with a little national Communism? Maybe your critics have a point. Maybe you're too alien from your people. You're like priests without congregations. Between you and me, comrades, there *are* too many Jews in the Party apparatus. The masses in your countries think the Jews are stepping on their throats and laughing behind their backs. I'll say this much for Stalin. If he didn't take care of the likes of Trotsky, Zinoviev, Kamenev, Radek, and company there'd be a lot more anti-Semitism in our country than there is. That's one of the ironies that our Jews haven't appreciated."

A long silence followed these ruminations. "One thing more, Comrade Secretary," Rakosi said, clenching his mastiff-like jaws. "If we go under in Hungary and Poland the dam will burst, and the Warsaw Pact will drown with us. Dulles and Adenauer and the imperialists will be very pleased."

"Let's not discuss it further," Khrushchev said, rising from his chair. "You don't have to spell out all the consequences. I know them very well. But maybe you're not the only alternative. Anyway, I'm not abandoning you, don't worry. I'm trying to help you, to convince you not to depend so much on us. Smerdyakov suggested the other day that I should remove Soviet officers from your armies—"

"No, no, you mustn't," Bierut said.

"It would be a calamity," Rakosi added.

Khrushchev smiled. "Comrades, settle down. This isn't Judgment Day. Before you interrupted I was going to say I didn't think it was a very good suggestion. I'm not going to remove our officers from your armies. You can rest assured on that score.

"Before you leave, comrades, a last piece of advice. Have nothing to do with the other members of the Politburo. You know who I mean. Keep your distance from them no matter how hard they try to approach you. 'A warning heeded is a life saved.'"

Following Khrushchev's advice the Communist Parties of Hungary and Poland went out of their way to assuage the "disaffected" groups. They began to "rehabilitate" the victims of Stalinist purges and release thousands of political prisoners. The most sensational "rehabilitation" occurred in Hungary, where the government confessed that Lazslo Rajk, once Premier, and four other high ranking officials, had been unjustly hanged in 1949 for "treason"—that is, for having followed "the Titoist line."

In Poland, events took an ominous turn. Bierut died in mid-March (some claimed of heartbreak over the Twentieth Party Congress speech) and the Polish Politburo was thrown into wild confusion as a surprisingly large number of insurgents—about a fifth of the members—insisted that he be replaced by a "liberal." But the old guard chose Roman Zambrowski, another implacable Stalinist. The insurgents stalked out of the conference and threatened to take their case "to the rank and file"—a revolutionary step.

That evening Khrushchev arrived in Warsaw, ostensibly to attend Bierut's funeral, actually to intervene in the selection of Bierut's successor. "Zambrowski's out," he shouted to the Polish Politburo. "Your folly defies understanding. A man with his record? And a Jew to boot? Give him a job as tax collector. And while you're at it send Berman, Goldschmidt, and Deutscher out to the provinces with him. They shouldn't be on the Committee."

The Polish Politburo heeded Khrushchev's advice and elected the "liberally oriented" and otherwise innocuous Eduard Ochab as Party secretary.

But these minimal concessions, as Bierut and Rakosi had predicted, scarcely satisfied the insurgents. "Salami tactics work both ways," the insurgent *Patofi Tribune* of Pecs (Hungary) wrote. "This time the regime must hand out the slices to the people." Matters came to a boil late in June 1956 when the workers of Poznan, Poland, "rebelled": they struck for higher wages, lower quotas, and for their own unions and councils. As the strike spread and gained support in the city, then elsewhere in the country, the government sent in troops (a number of whom joined the rebellion).

The government crushed the strike, but it also completely discredited itself. Even the most hardened Stalinist realized that popular discontent could no longer be reduced by mere poultices. During the Party Plenum meeting in July, the Stalinists executed an apparent about-face. They sponsored a broad series of reforms, some of them going beyond what the liberals sought. In fact, they conducted a tactical retreat. Their intention was to deflect the public from the more pressing issue of national Communism. As Wiktor Klosiewicz, a hard-bitten Stalinophile of long standing, stated in the Plenum debate: "If we raise a Tito here, comrades, we Communists are finished, *kaput.* We'll be sent packing. As far as I am concerned the insurgents can have their freedoms, so called, all of them. But if we break with Moscow, there will be nothing left. I favor a declaration of the rights of man, of Poles. I am against a declaration of independence."

The regime adopted the Stalinist-sponsored civil reforms. It also dealt leniently with the "hooligans and American and West German agents" who had "inspired" the Poznan "troubles." The trial of the "malefactors" and "ringleaders" was, indeed, a model of humane due process, and the sentences—when imposed—were mild.

"Yes, we welcome these changes," the radical student paper, *Speaking Out* editorialized in late September. "But the cult of personality hangs over our heads like a sword of Damocles. Wait till things calm down. The reforms, the changes, the sunny climate—all will disappear. Why? Because Poland is tethered to the Soviet Union, like an old draft horse to its wagon. Only a charter of national autonomy will save us. Without independence Poland will never be free. To say otherwise is a damnable lie."

By early summer the insurgents in Poland and Hungary were drawing strength from each other. The Poznan uprising brought thousands of Hungarians into the streets of the larger cities, and Hungarian workers, too, petitioned for higher pay, lower work quotas, etc. A "League of Housewives" paraded through Budapest demanding more consumer goods. The radical Petofi Circle, its ranks swelling daily, unloosed a torrent of criticism against "government by secret police and Byzantine bureaucrats."

Rakosi found it harder and harder to control the Hungarian Politburo. Early in July he decided to embark on a "draconian course," as he described it to his trusted aide, Ernst Gero. He would give Hungary "what she wanted and what she deserved: a fat carrot and a big stick." The Communist Party's Central Committee announced that the drive to collectivize agriculture would be "relaxed," that workers would be allowed more "autonomy," and that more consumer goods would be made available. At the same time, the secret police arrested hundreds of insurgents, sacked their meeting halls, and closed down the "anti-Party" publications.

Hungary was thrown into turmoil. The Soviet ambassador wired Khrushchev: "The crowds are growing by the hour. Budapest will make Poznan look like a love feast." Khrushchev called in Anastas Mikoyan. "That Jew swine. I knew it would come to this. Go to Budapest now and see what's going on. If it's a revolution, come right back. If it's not, get rid of Rakosi. If he's pulling another Ulbricht, if you think he's provoking the trouble, shoot him on the spot."

Hours later Mikoyan and Rakosi met in the heavily guarded Communist Party headquarters on Kossuth Square, directly across from a towering statue of Stalin. "I have already spoken to the Central Committee," Mikoyan said sharply, "and they agreed that you need a long rest. The situation is not yet critical, though it will be if you do not take your vacation. Comrades Khrushchev and Bulganin invite you for a cruise on the Black Sea."

"So be it," Rakosi replied with a weary shrug. "I tried my best. You know, comrade, I'm a Hungarian—never mind that slander about my being a Jew—and I know what Hungary wants: a blood-bath, a catharsis, a purgative. And when I'm gone there'll be one, sooner or later. The choice is this: bayonets or Titoism, nothing else. It will be 1848 all over again. You see, I wanted to prevent that from happening. I learned that you can't tamper with the tragic destiny of the Hungarian people. It gives me no pleasure to be a prophet vindicated. My bags are packed. I leave at once."

That day, on Mikoyan's urging, Ernst Gero became the First Secretary of the Hungarian Communist Party.

In both Poland and Hungary the insurgents refused to accept changes in leadership ordered from above. They rallied behind the two men who had been exiled from the party ranks of both countries for their "traitorous"—i.e., national Communist, or Titoist—views: Wladyslaw Gomulka of Poland and Imre Nagy of Hungary.

Gomulka had joined the Communist movement as a working class lad, having taught himself the dialectics of Marxism-Leninism. His zealousness, discipline, and stiff-necked pride earned him such nicknames as "Calvin," "Savanarola," "St. Jerome," etc. They also accounted for his rise to the summit of the Party. Stalin, however, had come to regard Gomulka as "too dangerous," "too prone to Titoism," and in 1949 he had been deposed as Party chief, stricken from the rolls, and thrown into prison. Gomulka's "mistake" was to have objected to Poland's total economic and political subjection to the Soviet Union.

Nagy had fallen from grace much later. He had been premier of Hungary in 1955, during a period of liberalization, and had ventured closer to national Communism than any statesman in the Soviet orbit. He had gone so far as to advocate the "neutralization" of the Balkan countries. "No small country, irrespective of its ideology, should be caught in the vice of big power politics," he had said openly. "Big power politics is the death of reform. We should *feel* a sense of solidarity with our Soviet brethren, not be chained to them."

At a fateful Party Committee meeting, Ferenc Bartók, the Minister of Education (and a Stalinist) had asked Nagy: "Do you think, therefore, that Hungary should withdraw from the Warsaw Pact and link up with the neutralists—Tito, Nehru, Nasser, Sukarno, and the others?" After pausing, Nagy had answered: "Yes, I do. That would be the best thing for Hungary."

Bartok had then called Khrushchev himself on the phone and explained everything. Khrushchev's message had been immediately communicated to the other members of the Committee. It was, "Oust the intellectual fool."

(Nagy was derisively called an "intellectual" because he discussed things "from every angle" and "in depth," as he liked to say, and because his office was a haven for Budapest artists, actors, and writers. Party officials complained regularly that he was turning his office into a café. His critics described his government as "comic opera," "absurd," "a Hollywood spectacle." Yet they had to admit that Nagy was efficient, much more efficient than his Stalinist predecessors. When Nagy had been ousted from the premiership, and from the Party as well, Rakosi told him, with a slap on the back, "Now you can spend all your time in the cafés.")

The pressure to restore Gomulka and Nagy to their former places was relentless, forcing the Polish and Hungarian parties to retreat further and further. Both were readmitted to their parties as members at large. They were warned, however, not to "canvass" for support. In allowing even this concession the old guard leaders were taking a chance. They knew that to readmit such "apostates" would antagonize the hard-core Stalinists to the point of desperation. For the Stalinists had reason to fear for their lives as well as their jobs.

Poland's Stalinist faction, the "Natolin Group," issued a manifesto early in October denouncing Ochab and the Party for permitting Gomulka to attend a recent Committee meeting. "Make no mistake," the manifesto declared, "if the Gomulka clique has its way it will exact heavy retribution. Shall we stand by and watch in silence as our executioners sharpen their knives?" In Hungary the followers of the notorious Georg Farkas ("Little Stalin") issued a similar statement, or warning: "Bring Nagy back and we will have civil war. We will not accept suicide as the price of our submission."

Khrushchev, growing more alarmed by the day, placed the Soviet armies in Poland and Hungary on standby alert.

In mid-October, a week after drawing up its manifesto, the Natolin Group decided to act. The Assistant Minister of Justice, who was one of its leaders, ordered the secret police to round up seven hundred of the most prominent insurgents in Poland. But the order was "leaked," and the public learned about it before it was scheduled to be issued. Immediately, masses of people poured out into the streets and towns. Work came to a complete halt.

On the afternoon of October 17 Party Secretary Ochab called Khrushchev in Moscow. "A revolution is building up outside," Ochab said, his voice trembling. "What should we do? The mobs are shouting for Gomulka, and the full Plenum will meet tonight. It is going to appoint Gomulka. We can't resist any longer. The Natolists are hiding like cockroaches. What should we do, appoint Gomulka or bring in Soviet troops?"

"Wait!" Khrushchev shouted at the top of his lungs. "Delay the Plenum. Hold them off. I'll be there in twelve hours. Promise the mobs anything, only keep them quiet. We'll settle it tomorrow."

To appease the crowds, the radio and newspapers announced repeatedly that Gomulka would become the Secretary of the Polish Communist Party and that his appointment awaited "formal ratification" at the next meeting of the Plenum.

The Soviet delegation arrived at Warsaw at dawn and went at once to Party headquarters on Proletariat Plaza. The thousands of people who lined the streets watched the procession of limousines in tense silence. Besides Khrushchev, the Soviet delegation consisted of Mikoyan, Molotov, and Kaganovitch.

Khrushchev had asked "the tough ones," Molotov and Kaganovitch, to accompany him as a "gesture of reconciliation." "In the face of this threat to the Soviet Union we must unite, set our

differences aside," he had told the Politburo just before departing. Molotov and Kaganovitch had preferred not to go to Warsaw. They regarded their presence on the delegation as another
of Khrushchev's "sordid tricks." If they should agree with his decision in Warsaw (whatever it might be), then they would share
the responsibility for its outcome. If they should disagree with it,
Khrushchev could accuse them of anti-Party activities.

The Polish "negotiating team" was led by Gomulka and
Ochab. "We will know before long," Gomulka whispered, as
the Soviet leaders filed into the Committee Conference Room,
"whether Poland lives or dies."

"Comrade Gomulka," Khrushchev said peremptorily, "you've
brought us to this pass. The fascists, the hooligans, the church,
the anarchists—they've conspired to bring down the government and the Party. You're their instrument. Do you deny it?"

"I deny it," Gomulka asserted, his face red with contained
anger. "It is the Polish people who have brought you to this pass.
And the Polish people have done so because they have reached
the end of their rope. I resent your accusation that they are
fascists and hooligans and anarchists. They act as patriots and
true Communists. They demand a party and a government that—"

"Don't lecture us, comrade. Tell me this. Do you repudiate the
slander against us, against the Soviet Union? Your press makes us
into beasts. Should we show you how beasts really behave? Your
supporters have no complaints about the West, but they say
with one voice: Down with the Soviet Union, down with Khrushchev, down with the Warsaw Pact. Do you say this too?"

"I do not," Gomulka replied. "I also resent your identifying
me with everyone who opposes the regime. Would you identify
me with the Catholic League? I am resolutely against any slander
of the Soviet Union. I am against any slander of Comrade Khrushchev. And I support the Warsaw Pact, provided it is not used to
suppress its member states."

"Ah, you see," Khrushchev yelled, thumping the table with his
fist. "We can't trust you. You'll have the Warsaw Pact on your
terms, is that it? What are your terms? Do you want complete
independence? Should Poland leave the Pact whenever it chooses?
Let me ask you this: Do you agree with Tito that the peoples'

democracies should join the neutralist bloc? Is that what you're asking for? Tell me right now."

He thumped the table again.

"I feel as though I were before the state prosecutor," Gomulka said. "I will tell you exactly what I think, Comrade Secretary. I do not favor neutrality. I consider Poland a loyal ally of the Soviet Union, and I wish the other peoples' democracies would remain loyal allies as well. But loyalty must come from devotion. How can you expect loyalty from the Polish people when you interfere in our internal affairs, when your officers run our army, when certain of our Party officials take their orders from the Soviet Union. The Polish masses are aroused, and if they think I, too, am willing to barter away their freedom they will throw me over at the blink of an eye. Then you will find no one whom they trust to support the Warsaw Pact. What I am saying, to come to the point, is that unless I come through for them there will be violence, and you will have to bring in the whole Soviet army. The blood will flow like water in the streets."

"Yes," Khrushchev said, "and it'll be Polish blood."

"Comrade Gomulka," Mikoyan asked gently, "what assurances can you give us that you will be able to control the masses? Perhaps they are too agitated and need the discipline of bayonets."

"Poles are not disciplined by bayonets," Ochab broke in. "It has never worked before. We are not Czechs, you know. Death does not terrify us."

"And neither does your bravado intimidate us," Khrushchev declared, pounding the table harder than ever. "Every person, every people, can be disciplined by bayonets. We have enough bayonets to do the job, too. We have done it before. Your martyrs mean nothing to us. Remember, comrades, your own lives are at stake."

Khrushchev was now livid.

"I want to answer Comrade Mikoyan's question," Gomulka rejoined calmly. "I can give you no hard and fast assurance. My ability to control the masses depends more on you, comrades, than on me. You must stop the movement of your troops toward the frontier. Take Marshal Rokassovsky home with you. Also his officers and commissars. Do not meddle in our domestic affairs. Then the Polish people will return to their homes and factories and obey the commands of the Party. And they will stay in the Soviet camp. They will be devoted to the Warsaw Pact."

There was a long pause while Khrushchev and Gomulka looked at each other.

"All right," Khrushchev said, standing up suddenly, "I'll take a chance. You'll have what you want. Everything. Rokassovsky is out. Our troops will pull back. No more Russians in your army. But mind you, comrade, if you fuck up, you're finished. Zhukov himself will lead our armies, and I don't care what happens to your lovely cities. I'm through with sentimentality. Keep the peace, perform your obligations to us, that's all I ask. As for your domestic policies, you can do what you want. Make every Pole a millionaire. I don't give a damn."

The next day the Eighth Polish Communist Party Plenum voted Gomulka Secretary without a dissenting vote.

Gomulka immediately went out to the multitudes who had gathered in the Plaza to await the results of the election. They cheered him for twenty minutes. His speech, however, was restrained. "The time for cheering is not yet. When the threat of conflict is gone we can cheer. We must do nothing to provoke a conflict. The crowds must disperse. Normal processes must return. Calm must prevail. Comrades, fellow Poles, it is not enough to win a victory. It must be preserved. Do you know how close we came to war? To destruction? The danger is not over yet. Only when it ends can we count ourselves free, truly free, truly victorious. We will be our own masters. All power to the people! All power to the Party! All power to Marxism-Leninism!"

These sobering words subdued the great crowd. Grumblings could be heard here and there. But Gomulka's appeal worked. The mood of insurgency, which had risen to such an intense pitch, collapsed. The "October Days" were over.

"I think Poland is safe," Gomulka said to the Party Committee, "provided nothing stupid happens."

Gomulka's ascendancy and the withdrawal of Soviet troops from the Polish border electrified the Hungarian people, who now created their own "October Days." On October 22 and 23 activity in Hungary came to a standstill in honor of the Polish "achievement." All over the country the cry went up for Nagy. The situation was even more volatile than it had been in Poland,

as many army barracks joined in "fraternal solidarity" with the
insurgents, the "free workers" and the "independent peasantry."
What was more, the Communist Party organization simply dis-
integrated (as it had not in Poland), and when, on October 23,
the Central Committee voted Nagy premier, scarcely a murmur
of opposition was raised.

The announcement of Nagy's election failed to disperse the
Budapest crowds. In fact, it set them in motion. They tore down
the enormous statue of Stalin, sacked offices, unlocked the jails and
freed the remaining political and "ideological" prisoners (i.e., non-
juring Catholics), and shot the more notorious members of the
secret police.

Nagy went on the radio and begged for order, invoking Tito and
Gomulka for support. "Beloved Hungarians, something dreadful
may happen. Please, please, go home. Stay off the streets, turn in
your arms. Everything has been won. We will punish our per-
secutors, but not this way."

Just as Nagy said this Ferenc Bartók was issuing a statement
under Nagy's name, though Nagy knew nothing about it. "I have
had to call in Soviet troops to maintain order. I regret that it has
been necessary to do so. The fascist and counterrevolutionary
elements among us are responsible. We will settle accounts with
them later."

Several hours before he wrote those words Bartók had spoken
to Khrushchev, who had himself given the order to the Soviet
commandant in Budapest.

For five days the conflict raged in Budapest as Hungarian
"freedom fighters" conducted a form of urban guerrilla warfare. No Soviet soldier or tank was safe from attack. Over and
over Nagy pleaded with the freedom fighters to put down their
arms. "It is a question of means, not ends, my people. I am with
you on every issue. Only stop the fighting. You will be granted im-
munity from prosecution. You have my word."

Meanwhile, a new Party chairman, Janos Kadar, replaced
Gero. Like Gomulka, Kadar had been imprisoned as a traitor,
narrowly avoiding Laszlo Rajk's fate. And like Gomulka, too,
Kadar was tough and authoritarian. He differed from Rakosi
and the Stalinists in policy, not in methods of leadership. Whereas

Nagy refused to justify Soviet intervention, Kadar welcomed it from the start.

"If we lay down our arms," one group of freedom fighters wrote, "Kadar will hang us high as Haman. He's nothing but a white-collar Rakosi. As for poor Nagy, a born dupe."

On the evening of October 27 Khrushchev asked the top Soviet military officers what was needed to crush the uprising. Their opinion was that many more tanks and men, and perhaps planes as well, would be needed. "The longer the battle lasts the more force we'll have to use," Marshal Georgi Zhukov said bluntly.

Khrushchev promptly instructed the Soviet commandant of Budapest to cease firing and move the troops to the outskirts of the city. At the same time he ordered five divisions, three of them armored, into Hungary. "With Hungarians one can't be too much of a gentleman," Khrushchev said, drily.

A day after the fighting stopped Nagy met with the "representatives of civil society." His office was crowded with people who had been disgraced or jailed or exiled in the previous ten years. Many of them had been leaders of the various suppressed constituencies of Hungary: peasants, workers, Catholics, military men, intellectuals.

"My friends," he said, "it is too soon to say we have triumphed. The Russians have drawn back, for how long I do not know. I do know this, however. Unless we act now they will surely attack us again, reinforced by the armies that are streaming into our country at this very moment.

"The hammer is on the anvil, gentlemen, and it will be struck either by us or them. I have, accordingly, decided on the following course. It is our only hope. I am going to establish a multiparty government, representing every segment of our national life. The Communist Party will be one of many. Let me add, for I know this is very much on your minds, in reaching my decision I have not consulted the Central Committee. I informed Kadar. He has said nothing. He wants me to pledge Hungary's 'fealty'—his word —to the Soviet Union. It is, he thinks, the only way to save Hungary. I disagree. Yes, it might save this regime. It will not save Hungary."

These words were greeted by tremendous applause and loud stamping of feet.

Nagy continued: "The revolutionary situation in which we find ourselves gives us an historic opportunity—that is why I have chosen the simile of the anvil—to announce our complete independence of blocs, cold wars, great power animosities. [Loud applause.] I am going to begin negotiating with the Soviet Union to terminate our treaty with the Warsaw Pact and declare our neutrality. [Applause.] You are familiar with my views on this matter. It is no secret. I revealed them even before Rakosi held the whip at our backs. Now you will ask: Suppose the Russians refuse to negotiate? Suppose they attack us? What can you do? Good questions. Indeed, how can little Hungary stand up to the great bear?

"Well, in the first place we have already stood up to the bear. We have fought well, I dare say, and the whole world has marked the heroism of the freedom fighters. [Tremendous applause.] Now let me ask this. How did Tito stand up to Stalin? Yes, his courage, of course. But there was something else. I mean support from the West, from the United States. It was the United States that gave him the strength to survive. Consider how much more likely it is the West and the United States would sustain us today, seven years later. I can tell you now that I have received assurances from the Americans that they will assist us. 'The United States will not stand idly by'—I quote Ambassador Harkavy—'and allow Hungary to be raped.' The U.S. government is committed to 'massive retaliation.' Fear of such retaliation, gentlemen, this is what will deter our Russian friends. Khrushchev is not so foolish as to risk the destruction of the Soviet Union in order to destroy us.

"My calculations may be wrong. I have miscalculated before. But we must take the chance now. For if not now, when? If the moment is lost it may never be recaptured. Gentlemen, do I have your support?"

A thunderous shout of Yes answered his question.

"Splendid. Let us get to work."

The next day Nagy saw Mikoyan and Suslov, who had hurriedly flown to Budapest as Khrushchev's emissaries. Nagy told them what he had told the representatives of civil society. He was determined, he said, that Hungary should be free, open, democratic, and, above all, neutral, neutrality being "the pivot on which everything else turned." When they pointed out that such a policy might prompt Soviet "intervention" under the terms of the Warsaw Treaty, he replied by threatening American "counterintervention."

"Dulles has stated there will be no Koreas. If Hungary becomes a battlefield, so will the Soviet Union."

Mikoyan and Suslov went to the Soviet embassy where they spoke to Khrushchev on the phone. The conversation was brief. He instructed them to submit to all of Nagy's demands and promise that negotiations on Hungary's withdrawal from the Warsaw Pact would start at once. They conveyed the message to Nagy.

"I am delighted," he said, "but the test of Comrade Khrushchev's sincerity is whether he removes the troops he has sent in." They said they would communicate his "understandable desire to be free of foreign troops" to Secretary Khrushchev.

On November 1 the Soviet ambassador and commandant told Nagy that Soviet troops would board trains and return home the following evening. "The orders are categorical," the ambassador said. "Your triumph is complete."

Several hours later Nagy received a call from a Hungarian colonel. "I've just seen Soviet battle orders for a full-scale assault on Budapest. I swear they're authentic. The Russian lieutenant who showed them to me is going to lead the attack on the Trade Union Institute. The orders are to wipe out all resistance. Airplanes are to be brought in. It's war."

Nagy sat down, placed his head in his hands, and wept. "I will take the bit in my hand, yes, I will take the bit in my hand," he said over and over.

Later that day Nagy sent Tibor Kodály, once a professor of law at Harvard University, on a "sacred mission": to plead with President Eisenhower for American "counterintervention" to save Hungary from "Soviet rape."

On November 2, at 1 P.M., Kodály was ushered into Eisenhower's office in the Executive Office Building. With the President were Secretary Dulles, Neil McElroy, the new Secretary of Defense (formerly chairman of the board of Procter and Gamble), Nixon, Admiral Radford, Senators Lyndon Johnson and William Knowland, and Representatives Sam Rayburn and Joe Martin.

"Gentlemen, my heart is heavy," Kodály said, his voice choking with emotion. "My people will soon be slaughtered by the Russians. Their battle plans are ready. We know this for certain. That is why I am here. To beg for your help in behalf of the Hungarian people."

"What can the United States do to help your people, Mr. Kodály?" Eisenhower asked.

"We do not know precisely. In two or three days the onslaught will begin. There is little time. Perhaps, Mr. President, you should warn the Russian leaders not to go ahead with their plans. Not an ultimatum, but a warning, a strongly worded warning that the Soviet Union can expect retaliation if Budapest is attacked. After all, the United States has given us, the captive peoples, her word that she will assist us if we would but throw off the yoke of Communist thralldom. Sirs, we have done that. Hungary is today a free and independent state, a democracy in the Western tradition, though we are, or will be, neutral, for reasons you can well understand. It is you alone who stand between Hungary and the apocalypse. Hungary throws herself at your mercy."

"I'm extremely moved, Mr. Kodály," Senator Knowland said, "and I go along one thousand per cent with what you've asked us to do. What's more, I don't see why we shouldn't fire off an ultimatum. Why should Hungarian freedom be less precious to us than Greek, or Turkish, or Korean, or West European? And Mr. Kodály, you're absolutely right in saying we have an obligation to Hungary. Why, we encouraged this uprising. We made a commitment to the captive peoples behind the Iron Curtain. I was on the Platform Committee in Chicago that approved the captive people's plank. [Turning to Dulles] Mr. Secretary, you wrote that plank."

"Now, Mr. President," Johnson said gently, "I don't want to keep saying I told you so, but you know how often Sam [Rayburn] and I have objected to the captive peoples' resolution. We always thought it was mischievous. Now look at the mess it's gotten us into."

"I'd like to put my two cents in," Rayburn added. "Mr. President, the captive peoples' thing is worse than mischievous. It's criminal. We're not going to send no warnings or ultimatums

or anything like that, are we? I'm really sorry, Mr. Kodály, that
I'm so blunt. But damn it, the American people aren't going to
have a hydrogen war over this thing. And if not a hydrogen
war, what else? Move in our boys? Do you want to make Hungary
a battlefield, Mr. Kodály? Another Korea? Besides, the American
people won't tolerate it a single second. Neither will the Congress,
right, Joe? [Martin slowly nodded his agreement.] What we've
got to do, I'd say, is put on ashes and sackcloth and beg the
good Lord's forgiveness for letting the Hungarians think we were
going to help them."

"Well reasoned, Mr. Speaker," said Neil McElroy. "You've
persuaded me."

"I tend to agree with you too," Admiral Radford said, speaking
very deliberately. "I never thought Eastern Europe was our
proper theater of responsibility. We should do everything to protect
Asia from the Communists. Well, the mistake was done. I don't
see how it can be rectified now short of all-out war."

"Foster, you haven't spoken yet," Eisenhower said nodding at
Dulles. "What's your opinion? Should we intervene? And if so,
how?"

"I feel as though the angel of death were gnawing away at my
bowels," Dulles said in a low voice. It was apparent that he was
not himself. He averted his eyes from everyone, either looking
down at his desk or up at the ceiling.

" 'It is a time of night, a time of travail,' said the Preacher.
'You are my witness, but you sufficeth not,' said Job. 'Rain
down your plagues, my heart has turned to stone,' said John the
Baptist.

"Have no fears, Mr. President, I haven't gone insane. For
days now I've been mulling things over, and I'm tormented.
I feel as though my soul were roasting in hell. The Hungarian
people have rebelled and become free. But we're impotent. I've
spoken to our NATO allies and they're not intervening. Their
argument is incontrovertible. If we go into Hungary the Russians
will go into Egypt, maybe into Europe itself. It'll be a two-way
street. The world will go up in flames. No, that can't happen.
No, Mr. President, we must stay out of Hungary. Not in my
whole life, never, in nothing I've done have I felt such a sense
of defeat, weary, hopeless—"

Kodály sprang to his feet. "You talk about *your* defeat! Don't
worry: Read the New Testament and you will be consoled. But
what will console the Hungarian people? I could hardly believe
my ears. I kept asking myself while all of you spoke: Are these
the men who represent the great and glorious United States
of America? Pardon my saying so but you sounded like politicians in a Swiss canton. Do you realize what your Radio Free
Europe and Voice of America have been telling us every day,
every hour, for years? What they have been telling us since
October 21st? Do you realize what the captive peoples' promise
has meant to us? Mr. Dulles, please be so kind as to tell me:
Were you lying when you wrote the resolution? And if you were
not lying what did you expect us to do—we who read it, memorized it, held it up as our beacon, our corposant? You must answer my question, sir."

"Now hold on there, Mr. Kodály," Eisenhower said angrily.
"That's rather impertinent. The Secretary doesn't have to answer—"

"It's all right, Mr. President," Dulles said sadly, "I'll answer
Mr. Kodály. They're fair questions. I swear I wasn't lying when
I wrote the resolution in '52. I swear I was sincere in everything
I said and did. My objective—I mean, I thought—I didn't
know—it was not my—I can't go so—I—I—please excuse me."

Dulles sobbed as he left the room.

"The Secretary has been under tremendous strain the last
week," Eisenhower said. "His stomach's been bothering him, and
he's going to Walter Reed tomorrow to get it fixed up. Before
I close is there anyone else? Dick?"

"I merely thought, Mr. President," Nixon said, clearing his
throat, "that we might be able to find some kind of compromise
solution. I don't think we need to issue an ultimatum. Nor do
we need to send in our troops. But perhaps it might be possible
to have the CIA quickly organize several battalions of Hungarians
and other Eastern Europeans to defend the vital sections of
Budapest. If Budapest holds out the Hungarian people will
develop a guerrilla army which we would supply and help train.
I don't see how the Communist empire can survive the outbreak
of guerrilla warfare."

"Does anyone agree with Dick Nixon's proposal?" the President asked. "No one?"

"All right, then, Mr. Kodály, I'm sorry to have to tell you—sorrier than you'll know—that the United States can do nothing for Hungary if and when the Russians move in. Especially since there's a presidential election in a few days. We'll help the Hungarian people in any other way we can. We'll condemn the invasion without let-up. I know that won't satisfy you, Mr. Kodály. But our hands are tied. I wish I could say something that will comfort you. My heart is heavy too."

Without a word Kodály rose and left the room. He went immediately to Washington airport and flew back to Budapest.

On November 3 Nagy declared the Hungarian army to be under the command of a "revolutionary tribunal." "We are alone," he solemnly intoned in his address to the people, "but we will resist the invading legions to the death." He then asked every Hungarian, "man, woman, or child," who could shoot a gun to serve in the revolutionary militia. "It is a struggle for our children and our children's children. They shall take pride in their country, in the valor of their fathers. Hungary's courage today will sustain the spirit of generations unborn, when our enemy will have been vanquished and destroyed." [. . .]

The hastily improvised militia, armed with an abundance of courage, was no match for Soviet tanks, artillery, and planes. The Soviet commandant was under orders to level every building that offered resistance, to "scour" every cellar and alley in pursuit of "Nagy's gangsters."

By November 6 the fighting was over. Budapest had been "secured." Nagy had found sanctuary in the Yugoslav embassy. The leaders of the revolutionary tribunal had disappeared. Hundreds of thousands of Hungarians had fled into neighboring Austria and Yugoslavia. Those who had participated in the uprising, or had shown sympathy for it, had been placed in detention camps, awaiting transfer to Soviet prisons for unspecified periods.

The workers, however, refused to submit. They took possession of the factories in the large cities and held on to them as long

as they could. Not until the end of the year were they finally
dislodged.

The new premier, Janos Kadar, repudiated the "insanities" of
his predecessor, swore "fealty" to the Soviet bloc, and promised
that "Socialist legality" would prevail, that the consumer, the
worker, and the peasant would be granted their "rights," once
order was re-established and the "culprits" punished.

Nagy's presence in the Yugoslav embassy embarrassed Tito,
who wanted to avoid giving the impression that he condoned the
rebellion, especially after its defeat. ("Why ours?" he asked his
deputy, E. M. Kardelj. "Why didn't he go to the American or
British embassies?") Tito worked out an arrangement with
Khrushchev for settling the "Nagy affair." Soviet authorities
would allow Nagy a safe conduct pass out of Hungary in a
"sealed railroad car."

When the Yugoslav ambassador informed him of the decision,
Nagy laughed. "I understand," Nagy said, *"raison d'état.* You
realize that I will never leave Hungary alive. What guarantee
has Khrushchev given that he will honor his word? I have reason
to know how faithfully he honors it. I will go on one condition
—that Kadar or Mikoyan, perhaps Khrushchev himself, stand
hostage for me in, say, the American embassy. If I reach
safety the hostage will be freed. You think I am joking, eh?
Maybe I am. Suppose I refuse to go?"

"I'm afraid you must go," the ambassador replied. "President
Tito would not have made the arrangement if he weren't certain
you have a safe conduct pass. You Hungarians have a gallows
outlook on life. You should be a little more positive."

Nagy laughed again. "That's because I have lived in the
shadow of the gallows so long. It's part of my life. All right, I am
ready to go. Please, when I am gone, say that my last words
were: Long live Hungary! Long live freedom! Long live the
memory of our struggle!"

Nagy left the embassy escorted by two Yugoslav guards. As
soon as they descended the steps, four burly men emerged from
a car and intercepted them. They hustled Nagy into the car and
drove him to the railroad station. They boarded a sealed car.
Only the train on which Nagy was placed took him not to the
West but to Romania. There he was thrown into a dungeon cell

of an ancient fortress prison. For over a year, unable to speak to anyone, unable to read or write, Nagy [. . .]*

The events in Poland and Hungary taught everyone two harsh and unsavory lessons in power politics. First, the subject peoples of the East learned the permissible limits of their independence: Gomulka yes; Nagy no. Provided a people's democracy did not stray from the Warsaw Pact, from the Soviet center of gravity, it could go far in its internal reforms.

The second lesson was that the United States, in its relations with Eastern Europe, was a paper tiger. The talk about captive peoples had proved so much vacant rhetoric, so much rodomontade. Americans could consume it with no ill-effect; the "captive peoples" nearly choked to death on it. The Cold War began thawing only because each side came to recognize (without, of course, saying so) the other's hegemony. Hungary thus fell tragic victim to the cruel imperatives of the modern age.

* Nagy was secretly tried and shot in Romania in June 1958. Evidently, Prescott intended to discuss his imprisonment and trial at some length. A note at this point in the manuscript says: "get more info from F. and B."—N.F.M.

9

HEGEMONY (*cont'd*)

ONE day in October 1955, while in Paris attending a conference of NATO foreign ministers, Secretary of State Dulles met at the United States embassy on the Place de la Concorde with Portland M. White, the president of the International Bank for Assistance to Underdeveloped Areas. This was no routine meeting. White (along with two State Department officials and two members of the British Foreign Office) had just spent several days with Egypt's President Gamal Abdel Nasser, discussing Egypt's request for financial aid to build a dam at Aswan that would control the waters of the Nile River, a project more imposing than all the pyramids of the ancient pharaohs.

"Nasser was very charming and cordial to us," White said, articulating every syllable carefully, "and he insisted on exploring every question, every difference between us. Egyptians, he told us, do not believe, and never practice, duplicity, not even against their enemies. I don't know about that, Foster, but I think we can establish an open and above board relationship with him. That's simply my opinion, or rather impression.

"First, we asked Nasser if it was true that he has imperialist designs in the Middle East. He said we must distinguish between imperialism, which is evil, and responsibility, which is necessary and desirable. With its twenty-five million people Egypt is the largest country in the region. It therefore has commensurate responsibilities. Egypt herself, he pointed out to us, is a 'synthesis' —that's the word he used—of Africa and the Middle East, of diverse religious, racial, and ethnic groups.

"We asked him what were Egypt's responsibilities. He said, and I quote him: 'To keep order, to make sure the Arab states do not leap at each other's throats, to reconcile differences, to establish a bridge between Africa and Asia, East and West, the old and the new.'

"We asked him what he thought of the Baghdad Alliance. He has no objection to it, he said, as long as Iraq and Iran do not intend to use the arms they receive from the West against neighboring countries. He does not consider himself their rival, though he often disagrees with them.

"I asked him if he has any ambitions—as his enemies charge —to take over the Suez Canal and challenge Western oil interests. He replied that he is content with things as they are because the canal company is doing a good job. He complained about Egypt's cut of the profits, but thought that problem could be settled in negotiation. As for the oil problem, he thought it silly to imagine that he wants to kill the goose that lays the golden egg. Almost all of the canal's revenues come from West European oil tankers. Why should he try to disturb the relationship between and West and the oil-producing countries and sheikhdoms?

"We asked him about his relations with Russia, whether there was any substance to reports that he wants Russia to have a bigger role in the Middle East so that he could exploit both sides against the middle. He regarded the question as 'cynical.' 'You Westerners,' he said, 'have a way of imputing squalid motives to other peoples.' Yes, he desires good relations with the Soviet Union, he admitted, and hopes to maintain his status as a neutral in the Cold War. For only as a neutral could he serve as a bridge. He admitted receiving arms from the Soviet Union, but only, he contends, because the West refuses to supply his needs. He feels that the safety of Egypt is at stake, and the Egyptian people, he said, would not tolerate him for an instant if it seemed to them that Israel—which, he held, is getting all the arms it needs—enjoys too much of an advantage. In any case, he emphasized, socially, culturally, and economically, Egypt is in the Western sphere, and that is how he prefers it.

"Finally, we brought up the most perplexing issue: Israel. We asked him why he doesn't sign a peace treaty with Israel, why he permits fedayeen commandos to operate out of Egypt against the Israelis, and why he has closed the Suez Canal to Israeli vessels, or vessels bound for Israel, and threatens also to

close the Strait of Tiran to vessels bound for Elath. His answer
was extremely long. I'll try to summarize it here as briefly as
possible.

"He said he has nothing whatever against the presence of
Jews in Palestine. He realizes how much the Jews suffered during
the war and how little the Western countries did for them, refusing
to admit them to their own countries. What he does not approve
of is the conversion of a Jewish settlement into an aggressive,
imperialist state, whose professed aim—so Nasser believes—is to
restore the Davidian empire, which extended from the Jordan to
the Tigris Euphrates.

"Nonetheless, he acknowledges the right of Palestinian Jews
to have their own state. What he refuses to acknowledge is the
legitimacy of the Zionist claims. He would be satisfied if Israel
were reduced from its present 'ill-begotten' size to that specified
in the 1947 UN resolution. Israel, he said further, must admit all
the Palestinian refugees whose land it appropriated. When these
conditions are met there will be peace in the Middle East. Otherwise, he said, Egypt and the other Arab states have no choice
but to remain at war with Israel.

"He concluded his discussion of Israel by calling our attention
to an amusingly ironic fact. Had it not been for the emergence
of Israel in 1948, and the subsequent defeat of Egypt's army,
King Farouk—'the lascivious one,' as Egyptians know him—
might still be ruling the country, and the revolution that brought
him, Nasser, to power never have taken place."

"Hardly reason for me to celebrate," Dulles said acidly. (He
had drawn doodles on his pad throughout White's lengthy exposition.) "Portland, do you favor giving him the loan? I'll tell you,
I don't trust him. The British think he's an adventurer. I don't
go that far, but I don't trust him. What do you think, Portland?"

"I say, let's give Nasser the loan. Getting the dam started is
the best way of keeping him in tow. The dam will take ten to
fifteen years to build. I think he'll become a lot more reasonable
during that time, and unfortunately he's the only man who can
bring peace there. He's a first-class demagogue all right, but he's
also a realist. He wants that dam pretty badly. He'd like to go
down in Egyptian history as another Cheops or Amenhotep. I
favor going ahead with it."

"You're a little too sanguine," Dulles said. "The pregnant problem is Israel, and it's not going to go away. Israel will never accept those conditions he set forth to you. Of course, he knew that Israel won't accept them. The last time I spoke to Ben Gurion about admitting those refugees he politely told me to jump into the Dead Sea."

"Well, I know that," White said, "but Nasser should become more flexible. I think it's worth the price to try persuading him."

The following month the United States, Great Britain, and the International Bank announced that they would jointly provide $300 million in loans and grants for the construction of the High Aswan Dam atop the Upper Nile River.

By the spring of 1956 Dulles had begun to regret his acquiescence in the decision. "I think we made a dreadful mistake," he confided to his brother, Allen. Nasser ordered the fedayeen raids into Israel stepped up, provoking Israeli counterraids into the Gaza Strip. In speeches sent out over Cairo Radio Nasser proclaimed himself leader of an Arab "holy war" against Israel. In the most inflammatory language he condemned the oil-rich Arab countries—primarily Iraq and Saudi Arabia—as "eunuchs" ("ball-less ones") of the West. He also presented himself as a "liberator" of black Africa, whose peoples, he declared, "groan, as we once did, under the heels of the imperialist aggressor."

Most ominous of all, from Dulles's point of view, was the prodigious quantity of arms, including planes, tanks, and heavy artillery, that Egypt was receiving from the Soviet Union. "Egypt," Nasser asserted, in an interview with *New York Argus* reporter J. Scott Mover, "has the right to buy arms—and mind you we pay for them with our cotton—from anyone who will sell them. To be honest, Mr. Mover, we would prefer to buy them from the West, but the West refuses to sell them to us. Of course, Turkey, Iran, Iraq, and Saudi Arabia get everything they want, and get it free, because they are reactionary regimes. They are the bootblacks to the imperialists. It is not—how do the British say it?—for the pot to call the kettle black."

"This man is an authority on blackness," Dulles commented to his brother when he read the interview. "It's the color of his soul. A filthy blackguard, Eden said a long time ago. He's absolutely right."

The worst news was yet to come. Early in July Dulles received a report from the CIA stamped, "Top Secret. To Be Handled Only by Authorized Persons: the President, the Prime Minister, the Secretary of State, the Foreign Secretary, and the Director of Central Intelligence." It contained the summary of a recent conversation in Cairo between Nasser and Soviet Foreign Minister Andrei Gromyko. It was signed "Operative CC."

"Their conversation dealt with their 'mutual and compatible interests' in the Middle East. Nasser stressed the fact that Egypt and the Soviet Union had much in common, both being opposed to Western imperialism. At great length he defined for Gromyko the 'scheme' by which the 'forces of darkness' (the imperialists and their Arab friends) intended to 'subjugate' the Arab world. It was to be achieved through a 'conjunction' of three 'alien' interests: the Zionists, the Lebanese Christians, and the 'feudal oil monarchs,' namely, Saud and Faisal. These three interests, he maintained, each in its own way, served as the 'cat's paw' of the imperialists.

"For her part, Egypt pursued two aims: to 'throttle' Israel before it conquered new Arab land; and to actively support the young Iraqi army officers who wished to overthrow the 'leprous' government of Nuri Said and Faisal and repudiate the Baghdad Pact.

"Gromyko of course agreed with Nasser that the Soviet Union and Egypt were united in their opposition to the 'forces of darkness.' The Soviet Union's goal, he said, was to rid the region of the Western imperialists. She had no designs of her own. She had more than enough oil for her own needs, and she also recognized the legitimate oil needs of Western countries. The 'patrimony,' however, of Iraq and Arabia should properly belong to the people of those countries, not to the sheikhs and kings and Western monopolists. The Soviet Union, Gromyko said, was prepared to throw her 'full support' behind Egypt's attempt to establish Arab 'autonomy' and order in the Middle East. Only a 'hegemonic Egypt' could ensure peace, justice, and self-determination in the region.

"Toward that end the Soviet Union would furnish whatever arms and other material resources Egypt might require. She would, furthermore, 'prevail' upon the peoples' democracies, in particular Romania, Hungary, and Poland, to stop the emigration of Jews to the 'criminal state' of Israel.

"Gromyko described the Soviet Union's friendship for Egypt as 'imperishable' and 'illimitable.' Neither country, he said, would rest until the 'imperialists' and 'aggressors' were 'permanently rebuffed.' The two men then embraced."

Dulles went at once to the White House and gave the President a précis of the top-secret report. "Why, he's nothing but a horse thief," Eisenhower said, frowning.

"Yes," Dulles agreed. "So they're the forces of light and we're the forces of darkness. That's rich."

"What do you make of it, Foster?"

"Well, each of them is using the other, and each of them knows it. Neither is deceived. But in the long run it will be the Russians who will profit—unless Israel somehow disappears. Nasser wants to dominate the whole area, get his hands on the oil, reach into Africa—the man is demonic. But Israel, tiny Israel, sticks in his craw like a tumor. That's why Russia doesn't want Israel to disappear. As Nasser's nemesis, Israel guarantees his dependence on Russia. That fact puts us in an odd position. Without Israel, Russia's influence will diminish. But Nasser's will increase. Nothing will prevent him from taking control of Syria, Lebanon, Jordan, and, who knows, Yemen and the Arabian peninsula as well."

"You paint a pretty dark picture, Foster," the President said. "What do you suggest we do?"

"Now that's really a question, Mr. President. One thing is certain. We must avoid the twin evils of Egyptian hegemony and Soviet influence. That's our aim. For the moment, I think we should make it clear to Nasser that we don't like his illicit love affair with the Soviet Union, and that we're not going to subsidize vast Egyptian projects, in effect underwriting his arms purchases, while he sleeps with the Russians. I'm meeting with the Egyptian ambassador tomorrow, and I'll hear what he has to say. Of course, I won't let on that I know all about Nasser's talk with Gromyko."

The Egyptian ambassador, Mohammed Masjeeb, was one of the most highly respected members of the Washington diplomatic community. Educated in the best Western schools (his English was perfect, his accent, Oxbridge), he was an old friend of Dulles's. He was surprised, therefore, by the grim and perfunctory welcome he received when he was ushered into Dulles's office.

"We've known each other a long time, Mr. Ambassador," Dulles said, looking over his glasses. "You won't mind, then, if I come right to the point. I can best express it in the form of three questions. First, what are Egypt's relations with the Soviet Union? Second, what is Egypt's attitude toward the Baghdad Pact? And third, does Egypt intend to destroy Israel? I trust, Mr. Masjeeb, that you're not offended by my bluntness. I thought we could dispense with the diplomatic brummagem."

"Yes, Mr. Secretary. I always find it refreshing when the cards are on the table. I must say, however, you presented your questions as though you expected me to submit to a catechism, a kind of confessional. But being an old friend and appreciating your concerns, I will answer them as directly as you asked them.

"First, Egypt's relations with the Soviet Union are unchanged. We are a neutral country in the Cold War. We are friendly with both blocs, though most of our trade is with the West. I need not rehash the matter of Soviet arms shipments. They are for purely defensive purposes. Israel is a persistent threat to us, to the Egyptian people, whatever the West may think about it. We seek parity, nothing more. That partially answers your third question. As you know very well, Mr. Secretary, Egypt does not want to destroy Israel, only secure the minimal conditions of justice for dispossessed Palestinians and Israel's beleaguered neighbors. As for the second question, President Nasser—and you know this too, Mr. Secretary—has no quarrel whatever with the Baghdad Pact so long as its member states do not use it for their selfish ends over and against the peoples of the Middle East.

"I assure you, sir, President Nasser's sole ambition is to improve the lives of the Egyptian masses. We are among the poorest, sickest, least literate, least productive nations in the world. There is enough work to do at home for decades to come. We want only to live at peace—with justice, however."

"As usual, Mr. Masjeeb, your eloquence is fairly overwhelming. On the face of it it's terribly persuasive. But here, read this report on the recent conference between President Nasser and

Foreign Minister Gromyko. It would seem to flatly contradict everything you've been telling me."

Masjeeb scanned the report. "It's a lie through and through," he said insouciantly. "Your secret agent is deceiving you. It's ridiculous."

"I've had it checked and double-checked. So have the British. The intelligence people say it's incontrovertible. I accept it as true."

Masjeeb smiled. "Let's say it is true. In that case why have you asked to see me? To embarrass me or my government? To catch us at an inconsistency? Do you think we talk out of both sides of our mouths? So be it. Of course, you Americans have never been known to do it. Oh no, hypocrisy among Anglo-Saxons, and I might add among Christians, is unknown, an aberration at most."

He continued smiling. "If you want to hear the truth, Mr. Secretary, it is this. Egypt, too, has a destiny, and President Gamal Abdel Nasser is its instrument. And yes, whoever assists us in realizing that destiny is our friend. Whoever attempts to thwart us is our enemy. I will be ruthlessly candid, Mr. Secretary. It is the West that thwarts Egypt, and it is the Soviet Union that assists her. The West stands with Israel and the present regime in Iraq. You, the United States and the West, have tried to stop us, and you cannot. I am pleased that I can tell you this directly, without 'diplomatic brummagem.'"

"And I can tell you this, Mr. Ambassador," Dulles said through his teeth, his grey eyes fixed on Masjeeb's smiling mouth, "the United States will *not* be the instrument of President Nasser's destiny. He had better be careful not to bite off more than he can chew. It seems to me that Egypt's problems are great enough as they are. Just staying alive is a struggle for you. The United States wants to help Egypt stay alive. That's why we agreed to contribute to the Aswan Dam project. But the United States will withdraw its offer now, or at least until we're convinced President Nasser has come to his senses.

"You know, if he persists in his ambition, he'll end up with nothing, only his servitude to Russia, who exacts a heavy price for her favors."

Smiling still, the ambassador clenched his fists as he spoke.

"Hypocrisy again, Mr. Secretary. Do you mean to say that the United States was interested in financing the Aswan Dam because of her compassion for the suffering of our felaheen? American aid, of course, is always gratuitous. You never exact a price for *your* favors. You're not lecturing your Sunday school ladies. If you were concerned about the suffering of our poor you would continue to finance the dam, regardless of political considerations, wouldn't you? For you, too, everything is power politics. Only you conceal your motives under a thick layer of moral treacle. You are, if I may say so, a nation of Pecksniffs. To hell with your offer, sir. Buy someone else's friendship."

"Mr. Masjeeb," Dulles said excitedly, "I'm going to ask you to leave my office. I have a mind to order your recall. Remember, Egypt isn't yet the ruler of the world, and I'm not obliged to sit here and listen to your insults. You may go."

"As you wish, Mr. Secretary," Masjeeb said, smiling.

At a hastily called press conference that day Dulles announced that the United States would withdraw its part of the Aswan Dam aid program until Egypt had "worked out a number of problems related to the Nile River with the other riparian states involved, mainly Ethiopia and Sudan." He went on to emphasize that the moment Egypt reached an agreement with them the United States would be "delighted" to resume the loan.

Later, the British Foreign Office and Portland White for the International Bank announced that they, too, were "temporarily" withdrawing from the Aswan Dam project and looked forward to "refinancing it in the near future."

Nasser responded at once. Speaking over Cairo Radio he declared that he had expected this "act of perfidy" from the West. "The United States and Great Britain and the big bankers who control them once again disclose their lowly and corrupt natures. 'You will know evil ones not by their faces or their words but by their deeds,' Mohammed teaches us. The representatives of the United States, Great Britain, and the Bank said to me: We will help Egypt if Egypt does what we say, if Egypt becomes a base for our imperialist operations. When I told them no, they said to me: Your dam will not be built. I have news for them. The dam will be built. Premier Bulganin of the Soviet Union has just sent me a cable promising that the Soviet Union, whose dams are the greatest in the world, will assist us in every-thing. 'What Allah takes away with one hand He gives with the other.' I will soon have more bad news for our perfidious Western friends."

The bad news, made public late in July 1956, was that Egypt would, for a generous sum of money, forthwith nationalize the corporation—Suez Boat and Waterway, Limited—that ran the Suez Canal. The act was perfectly legal under international law. Governments have the right to expropriate foreign proper-ties, provided they are justly compensated for the loss.

But Suez Boat and Waterway Ltd. was not simply another corporation. Though its shares were sold on the open market, it existed as an adjunct of the governments it mainly served: Great Britain and France. The Suez Canal had once been Britain's shortcut route to India. Hence Britain's long dominion over Egypt. India and Egypt were now free. Yet Britain—and the rest of Western Europe—were more dependent on the canal than ever, for without it the cost of shipping oil from Iraq and Iran would rise prohibitively—or so it was assumed.

The announcement of Egypt's nationalization of the canal sent a shudder through Europe. France's premier, Guy Mollet, said he was "shocked beyond words at this grossly irresponsible act against the entire international community." "The seizure," NATO Secretary General, Maurice St. Jacques, asserted, "places three hundred and fifty million people at the mercy of a single man. Must we be hostage to a dictator's whims?" British Prime Minister Anthony Eden quietly stated that "neither the people of the United Kingdom nor the people of Western Europe will countenance this brazen outrage." Dulles was more restrained. "We rather anticipated this," he said. "President Nasser has been planning to take the canal for years, and if it hadn't been the Aswan Dam pretext it would have been another."

In mid-August Dulles met with Eden and Mollet to work out a "solution" to their dispute with Nasser. At first the two prime ministers opposed any compromise. "We shall have to punish this gangster and settle accounts with him in our own way," Eden said.

"I don't think this man can be reasoned with," Mollet added. "He's like Hitler."

"That's precisely what he is," Eden agreed. "A Hitler in miniature."

Dulles, however, advised caution. "We should try in any case to come to terms with him. I suggest that all of the European canal users form an association and press for the international operation of the waterway. After all, we have got to think of reality. No one's going to go in there and knock Nasser on the head. And there's no possibility of returning Suez to private hands, back to you. Nasser's move is very popular with his own masses and with the non-European world. That's the unhappy fact of the matter. He's a clever demagogue. My concern is to get the canal away from him without antagonizing the neutrals and the colored peoples."

Eden and Mollet agreed to establish a "Canal Users' Association" and to seek the internationalization of Suez. A delegation representing the Users, with Ian Ziemens, the Prime Minister of Australia serving as their intermediary, met with Nasser in Cairo.

After five days of angry exchanges and mutual recriminations the conference broke down. The talks had in fact been doomed long before they started. Nasser had vowed to his cabinet "never to surrender Suez" and had characterized the Canal Users' Association as an "imperialist front." Internationalization he rejected as an "insult." "When the Panama Canal is internationalized," he said, "we will discuss it."

At the conclusion of the Cairo conference Ziemens spoke to reporters. "There have been differences, profound ones, acrimoniously set forth by both sides. But I am not a pessimist by nature. President Nasser, it certainly seems to me, is amenable to compromise. He wants to study the Users' proposals. At a date still to be determined, probably before the end of the year, we will all meet again. By then, President Nasser will have worked out Egypt's counterproposals. The whole affair, I am confident, can be settled amiably, to the satisfaction of everyone concerned."

One day early in October, at exactly midnight, Prime Minister Eden received two visitors at his private home in Cruttwell, outside London. They were Prime Ministers Mollet of France and David Ben Gurion of Israel. The public at large had no idea these distinguished men were in England, for they had come disguised as lawyers from their respective countries attending the biennial meeting of the International Barristers' Association.

Not even their friends would have recognized them. The make-up men had no trouble disguising Mollet (his assumed name: Émile Charlus, professor of law at Dijon University) because of his neutral appearance. He looked like the small-town high school teacher that he had been before rising in the French Socialist Party organization. His height was medium, his features were regular, he wore rimless glasses, and combed what remained of his hair straight back. Now, as Émile Charlus, he wore a reddish-grey goatee, parted at the center, a slight reddish-grey mustache, and horn-rimmed glasses.

Ben Gurion presented a more formidable problem. He was short and stocky, and his large, round, ruddy face and bald head were set off by a great shock of wispy white hair. Like most Israeli Socialists of his generation (he was in his late sixties) Ben Gurion rarely wore a tie or a hat, always affecting an appearance of egalitarian informality. On this occasion he wore a black, tight-fitting, pin-striped suit, a high-chokered collar, a flowing silk tie, and a black fedora hat. Elevated shoes added three inches to his height. Very little of his distinctive face could be seen behind a long dark-grey beard. His name was Yehuda Ben Kochbar, a renowned Talmudic scholar.

"How do I know I'm talking to my friends Mollet and Ben Gurion?" Eden asked, smiling imperceptibly, after his two guests had seated themselves around the library fire and taken up their glasses of sherry. "If you are they, you are a convincing professor of law and Talmudist. A tribute to your make-up people."

"But Monsieur Charlus and I cannot be sure you are Sir Anthony," Ben Gurion rejoined, drawing a chuckle from the others. "You sound like him, and this is his house—apparently."

"Enough levity," Mollet said. "We must get down to business. Tomorrow morning the Chamber takes up the Algerian conflict, and I must be prepared. Another sleepless night."

"Yes, of course," Eden said, pursing his lips tightly. "There's no reason why we need to deliberate for more than an hour or two. It's obvious why we've come together this way. The secrecy is excruciating. Only a handful of my most trusted lieutenants have any inkling of what's going on: Alec Home, Macmillan, Salisbury. But we couldn't meet any other way, could we? We couldn't draw suspicion on ourselves. We have the same enemy, or should I say, tormentor. So far as I'm concerned, gentlemen, he's a bloody tyrant, a megalomaniac, a little guttersnipe, like Hitler. We should be making a grave error if we continued to deal with him as though he were an honorable man, as though his word could be trusted. I reluctantly went along with Dulles's suggestion to compromise with him. I shouldn't have, of course. The Users' Association is a damnable farce. There's no question of it any longer. We must do something about him at once."

"Before you go any further, Mr. Prime Minister," Ben Gurion said, "let me take minor exception to your analysis. He's a megalomaniac, yes, but he's no Hitler. Nor are the Egyptian people Germans. The man is no racist, though we are worried about the fate of the thirty thousand Jews who still live in Egypt. Once upon a time we hoped that we could reach an accommodation with him. We liked his domestic reforms, and only he was popular enough to do some disagreeable things—recognize Israel, for instance. Now, we know, nothing more is to be hoped for. He has to be overthrown, discredited, beaten down like a dog. We are tired of sending our army across the border to punish the fedayeen. This is bad enough. Now his alliance with Syria and Jordan, his big tanks and guns. If we do not strike him first he will strike us on three fronts.

"You realize, gentlemen, that if we lose the war we cease to exist as a nation. He will throw us into the sea. That is what he threatens to do. We did not leave the ghettoes and concentration camps of Europe for those of Palestine. We will all die rather than endure that fate."

"Gentlemen, let us be absolutely clear," Mollet said. "The issue for France and the United Kingdom, and I might add, the rest of Europe, is not merely the freedom of navigation through the Suez Canal. The issue is whether a street tramp like him will encourage other peoples to rebel. Indeed, he has promised to help the Algerians, and he gives promises to African revolutionists. It is like promising candy to children. Now France believes in the self-determination of all peoples, which is why France will never allow demagogues to presume to be their spokesmen. All these demagogues want is power for themselves. They are not interested in the welfare of the people whose emotions they selfishly exploit. France is determined that they shall not get their way. I say again, Suez means more to France than the right to use an international waterway."

"Brilliantly put, Monsieur Mollet. I couldn't agree with you more enthusiastically," Eden said with feeling. "Though each of us has his own reason for opposing him, we agree on one quintessential thing, that the man is an outlaw. I hold no brief for the Holy Alliance and the Concert of Europe, but in the old days the responsible powers would convene and discipline such a troublemaker and scoundrel. There is no community of nations today. The Soviet Union chortles over our embarrassment, where she does not cause it. The neutrals are against us too. And the United States would like to be the honest broker and fair dealer—commendable, but foolish and unrealistic in the extreme. Her naïveté never ceases to astonish me.

"So I will get to the point. We three must take it upon ourselves to discipline this man and everything he stands for, and restore law and order and respect for just authority, especially to those parts of the world he has subverted. I pray we're not too late."

"And by law and order," Ben Gurion said, "you mean opening up all the international routes of commerce. The Suez Canal and the Strait of Tiran must never again be closed to Israeli ships. Is that what you mean?"

"That, among other things, is exactly what I mean. Should we succeed in our purpose, peaceful commerce through all waterways will be guaranteed."

"Nevertheless," Ben Gurion said, "there is an apparent difference of objectives between us. You, Great Britain and France, want to secure the Suez Canal. Israel wants to secure her borders and allay the anxieties of her people. Our task, it seems to me, is to coordinate our strategies so that we may gain our separate objectives."

"I do not think it could be expressed better than you have just expressed it, Monsieur Ben Kochbar," Guy Mollet said, blinking his eyes humorously. "What do you propose?"

"To be frank, Monsieur Charlus, I am not sure. But I will tell you this much. Israel will launch an attack on Egypt early next year, around February 1st. We will occupy the Gaza Strip and the whole Sinai Peninsula, from the Suez to the Negev, from the Mediterranean to the Gulf of Aqaba. We will hold these areas until we are satisfied that no more commandos are sent into our land, until the Arab states recognize us and work things out with us as equals. We are out of patience. The invasion is a categorical imperative. It is only a matter of when and how."

"Of course, we—France and England—cannot wait until next year," Mollet declared. "For us it is not a matter of patience. It is a matter of prudence. If we procrastinate we shall lend legitimacy to Nasser's action. Time is of the essence. I submit that we, France and England, undertake an action of our own before the month of October is out."

"In that case," Ben Gurion pointed out, "Israel will find herself in a very peculiar position. Let us say you have secured the canal, but you haven't been able to stop the fedayeen raids into my country. If we then moved into Sinai we would be either opposing you or occupying a part of Egypt with your consent. He would then say to his countrymen: See, if only France and Britain had not invaded us, we would have crushed the cowardly Israelis, and so forth. Inevitably, he or his successors would be tempted to try us again. Defeat of Israel would be the permanent, ineffaceable measure of Egypt's pride."

"Mr. Ben Gurion," Eden said, "I must commend you for your logic and also for your very fine presentation. How did you achieve such mastery of our language?"

"I am flattered, Mr. Prime Minister. English, may I say, is no one nation's language any longer. It belongs to mankind. So does French, of course. Whatever competence I have acquired I owe largely to the King James Bible, Shakespeare, Jowett's translation of Plato, and the writings of William Morris and Winston Churchill."

"A remarkable selection," Eden said, staring intently at Ben Gurion.

"My favorite writers in English," Mollet put in, "are Bernard Shaw and the Webbs, Beatrice and Sidney. When I was a young man they made a great impression on me."

"Well now," Eden said, pulling himself up in his haughtiest

manner as he realized he was talking to two Socialists, "we really must return to the business at hand. I think I have found the solution to the problem that Mr. Ben Gurion has made us aware of. In broad outline, here is what I propose. Our military and intelligence can iron out the details. Monsieur Mollet, are your troops prepared to move out in a month or so?"

"Yes, of course."

"So are ours. And Mr. Ben Gurion, can Israel mount an assault on Sinai by the end of this month?"

"If we must, yes. We can mobilize in hours if necessary. Three weeks is ample time."

"Good. Here's what I have in mind." Eden leaned forward and lowered his voice. "If Israel attacks Egypt as planned, we, the Suez powers, will be able to intervene in the interest of protecting the canal. We would go in for defensive reasons to prevent its destruction. We would also be in a position of head off any UN sanctions against Israel. We would remain in the canal zone and Israel would remain in Sinai until all of us obtained what we desire—an Egyptian government that we can trust, that will respect international laws and obligations."

Mollet and Ben Gurion accepted Eden's plan. The three men drank a champagne toast to "the successful outcome of our deliberations," as Mollet phrased it. Ben Gurion added another toast, taken he said from the Talmud: "May thought, not impulse, be the author of our deeds."

Later that morning the professor of law and the Talmudic scholar flew back to their countries.

On the morning of October 29 an Israeli armored column drove deep into the Sinai Peninsula. Within two days the Egyptian army lay in ruins, most of its Soviet-built tanks and artillery destroyed or captured. The whole of Sinai lay open to Israeli conquest.

On October 31 Great Britain and France issued an ultimatum to the "belligerents": "Within twelve hours the Suez Canal area must be cleared of all hostile forces. If it is not, the military forces of Great Britain and France will intervene to protect it."

It was not, of course, and twelve hours later the bombing and shelling of Egypt got under way. Three days later British and French paratroopers descended on the canal zone and quickly subdued the Egyptian garrisons there. "The objective is secured," General Brian Spencer, commander of the operation informed Prime Minister Eden. "The route to the East is ours again. I await further orders."

Eisenhower was taking a bath when Undersecretary of State Christian Herter—Dulles was in Walter Reed Hospital for a stomach operation—told him of the Anglo-French assault on Egypt. "Goddamn it to hell," Eisenhower shouted. "Yesterday the Russians go into Hungary. Last week Israel goes into Egypt. Now this. What in tarnation is this world coming to?"

Still in his tub he sternly asked Herter, "Did we know anything about this invasion? Did State know anything? Or Central Intelligence?" Herter replied that he had just spoken to both Dulleses, and both were shocked and surprised.

"We can't trust our own allies then, can we?" Eisenhower asked indignantly. "Well, I've got a mind to tell them they're on their own if the Russians step in, and sure as creation the Russians are going to. What a goddamned mess."

Prophetically, Eisenhower uttered these words moments before the Soviet representative to the UN, Boris Novikov, addressing an emergency session of the General Assembly, called on the United States to join with his government in forcibly putting down the "imperialist aggressors." "We collaborated against the Hitlerite fascists. We can collaborate against the imperialist pirates."

But the American delegate, Henry Cabot Lodge, rejected the appeal as "nothing more than an effort to pour oil on the fire." Lodge recommended that the two countries join instead in supporting resolutions currently before the Assembly ordering an immediate cease-fire preparatory to the removal of foreign troops from Egyptian soil and the establishment of a UN peace-keeping force in the area.

These resolutions [. . .]*

Eden and Mollet had anticipated these moves at the UN, and they were hardly daunted by them. What did daunt them were the threats voiced by Soviet leaders, fresh from their triumph

---

* Prescott's narrative peters out here in the middle of the paragraph, as though he grew tired of pursuing the subject any further. Undoubtedly, he would have returned to it later.—N.F.M.

over Hungary. "If the UN does not act," Bulganin asserted over Moscow Radio, "the Soviet army is ready."

Khrushchev was more specific. "If the criminal aggressors do not leave," he thundered in a speech to the Voloshin Military Academy, "Soviet volunteers will go to Egypt and make them. Every minute thousands of Soviet patriots are signing up for duty. Do you imperialists of England and France know what I'm saying? We're finished with the Hungarian fascists. We can now start on you.

"And you should know this, too. We won't hesitate to give you a taste of our rockets. Listen, England! Let me remind you, you're a small island. We can sink you with a few of our bombs, and nobody will ever know what happened to you. Take heed, you imperialist adventurers, take heed, I won't warn you again."

Early in the morning of November 6 a delegation of Tory leaders called on Eden at 10 Downing Street to tell him what he already knew, that opposition to the invasion was mounting "dangerously" in the country, that "Labour will soon have us on the ropes in Commons," and that unless Eden yielded to the UN the Conservative Party would "disintegrate." "Nasser and the bloody canal aren't worth that," said R. A. ("RAB") Butler, who spoke for the delegation.

While listening to the catalogue of complaints Eden was fidgety and restless. His mouth twitched nervously and he blinked his eyes incessantly. "When I need your support," he said rapidly, "you desert me. I acted in the interest of the nation, of humanity, and I'm confronted by the basest party spirit. On every side I hear threats: from you, from that squalid little fat man in Moscow, from Eisenhower, who preaches righteousness to me. If only you, yes you, could have done your share, we could have seen this thing through. In the long run we would have prevailed. But that's over.

"I'm going to order a cease-fire. If it's a humiliating defeat you want, you can have it. And I'll do you another favor. I'll take the blame for Suez. The Party will be exonerated. Not because I think very much of our Party. If there's anyone less responsible than you it's the bloody Socialists. They mustn't come to power. All right, please leave."

Eden was now sweating and speaking through tightly clenched teeth.

That afternoon he called Mollet to tell him of the decision. "But," Mollet protested, "we have won everything. We cannot leave now. Are you afraid of the Russians? Nonsense! And if some of the volunteers come in, why we'll give them a bloody nose. I emphatically do not—"

"You don't understand at all," Eden said nervously. "My own people, my own Party, are opposed to it. If I don't stop it they'll heave me out and stop it themselves. I'm helpless. I've already cabled Spencer to prepare to evacuate as soon as arrangements are made with the bloody UN. So far as I'm concerned—"

"But, Mr. Eden," Mollet broke in, "have you cleared your decision with Ben Gurion. What about the Israelis?"

"They can take care of themselves. They don't need us. They never did. Monsieur Mollet, I urge you to join me in making a statement accepting the UN resolutions."

"It is capitulation. I am finished. The Chamber will dismiss me like an old rag."

"We've no choice. I must hang up. I feel terribly ill."

That evening Great Britain and France released a joint statement. It read: "The task is completed. The Suez Canal is preserved. Peace is restored. Our forces can now turn over full responsibility for maintaining the peace to the proper international authorities."

News of the "capitulation" brought rejoicing everywhere except to Great Britain, France, and Israel. "We celebrate a triple victory," Khrushchev exultantly told a gathering of Soviet career diplomats while drinking a huge goblet of vodka. "Hungary, Suez, the anniversary of the Revolution—all within two days. The old adage is true, comrades, 'To him who has much will be given even more than he has. From him who has little will be taken even the little he has.' Down with the imperialists!"

From his Gettysburg farm Eisenhower praised the UN for "solving this conflict and affirming the rule of international law."

UN Secretary General, Dag Hammarskjöld, congratulated the United States and the Soviet Union for "uniting their strengths in the service of world peace. May this be a bright augury of the future."

And President Nasser came out of hiding (he had not been seen or heard from for a week) and thanked his people and his soldiers for "routing the armies of Great Britain and France," and for "proving that Egypt's destiny cannot be thwarted."

Two problems remained to be settled, one minor, the other major. Nasser demanded that Britain and France pay the cost of clearing the canal, which had been rendered unusable in the fighting. They refused. Finally, under a compromise formula the UN (meaning the United States) assumed the full cost. The second problem was Israel's refusal to surrender the territory she occupied. Here, too, a compromise of sorts was worked out (thanks mostly to American prodding). The Egyptians repossessed Sinai and the Gaza Strip, the UN emergency forces were placed in the areas of greatest friction. Reluctantly, Ben Gurion agreed [. . .]*

Prime Minister Eden collapsed under the strain of events. Even before the invasion his aides had noticed his nervousness, his twitchings, his heavy sweating, his distempers. After November 6 these symptoms grew progressively worse. On November 15, the day UN troops began to replace the Anglo-French army, he fainted while dictating a letter. The letter was addressed to Queen Elizabeth II. It expressed his wish to resign as Prime Minister.

The following day Butler, Lord Salisbury, and the rest of the Conservative Party hierarchy visited Eden at his home. Lying in his bed, he looked pale and haggard. Afterward, they remarked how he had "overnight" become an old man, "a shadow of his former self." Speaking for all of them, Salisbury, the architect of Tory electoral victories, said they had decided that he, Eden, should go away and rest for a while. When he returned, "in a month or so," he would resign, and Harold Macmillan (Chancellor of the Exchequer) would take his place. Eden listened with half-closed eyes and nodded slightly.

Everything went off as planned. Eden vacationed in the West Indies, where he only partially recovered. Early in January

---

* Prescott's comment on the margin reads: "Too much? Too little? Something wrong. Change drastically."

1957, he resigned. By then, the storm had blown over and the Conservatives were firmly in control again.

"Typical of the Tories," Harold Wilson, a prominent Labour Party intellectual, wrote in the *Tribune,* a Socialist weekly. "Here they commit one of the greatest fiascos in English history. What is the consequence? Nothing. The Prime Minister is served up as the sacrificial lamb. No one else is punished. The Party governs as though nothing more untoward happened than the loss of a cricket match. Pity we lost, eh old chap? Something must be wretchedly at fault with our parliamentary system."

With his usual acumen Washington columnist Stanley Fannin assessed the long-term implications of the Suez affair. "Suez marks the end of an era," he wrote in the Christmas 1956 number of the *Saturday Evening Post.* "The Anglo-French failure underscores the limits of the second order powers in the world. Without American support they were unable to sustain even the initial phase of their assault. They simply caved in under the pressure.

"The lesson, in other words, is this: only the superpowers can undertake great actions in the modern world. And, as Hungary demonstrates, even their actions are confined to their own hegemonies, or spheres of influence. Suez sounds the knell of knells to nineteenth-century colonialism."

10

KHRUSHCHEV

"THIS will be my critical year," Khrushchev remarked to Smerdyakov, his aide-de-camp, as he dressed for the 1957 New Year's Day ball at the Kremlin Palace. "It's the year of reckoning between us, the pack and me. They're plotting, plotting, plotting. I call them the Four Horsemen of the Apocalypse."

"How can they go on, Nikita Sergeyovitch? They despise each other, and they also disagree."

"But they despise me more. Once they get rid of me they'll fight it out among themselves. That's how we felt about Beria. But I'm watching them all the time, day and night, night and day. It's not enough to be a liar, Chmielnitzky said three hundred years ago, 'one must also be a hawk, a fox, a serpent, and a lion.' Comrades Malenkov, Molotov, Kaganovitch, and Shepilov will learn that I can become all of these at once.

"Soon I'll give them something else to complain about. Remember our conversations about the administration of industry last year? You were absolutely right, Semyon. The bureaucrats are chasing out the Party members. No one can tell them anything, these 'experts.' They think they know more than anybody, and they answer only to each other. They're above ideology, above Marxism-Leninism, above Party. They'll learn who's above *them*. I've decided that the local Party people must have more to say about running the factories. I've ordered Pugachev to draw up a master plan for decentralizing industry and the entire managerial bureaucracy. We're going to create regional councils of industry. When they see the plan the old bureaucrats will shit in their pants. They'll cry like babies, and they'll plead with our enemies to save them. Nothing will save them."

Khrushchev presented his "Plan to Reorganize Industry" in late
March 1957 in a speech before the 133-man Central Committee.
The virtue of reorganization, he emphasized, was that it would
increase efficiency and stimulate production by giving more responsibility to the managers who ran the factories and at the
same time involve "the representatives of the proletariat" in the
decision-making process at the local level.

"Bureaucracies proliferate like fungi," he stated, shaking his
finger in reproof, "and like fungi they have a life of their own.
They are suffocating us here in Moscow. Every day you bump
into a new bureaucrat just brought up from the provinces. What
is his task? Let us say he works in the administrative department
of the woman's wear industry. Does he know a blessed thing
about woman's wear? No. He is a friend of a friend of X who
is in charge of making new jobs, building his own little fiefdom.
What does our little bureaucrat do? He signs papers and then
sends them on to another comrade who also signs papers who in
turn sends them on to another, and so on until they reach our
little bureaucrat again. Meanwhile a month has passed.

"Comrades of the Central Committee! Reorganization of industry will put an end to that kind of waste and stupidity.
Sabotage is built into the present system. And I'm tired of provid-
ing our satirists with raw material. If Gogol were alive today he
would say in delight, 'What an embarrassment of riches! Why,
this bureaucracy, this society of clerks is worse than anything I
saw in the good Czar Nicholas's day.'

"No, comrades, our superfluous bureaucrats and petty clerks
will have to find socially useful jobs. We need more manpower
in our factories, mines, and fields. Better that they should break
their asses than sit on them."

After the speech the familiar pattern began: it was circulated
to the tens of thousands of Party meetings in the country where
"symposia" were held to discuss the merits of reorganization.
Critics of the present system were encouraged to "come forward"
and tell of their experiences, their observations of inefficiency,
mismanagement, etc. Many of these criticisms were printed in
Pravda, Trud, Izvestia, and the countless trade and technical
journals published in the Soviet Union.

For months Khrushchev's opponents in the eleven-member

Presidium (once the Politburo)—the summit of the Communist Party hierarchy—had been sharpening their knives, preparing for the decisive June meeting, when policies were to be framed and officials elected.

It was an historic meeting. Not since the early 1920s, before Stalin's conquest of power, had such a debate taken place within the ruling circles of the Soviet Union. The debate was, for the most part, a free-wheeling affair between Khrushchev and Malenkov, enemies now to the death.

Malenkov started it off by accusing Khrushchev of "foisting" the reorganization "scheme" upon the Party without its consent. "This is reminiscent of the cult of personality," Malenkov asserted.

"I have foisted nothing on no one," Khrushchev shot back. "I offered the plan to the Party in good faith. The Party may accept or reject it. What objections do you have to it, comrade?"

"This. It is an invitation to chaos. Decentralization is fine when it comes to food, say, or certain articles of clothing. But how about steel, chemicals, hydroelectric? And planning, Comrade Secretary, what does your scheme do to planning? Your idea, to say the truth, smacks of syndicalism. Regional councils of industry! How are you going to coordinate these so-called councils? Yes, of course, the bureaucratic concentration here in Moscow and in the other centers is something to behold. The solution, however, is not to destroy planning, as your reorganization would do, but perfect it."

"Oh, come now, comrade," Khrushchev replied with a sneer. "Lay your boots on the table so we can see them. Why do you object to reorganization? All of us know the reason. Because you fear that you, the bureaucrats, the administrators here in Moscow —admit it, comrade—will lose your power. You're afraid that the Party will check the bureaucrats, will check you. Let me tell you, your fears are justified. I know what you're up to. 'Knaves deceive themselves.'

"In a private talk we had early last year, Comrade Malenkov, you—and you too, Comrade Kaganovitch—admitted that we were sinking into a swamp under the weight of the bureaucracy. You said then that we needed to 'break up this empire within an empire'—am I quoting you correctly, comrade? No, it's not decentralization that churns your bowels. It's the Party, it's me, my leadership. Admit it, comrade; if you, or Molotov, or Kaganovitch, or Shepilov, were Secretary would you hesitate to do what I'm doing? Is there any other way? Is there? I want an answer."

"You're acting in an unseemly and uncomradely manner, Comrade Secretary," Malenkov said in his most refined and literary Russian, a language wholly different from Khrushchev's. "Let us agree that the reorganization scheme is inseparable from your leadership of the Party. So that whether we think well or badly of decentralization in the abstract we—those of us in the Presidium who feel as I do—are unanimous in objecting to the manner in which you have presented it to us. We were not consulted. We were told to take it or leave it. Some choice for the Presidium of the Communist Party of the Soviet Union!

"But Comrade Khrushchev, this has been your manner all along, for the four years you have been our Secretary. How painfully we have learned what troubles can befall us from your leadership! It is you, you more than anyone, who encouraged the Titoists in the peoples' democracies. When the Titoists went too far—wasn't it inevitable?—of course we had to crush them. Nagy was your protégé. He has given you a few surprises, though, hasn't he? You failed to provide strict and definite guidelines for our allies in the Warsaw Pact. That was why we found ourselves on a seesaw last year, going up and down, up and down against our will like a helpless child. That is exactly the feeling I have—it approaches nausea—with your decentralization scheme, and I might include your agricultural policies as well. With you as our pilot we are always on a whirligig. The future is a blur."

"Comrade Malenkov," Khrushchev said loudly, his face now rubicund, "if you suffer from nausea why don't you see a doctor. I think it's a symptom of your intellectual confusion—*your* confusion! Why do you accuse me of everything? Was I responsible for creating the modern world? When Stalin died the center fell apart. One thing we knew, though: without him, his policies, his way of ruling would not continue. Even you who wanted more terror, who felt secure only when the secret police roamed the streets at night, stealing people from their homes, people never seen again, even you wouldn't take such power in *your* hands.

Who could do it? And how long would the people stand for this kind of treatment?

"Let me ask you another question. Who didn't want a relaxation of tensions with the bourgeois democracies? Who didn't think we had gone too far in cutting ourselves off from the neutrals? And as for the peoples' democracies, how reliable, how loyal to us were they while Jews and Stalinists sat on them, used them as footstools? Yes, I've been Party Secretary in this period of readjustment. Life doesn't move along smooth rails. No, life is full of jolts and sharp curbs. Sometimes it goes off the rails. I've no apologies to make to you. Let's get on with the vote."

In a sense, the debate merely enacted a drama already written. Everyone on the Presidium knew that Khrushchev would be voted down as Secretary, the "Four Horsemen" having won two others over to their side, thereby ensuring a majority. As soon as the vote was taken Khrushchev sprang to his feet and demanded that it be "ratified" by the full Committee (which nominally represented the Party as a whole and nominally appointed the members of the Presidium).

"To ensure that there's no disorder," Khrushchev said, smiling ironically, "I've asked the Army to protect the Kremlin."

Two days before, he and General Georgi Zhukov had secretly worked out the arrangements for military support during the "showdown" with the "anti-Party faction," as Khrushchev labeled his opponents. Zhukov had led them to believe that he and the army would stay neutral. "This is a political matter," Zhukov had told Malenkov, "and the army must keep out of politics." Khrushchev, however, had already promised to make the general his "right-hand man," in fact, his co-leader of the Party and the state.

The final scene of the drama was therefore an anti-climax. With the army standing guard outside, with tanks ringing the Kremlin, the 133-man Central Committee gave Khrushchev a resounding vote of approval.

Re-elected Secretary, he promptly excised the entire "anti-Party faction" from the Presidium. "I want to prove that Stalin is dead," he confided to Smerdyakov. "I'll be civilized toward these black sheep. I won't chop off their heads or put them in a pen. I'll send them out to pasture where there's a lot of land and open spaces."

"Pasture" meant menial jobs in remote provinces. Malenkov became a manager of a hydroelectric station in East Kazakhstan; Shepilov, a grade school teacher in Central Asia; Kaganovitch, chief of a cement factory in the Ural Mountains; and Molotov, ambassador to Outer Mongolia. Among those named to succeed them (and three others on the Presidium) was General Zhukov, who was also appointed Minister of Defense. "If the anti-Party comrades do their jobs well," Khrushchev remarked jocularly to a group of foreign Communist leaders in August, "why they can return someday on a nice pension and die in peace surrounded by their families and friends."

That Khrushchev continued to be troubled by his enemies was obvious from the farrago of articles and reports on "anti-Party cliqueism" that appeared in official publications. Early in October *Komsomolskaya Pravda* carried a story on "Problems in the Military." The chief problem, it seemed, was that army officers were "arrogating to themselves too much authority," were "disregarding the orders of the Party," and were, accordingly, "violating the teachings of V. I. Lenin."

The target of these attacks was, as Western Kremlinologists suspected, none other than Zhukov. He had made the mistake of taking Khrushchev's promises too seriously. Never a man to rein in his swagger and exuberance, Zhukov began delivering pronouncements on affairs of state wherever he went. He even made policy. For example, he and Eisenhower, as World War II friends, had been writing warm letters to each other since the spring of 1955. Suddenly Zhukov "broke off all personal relations" with Eisenhower because of Soviet-American differences over the Middle East. "Who told him to stop writing to Eisenhower?" Khrushchev indignantly asked Bulganin. "Is he giving orders around here now? I'll have to teach him some battle lessons."

During a routine trip to Yugoslavia late in October—while he was away from his command post—Zhukov was summarily stripped of his powers; he ceased to be Minister of Defense and a member of the Presidium. *Pravda* accused him of "arrogance, intemperance, and pursuit of the cult of personality." He was retired to a tiny house in the Crimea, overlooking the Black

Sea. There he would spend the rest of his life writing his memoirs of the Great Patriotic War.

By New Year's Day of 1958 Khrushchev could say to Smerdyakov with a pinch on the cheek: "You see, my young friend, we have passed this last critical year with flying colors, with pennants waving, with bands playing. We have sent the troublemakers packing. We have nothing to fear, do we? But we haven't settled accounts in full. You remember the words of Pushkin?

Avenge your wrongs, you who would live as men, lest the past lie like the Urals upon your quailing heart.

Semyon, I will sweep the past clean."

A few months later, at a meeting of high government officials at Communist Party headquarters Khrushchev suddenly turned to Premier Bulganin: "You won't be forgiven your misdeeds, Nikolai Andreyovitch." Bulganin's face grew pale as snow. He blinked in stupefaction.

"I know everything, Comrade Premier. I've known it for months. 'The cow always returns to his manure.' How foolish I was to trust you. So you, you, too, betrayed me. You thought you were shrewder than the others, eh? You were going to vote with the anti-Partyites to bring me down, maybe send me to the wall, right, old comrade? Then you switched your vote at the last minute when you discovered that Zhukov was with me. Your friend Shepilov, who's not happy teaching Muslim children the Russian alphabet, has squealed to us like a pig. Squealing pigs make bad plotters.

"Well, you're through, Comrade Premier. In a few days you'll be a private citizen. We'll find something useful for you to do. You'll have time to thank God you didn't lose the head you were born with. Foolish old man!"

Khrushchev then wheeled and glared for a long time at Smerdyakov, who shrank and cowered in his chair. Khrushchev spoke slowly, shaking his head.

"And you. What shall I say to you, you whom I treated as a son, you to whom I confided everything? What possessed you to join those scoundrels? My heart stopped beating when I heard you were with them. You also wanted to see me dead and buried.

You thought my number was up. Poor Semyon! Afraid to die, aren't you?"

"I don't know, I don't know," Smerdyakov sobbed, holding his head in his hands. "Shepilov threatened me. He said I could save myself and my family if I went with them. They couldn't lose, he said. They asked me for information—summaries of our conversations, your plans, intentions, the like. I told them nothing of value. Ask Shepilov. I don't care if I die now. I'm disgraced. My poor mama."

"Stop it," Khrushchev shouted. "You're not going to die. Don't worry about your family. Lucky for you you didn't give away any secrets, not the important ones anyway. I'm changing your job. You're going to Alma Ata to be a clerk in a paper mill. Consider it your purgatory. You're young. After your penance you can start over again. Nothing will be held against you. Now get out."

Two days later aged President Klement Voroshilov, one of the last of the Old Bolsheviks to survive Stalin, appointed Khrushchev Premier. "N. S. Khrushchev embodies the Soviet theory of sovereignty," Pavel Smirnov, a Party "theoretician," wrote in *Kommunist*. "As Premier and Party Secretary he is at once the source and executor of policy, the *terminus a quo* and *terminus a quem*. Lenin taught us, 'It is insufficient merely to *ascertain* the will of the proletariat. Our leaders must be able to *carry out* their will. Socialism is the unity of power and purpose.' Comrade Khrushchev represents the unity of Soviet power and purpose."

I I

KHRUSHCHEV (*cont'd*)

WESTERN experts on the Soviet Union speculated on the reasons for Khrushchev's amazing rise to pre-eminence. They all stressed the obvious point, that he followed Stalin's route through the Party apparatus, deposing one rival after another. The question was whether Khrushchev would also follow Stalin in raising himself above the Party and every other institution, making himself a classical tyrant; one who ruled in imperial isolation from his society and who therefore kept that society in continuous flux and fragmentation, destroying any force that might crystallize and lay claim to political rights.

No reputable Kremlinologist believed that Khrushchev would be a tyrant in the Stalin mold. He seemed too visible, too restrained, too reluctant to initiate a purge. Besides, the experts maintained, the Soviet Union could no longer *afford* a Stalin, given its advanced stage of technological development and hence its dependence on scientists, engineers, and the learned professions in general, and given also its international responsibility as the leader of many nations, comprising over a billion people inhabiting an area five times the size of the United States.

One Kremlinologist, Henry Sforza of the New York *Argus* offered another observation. Khrushchev, he pointed out, was the beneficiary of the Soviet Union's spectacular achievements in space exploration.

Sforza, as usual, was correct. On October 4, 1957, the world was astonished by the news from Moscow Radio that an artificial satellite, "Sputnik I," had just been successfully launched into an orbit around the earth. Great crowds of people gathered in the streets of Moscow, Leningrad, Smolensk, Tashkent and other cities to celebrate the achievement, which heralded Soviet supremacy in space technology. President Voroshilov attributed it to Communism. "Sputnik is no accident, citizens," he said on Moscow Radio. "We have the principles of Marxism-Leninism to thank. The triumph of the Soviet Union in space is the triumph of the proletariat. Sputnik is the doom of capitalism and imperialism."

Khrushchev was sitting with the other members of the Presidium, nervously awaiting the results of the launch. When told it was successful he clapped his hands in ecstasy and embraced everyone in the room. His brief speech on television that evening sounded the same theme as Voroshilov's. He introduced one ominous note, however. "Imperialists take pause," he said. "Our rockets can travel thousands of miles in any direction."

Sputnik stunned the American people. They had always taken their technological superiority for granted. Who was America's equal in applied science? Americans celebrated their inventor-industrialists—from Ben Franklin and Eli Whitney down to Bell, Ford, Edison, the Wright brothers (to name only a few)—as mighty folk heroes, the demigods of their race. They smiled in derision at the Soviet Union's fantastic claims that Russians had been the first to harness electricity and steam and had discovered the wireless transmitter, the automobile, the airplane, the open hearth furnace, the vacuum cleaner, the samovar, etc. Now Americans were not so sure of themselves. This much, at any rate, was certain: their avowed opponent in world affairs was very far ahead—years perhaps—in the technology of the future.

Some Americans even asked themselves if the Soviet boast that Communism correspondingly represented the *ideology* of the future was also true. During one of his press conferences President Eisenhower commented on the "self-indulgence and permissiveness" of American society. "Why, yes, I sometimes wonder if we're not too free to do all the things we do, spend all the money on cars with big tailfins, on cosmetics, and other such things. I'm not being critical now. I sometimes wonder. Why, one day when I was riding through Moscow with Zhukov he explained that Communism was a great goal for all those people lining the streets, cheering. They were poor, they had little, he said, but they had a faith. Now, to tell you the truth, I didn't have an answer for him because I wondered what our American faith was. Why, yes, we believe in freedom. But what kind of freedom? I'm still a little perplexed. What's our faith?"

Their pride wounded by Soviet space accomplishments, which grew ever more manifest in 1958, Americans embarked on one of their favorite pastimes: self-criticism. The central question that government officials, educators, intellectuals, businessmen asked themselves was what accounted for the Soviet lead in space, aeronautics, and other technologies.

Delegation after delegation visited the Soviet Union in search of the answer, surveying every aspect of Soviet life they were allowed to see, the school system in particular. The plethora of reports that emerged from these studies generally agreed that Soviet education in the sciences was far mort disciplined, rigorous, and extensive than the American. Soviet school children were required to solve complex mathematical problems; Soviet colleges graduated two and a half times as many scientists and engineers as American; and in the Soviet scale of values scientists ranked highest. One Harvard professor, after a brief tour of the Soviet Union, wrote: "The United States honors athletes, actors, businessmen, and politicians. How many Americans know who among their countrymen has won the Nobel Prize in physics, chemistry, biology, and, for that matter, literature and peace?"

As a direct result of Sputnik the United States placed increasing emphasis on science and engineering. School curricula at every level was radically revised; colleges began to undergo a gigantic expansion of facilities; government subsides to individuals and institutions proliferated; and the President appointed a special science adviser.

"We have to thank the Russians for what is, belatedly, going on in this country," *Scientific National* commented. "They made us aware of our shortcomings and our smugness; they aroused us from our torpor; they prompted us to action. We hope this is only the beginning."

But other Americans were alarmed by the growth of technology, by "the maniacal obsession with science that has seized this society," as Steven B. Buttner, the historian, wrote in *The American Thinker* (in a special number on "Science and Human Values"). "Science for the sake of improving life and satisfying 'the instinct of workmanship,' in Veblen's words, yes, by all means," Buttner argued, "but science for the sake of power and dominion—this is madness. Ultimately, it will prove to be our hubris. Does anyone ask how science will affect our environment, our relations with each other, our inner peace. But then these are trivial concerns compared to the quantity of instruments we produce for conquering space and the earth we inhabit. I fear humanists must stand aside and watch in silent perturbation while this madness runs its course, as it must."

The American military establishment also had reason to thank Soviet space superiority. "Sputniks I, II, and III make us realize how obsolete our military hardware is," the *Army Times* editorialized in June 1958. "We have been cutting back, pinching pennies, while the Russians have spared nothing. If we don't move now to develop our rocket and missile systems we may never catch up to them. Then we may as well pack up our old kit bags and go to Antarctica or Australia."

The refrain of American unpreparedness was heard often in the press and in Congress (where the military lobby was extremely powerful), and for the first time since his election President Eisenhower himself came in for sustained criticism.

Moreover, his hope that he might produce a balanced budget was shattered into a thousand pieces as he ordered the armed services to "proceed full steam ahead, without fear of cost" to develop a "rocket and missile capacity second to none." The yearly cost, in fact, would run into countless billions.

Before long the country was informed of the existence of a large and grotesque series of missile projects—the Zeus, the Atlas, the Jupiter, the Saturn, the Hercules, the Colossus, the Cronos, the Priapus, the Mars, the Cyclops, the Moloch, the Gehenna, the Golem, and the Mammon, among many others— all of which were designed to convey missiles of mass destruction deep into enemy territory from impregnable launching sites in the United States and from bases abroad.

The two most promising projects were the Priapus Intercontinental Ballistic Missile (ICBM, or "Big Cock") which, when perfected, would carry hydrogen bomb warheads (each able to annihilate millions of people) from underground silos in Kansas or Montana all the way to Moscow; and the Polaris missile, whose range was much shorter, but which could be installed in atomic submarines, the virtue of atomic submarines being that they could remain on the ocean floor only miles from Soviet shores for months at a time.

"How long before we have Priapus and Polaris?" Eisenhower impatiently asked the Joint Chiefs of Staff after the Soviets had sent up a three-thousand-pound satellite—the United States having been able to do no better than launch a thirty-one-pound trifle ("a tiny, shriveled up thing," *Pravda* wrote derisively). "They seem to be beating the piss out of us in this rocket thing, and I'm getting all kinds of flak from Congress and you people." He was told that the first ICBM should be ready by the end of the year at the latest and that the atomic submarine fleet should be outfitted with Polaris by 1960. He was told further that the United States would one day produce many more of these missile systems than the Soviet Union.

"They'd have a few good ones, no doubt about it," General Adrian Cooke, the Army Chief of Staff, explained to Eisenhower, "but we'd swamp them in numbers before long. All we need is the commitment for funds."

The commitment was forthcoming. The military received everything it asked for, and more. By the end of 1958, the arms race had entered a new and fateful stage. [. . .]*

"I'm not boasting," Khrushchev said to his son-in-law and new aide-de-camp, Alexei Adjhubei, early in the summer of 1958, "but the Soviet Union has never been better off than now. Relations with the West are stable, and the rest of the world respects us. Crops and production are breaking records every month. The leadership is strong and confident. The people are happy. If the intellectuals get out of hand I'll stuff them in my back pocket and sit on them.

"There is one problem, Alexei, that bothers me like an open sore. It worries me. I mean China. We're dealing with unknowns, with phantoms, sometimes I think with lunatics. They give me nightmares. We'll hear what Suslov says in his report to the Presidium tomorrow."

M. A. Suslov, the chief "theoretician" of the Soviet Union, had just completed a long trip through China. He had gone at Khru-

* Prescott crossed out the remainder of this page in his manuscript.—N.F.M.

shchev's behest to report on the recent changes there—changes
that had left Soviet leaders alternately perplexed and disturbed.
Especially significant was the fact that Suslov had been considered
one of China's staunchest friends in the Soviet government. It was
he who had persuaded Stalin in 1950–51 against the latter's
better judgment (for Stalin disliked and distrusted Mao Tse-tung)
to provide all-out economic aid to impoverished China.

Frol Kozlov, a Presidium member, was hardly exaggerating
when he said: "The future of world Communism may well depend on what Comrade Suslov tells us."

Suslov delivered his talk before the rest of the Presidium in
Khrushchev's main office in the Council of People's Commissars
Building. Suslov bore a thick bound manuscript which, he explained, was the full report. "Before the end of the day," he said,
"each of you will have copies of it. What follows is a synopsis of
its contents.

"Having spent the past two months in the People's Republic
of China, having spoken to the Party comrades there, from Comrade Mao and Comrade Liu down, having spoken also to our
own people there—Ambassador Schedrin, the heads of our missions, et cetera—and having read the state papers compiled by
our experts, I now have a clear picture of what is going on in
China and what, accordingly, the Soviet Union is up against. As
you will see, I do not use that last phrase frivolously.

"Why did the picture become unclear to begin with? Let me
recapitulate. During our period of troubles with Hungary and
Poland two years ago our Chinese comrades embarked on an experiment. 'Let us enjoy a great blossoming,' said Comrade Mao—
I quote from *Jen Min Jih Pao* of July 1956—'for it is a fruitful
and happy season, and the sun glows brightly. Let ten flowers
bloom, let one hundred flowers, even a thousand, yea, a million.
Let our fertile fields become the garden of the world.'

"Why did Comrade Mao encourage a sweeping criticism of the
regime? We often wondered why, did we not? There are three
answers. First, because he wanted to find a solution for China's
economic problems, which were getting worse: industrial production lagged and crops diminished. Second, because he wanted
to know what the masses were thinking, the Party apparatus
being notoriously unreliable. We know the condition, comrades.

And third, because criticism would also flush out the enemies of the Party and the state. It was a bold move.

"What our Chinese comrades learned, to their dismay, was that many, many thousands of flowers were poisonous. We will remember how vehement and widespread the criticism was in those days against the regime, the leadership, the Party. Much of it was counterrevolutionary. I read some of the essays and poems that recalled the happy old days of Sun Yat-sen, Yuan Shi-kai, and the bandit Chiang, even him. The evidence of apathy was shocking. The 'thousand flowers' showed that China was as conservative as ever, that the masses still adored Confucius, Mencius, and Lao-tse, that the family and the village were more important than Communism, more important than China itself.

"The village peasants looked upon the Party leaders as mandarins, who were tolerated as long as they left them, the peasants, alone. This was the way it had been in China for thousands of years. The alarming fact, as Comrade Mao discovered, was that the Party leaders in the regions and localities were content to be mandarins, in some cases war lords. It was as though nothing had changed. China's historic conservatism had infected the Party apparatus through and through, and instead of China being Communized, Communism was, so to speak, Sinocized.

"Comrades Mao, Liu, and Chou drew the appropriate lesson. 'We are going to re-create the Revolution,' Comrade Liu declared before the Central Committee last December. 'We will smash the mandarins, the war lords, the whole dead weight of the past. The time of action approaches.'

"At the time we thought Comrade Liu was threatening a purge of the Party, accompanied by an acceleration of the Seven Year Plan, an increase in the work quotas, etc.—all perfectly normal and comprehensible. Little did we realize how *literal* his words were, how far our Chinese comrades would go in making a 'revolution within a revolution.' Early this year Liu's Standing Committee was given the task of formulating the blueprint of this revolution from above. Three weeks ago Liu presented the committee's tentative proposals. We received an incomplete copy of them through unofficial channels. Here, comrades, is what is in store for the People's Republic of China. I will be absolutely objective and dispassionate in summarizing these proposals.

"They fall into three categories: internal reconstruction, foreign policy, and education.

"First, internal reconstruction. China will undergo a complete, root and branch transformation. The village system and the family system will be replaced by 'communes,' each of them a Spartan republic in miniature. Everything will be collectivized. The Party will exercise 'comprehensive control' over every aspect of life, public and private—toilet practices, love-making, everything. These communes will form the basis of a miraculous industrialization. Each will produce light or heavy industries, as factories spring up in back yards, in woods and fields. Each will participate in the building of roads and dams, each will mine raw material, grow the most specialized crops, whatever the state requires. The blueprint invokes such phrases as 'A Great Leap Ahead,' 'Twenty Years in a Day,' 'Full Communism within Five Years,' and the like to describe the anticipated progress. Soon China will be the richest nation in the world. It will also be the strongest, for each Chinese man, woman, and child will be as obedient to the call of arms as to the discipline and love of work.

"Second, foreign policy. Revolutionary militancy abroad will correspond to revolutionary militancy at home. This is the program laid down in the Standing Committee's plan of the future. 'China'—I now quote from the report—'must wage relentless war on all fronts against the imperialist aggressors, first among them the United States. China must recover the lands that were stolen from her over the last three centuries. She must recover Taiwan and the offshore islands held by the renegade clique of Chiang Kai-shek with the help of the American aggressors. She must unpityingly set her face against the so-called neutralists who in reality serve the interests of the imperialists. She must expose the lies of Titoist revisionism in all its manifestations, behind all its disguises. She must befriend the struggling masses of workers and peasants in Latin America, Africa, and Europe as well as Asia. Above all, she must resolutely and fearlessly confront the United States imperialists. They may brandish their weapons. The People's Republic of China will not flinch.'

"Comrades of the Presidium," Suslov continued, "these remarks are not taken out of context. They represent Peking's foreign policy in the years to come.

"Third, education. By education our Chinese comrades mean injecting the doctrines of Marxism-Leninism into the minds of the masses, reconditioning habits of thought—we might say psychological instincts—established in the course of the previous four thousand years. The problem, according to the blueprint, is to replace Confucianism and Taoism with a new philosophy. That philosophy, comrades, is none other than Maoism—Marxism-Leninism as refracted through the ideas of Comrade Mao. The Chinese masses will be forced to school themselves in the teachings of Comrade Mao, to memorize and recite whatever he tells them to. For there is no mistaking it, Comrade Mao regards himself as a 'creative Marxist,' the equal perhaps of Engels and Lenin, and, who knows, even of Marx himself.

"If you ask me my assessment of developments in China, comrades, I can do no better than repeat Schedrin's words when I spoke to him in Peking. 'What our Chinese comrades desire,' he said, 'is revolutionary pre-eminence. They feel they have arrived at a choice point, and unless they bound ahead, they will fall back, stagnate, die of inanition. Hence the extraordinary innovations, the xenophobia, the reverence for Mao. They seek not only their own salvation as Communists, they seek to restore, in Peking and in the person of Comrade Mao, the center that the world Communist movement appears to them to have lost.'

"I fully agree with Ambassador Schedrin. What are we to do? Comrades, we must deliberate on that question long and hard."

After a tense pause, Khrushchev, obviously agitated, rose to speak. "Comrades, the report from Comrade Suslov confirms our worst fears. We dared not say what was in our minds and hearts. The fox is in the open now. But before we delve into the matter further—and I'm restraining myself with all my might—before we deliberate and think about decisions, I suggest that I and Mikoyan meet Comrade Mao in the next weeks. Then we'll deliberate on the question long and hard.

"The report, Comrade Suslov, was splendid."

Late in July 1958 Khrushchev and Mao and their entourages met secretly (even the West knew nothing about it) in Ulan Bator, the capital of the People's Republic of Mongolia, which lies adjacent to both the Soviet Union and China. They conferred for three days in President U. Tsedenbal's palace, a converted seventeenth-century Buddhist monastery overlooking the greenish-grey Tola River. Khrushchev and Mao had met only nine months before, at the fortieth anniversary celebration of the Bolshevik Revolution in Moscow. At the time Mao and his right-hand man, Liu Shao-chi, had both publicly acknowledged the Soviet Union's "paramount position in the ranks of world Communism." It had struck the Soviet leaders as odd even then that the Chinese hierarchs should acknowledge what was unsolicited and taken for granted. "Why do they say this unless they doubt it," Gromyko had been heard to muse under his breath.

But now, in President Tsedenbal's palace, Mao and Liu were stiff and correct when, having arrived first (itself an act of impudence), they greeted the Soviet delegation. The toasting that evening was platitudinous and perfunctory. The vows of friendship between the two peoples lacked the warmth and spontaneity that characterized their previous meetings, few as they were.

None of these ceremonial nuances was lost on Khrushchev, who fully appreciated the importance the Chinese assigned to them. "We are dealing with mandarins dressed up as Communists," he told Mikoyan before they retired for the night. "Tomorrow I'm going to tear away the cloak of ritual. Everything will be out in the open."

Khrushchev was as good as his word. The following morning, after everyone had been seated around a long hexagonal table in what had once been the monks' dining room, Khrushchev asked Mao to explain the meaning of the "revolution within a revolution" that was about to begin in China.

"Chen Yi will explain it," Mao replied, his face a puffy mask of mottled yellow, reds, and greens.

Reading from a prepared text, Chen Yi, Chairman of the Central Committee, proceeded to cover the same ground that Suslov had. With one difference, however. Chen Yi's description of the "educational campaign" omitted any mention of Mao. "The theory and practice of Marxism-Leninism," Chen stated, "are to be brought to the masses in ways that the masses will understand and assimilate."

"Very well," Khrushchev said abruptly, "then tell me this, for I'm puzzled. How do you reconcile the communes with the theory and practice of Marxism-Leninism? I'm not aware that the communes they discussed are the same you wish to build. We know what they meant by a commune: an urban, proletarian complex. Such a commune seems to be altogether different from yours."

"Marxism-Leninism is a creative science," Mao said behind a curtain of cigarette smoke. He spoke slowly, measuring each word, closing his eyes periodically, hardly deigning, it seemed, to look at Khrushchev.

"Marx, Engels, Lenin were Europeans, not Chinese. They laid bare the laws of society and life. We are their inheritors. We apply their laws. The communes will carry us like eagles into the industrial stage of development. In this way we are faithful to the imperishable truths of Marxism-Leninism."

"Do I understand, Comrade Mao," Mikoyan interjected, "that your rural communes will soon produce steel, hydroelectric facilities, assembly lines?"

"They will lay the groundwork, as I have said," Mao replied, looking over Mikoyan's head.

"But if you are only laying the groundwork," Khrushchev asked heatedly, "how can you propose to confront the United States, which has large industries, stockpiles of hydrogen bombs, and what not? I don't understand."

"Understanding is reached through sympathy and with bonds of solidarity. Perhaps, comrade, you do not want to understand? The Chinese masses will not suddenly take courage when they too have huge industries and stockpiles of bombs. Strength does not give courage. It is courage that gives strength. The wolf who runs away is no stronger than the sheep who cannot fight. We do not fear the United States because its strength will fail it when its courage is tested. Our revolutionary spirit will test the imperialists' courage in the days ahead. Our courage will give us the strength to advance with great strides. By us I mean the international Communist movement."

"I see," Khrushchev said, the veins of his temple and neck dilating. "Suppose, however, your policy of confrontation with the United States leads to war? Suppose the wolf doesn't run away? Suppose the imperialists surprise you and show a little courage—just as the Hitlerite aggressors did. What then? You realize that millions will be liquidated, your cities burned to cinders, the whole country, including your communes, devastated. Will you pay that price, comrade?"

"You sound like a businessman I worked for when I went to the university. He would calculate every act he would make far into the future, months, years. How cautious he was. He never lived in the present. Of course, he went bankrupt. Comrade Khrushchev, you will find in the future whatever you look for. You create the future. You foresee hydrogen bombs falling everywhere if we challenge the United States aggressors and their bandit allies. We do not see them falling. On the contrary, only the revolutionary upsurge of the masses will guarantee peace. The imperialists become aggressive when they think we are weak, defensive, hesitant, courteous, deferential.

"Once we fear their weapons we are no longer revolutionaries. Yes, Comrade Khrushchev, we will talk revolution, we will sip our tea quietly after a big meal, sleep on a thick bed next to our fat wives, wake up fresh and go to work thinking about our jobs and families. That night we will talk revolution again. That is not our idea of a true Communist, of a true revolutionary. We should be lean and hungry, as Mo Ti once said. China will rend her fat and dedicate herself to revolution everywhere."

"An interesting lecture, but please answer my question," Khrushchev persisted. "Suppose confrontation leads to war with the United States. Are you prepared for that?"

"Confucius once told his disciples that there are two kinds of questions: one asked because the questioner knows the answer, and one asked because he does not know it. I assume, Comrade Khrushchev, that you are the second kind of questioner. Do you expect me to give you the answer you want to hear? My answer will displease you. 'He is always pleased who never hears the truth,' Cheng Hinh wrote. We Communists do not flinch from war. War will be a worse fate for the imperialists than a revolutionary peace. In peace they will lose everything slowly. In war they will lose everything at once. History is my witness. The Soviet Union emerged from the First World War. The People's Republic of China and the other peoples' republics emerged from the second. A Communist world will emerge from the third."

"Are you certain the world will survive such a war?"

"As certain as I am that the willows will send up their shoots on the banks of the Tola. You may have forgotten, Comrade Khrushchev, they can afford to lose less than we can. The United States has fewer than two hundred million. China has seven hundred million. The Soviet Union and the peoples' republics another three hundred million. Many, many will die in a war, but Communism will prevail. The Heavens themselves have decreed the outcome.

"Now, let me ask you some questions, Comrade Khrushchev. Will the Soviet Union back us in our struggle against the U.S. aggressors? Will we work together to build a revolutionary movement of workers and peasants on every continent? Will we march arm in arm as Marxists-Leninists?"

"This is madness," Khrushchev exploded, his face crimson and tumid. "You want me to back you in this grotesque folly? So you'll destroy everything to build anew. We've heard that nonsense before. We heard it from Nachayev and the Nihilists. We heard it from the infantile leftists in our own Party. My God, how Marxism-Leninism falls from your lips like honey! But, comrade, we're not talking in cafés, writing revolutionary manifestoes. You're the leader of hundreds of millions. Their fate's in your hands. Doesn't any responsibility come with such power?"

"Your anger and insults do not make you wiser, comrade," Mao said imperturbably. "Why do you call yourself a Communist? No one compels you to be one, or say you are one. Responsibility! Revolutionists are responsible for revolution. Capitalists and imperialists are responsible for capitalism and imperialism. Are we to be one or the other? We do not agree on the meaning of responsibility. Your responsibility is not the revolutionary's; it is not the Marxist-Leninist's responsibility. In the struggle today the lines are drawn between the masses and the ruling cliques, armed, advised, led by the American pigs. We stand with the masses, even if the ruling cliques are neutralists, or Socialists. Nehru, U Nu, Tito are Socialists, too. Their Socialism makes me smile. Chiang once called himself a Socialist."

"So that's what it is," Khrushchev asserted calmly, the storm having abated. "It's clear to me now. China is the foremost, the vanguard Communist nation. All who disagree with China are its enemies. And who is the sole interpreter of Marxism-Leninism? Why you, Comrade Mao. Soon, no doubt, we'll have Marxism-

Leninism-Maoism. We'll all have to look to *you* for guidance and instruction. *Your* communes and policy of confrontation will point the way for us too. The Soviet Union and the peoples' democracies will place their resources, their lives, at *your* disposal, to be used in *your* game of Chinese roulette. If you win, the world will be Communist—Maoist, I mean. At the least, hundreds of millions will go up in smoke. Poof! And if you lose—but no, that's impossible because Comrade Mao, who reads Heaven's decrees, assures us of victory. This is a farce!"

"From what I have heard and seen, Chairman Khrushchev, everything you do turns into a farce. No man can escape from his own skin, as one of our sages taught us. You have the skin of a revisionist. I see no difference between you and Tito. Where is the difference? Both of you think that revolutions ripen like oranges on trees. That is why you can give so much to bourgeois nationalists like Nehru. Support Nehru, you say, and meanwhile Indian Communism will slowly ripen. Let us go slow, you say. Let us wait for conditions to develop. Let the revolution evolve, one little step at a time. This is what you think. It is what the renegade Kautsky thought. It is what the father of revisionism, Bernstein, thought. It is what Tito thinks. Comrade, you have repudiated Marxism-Leninism. Deny it all you want, but it is written on your revisionist's skin."

"I've heard enough," Khrushchev said, rising from the table. "I've begun to think I'm in a madhouse. There's nothing more to say. We'll return to Moscow after supper. Before we go, Mr. Mao, allow me to remind you of the help we're giving you. The help won't continue if you turn China into a madhouse. We won't be dragged down with you."

"Speaking to you convinces me of how right we are," Mao said, standing up too. "You represent the degeneration of Communism. What worse fate than for a Communist to be a complaisant, self-satisfied revisionist like you. China will avoid that fate."

The differences between the two mammoths of world Communism, profound as they were, remained a secret, and each nation refrained—for a while at any rate—from openly criticizing the other. The Chinese press did speak from time to time of "revisionist tendencies" in Soviet policy, but mutedly, without polemics. For its part, the Soviet regime maintained a discreet silence, hoping that the Chinese would "come to their senses."

Sharp-eyed Western observers, however, perceived that something was amiss, as reports filtered through telling of an exodus of Soviet technicians from China. These observers also noted that the Soviet Union did nothing during the period, August through October 1958, when China and the United States confronted each other over the offshore islands of Quemoy and Matsu and very nearly came to blows. [. . .]*

* Prescott wrote here: "Pursue this further? Dull? Trivial? Use quote from Walter Request? Henry Sforza's inside dope? Needs more work!!!"
—N.F.M.

12

EISENHOWER

JOHN FOSTER DULLES died of stomach cancer in mid-May 1959. After the funeral President Eisenhower drove down to his Gettysburg farm. He was accompanied by three guests: his brother Milton, Vice President Nixon, and Senate Majority Leader Lyndon Johnson. That evening the four men sat and talked in the mahogany paneled library, richly adorned with swords, muskets, drums, medals, ancient coins, cups, stamps, books, etc., the mementos of a distinguished public career.

"I must tell you about a dream I've been having lately," Eisenhower said with a slight chuckle. "It keeps coming back to me. I think it began when Foster went back to Walter Reed to die. It's been bothering me, and, if you don't mind, I'd like to know what you guys think of it. I feel like the Pharaoh. Who's going to be my Joseph?

"The setting is always the same. I'm back in Abilene, on the farm. I'm with my mom and dad, and I'm dressed all in black. We're walking hand in hand over the fields, and I enjoy that because we move so easily and gracefully. The sky is blue, it's warm, and the ground is yellow as far as the eye can travel. Then, suddenly, I feel unhappy. Instead of wheat and alfalfa and corn I see nothing but crosses all around me. They're different sizes and colors. I look up at my mom and ask her what it means. She looks down at me with her sad and beautiful eyes and says—the words vary, but this is the sense of them—'Don't worry, David, just keep walking. You'll understand everything someday.'

"I'm terribly confused and troubled and I ask her again what it means, and she again repeats what she said, only more sadly. I ask my dad. He stares ahead sternly—he was usually stern, you know—and says, 'Be firm, don't give in. Do what's right.' I plead with him to explain what he means, but his lips are closed. By now I'm really agitated and a little sore. The dream disappears. Once or twice it's gotten me up at night. Well, what do you think?"

"I was fascinated by your dream, Mr. President," Johnson said, "and I confess I find it a little eerie. I've sometimes had dreams like that. I had them when I was sick, and I guess, subconsciously, I was thinking about death a lot. Those wheat and corn fields that turned out to be a cemetery? You were probably worried about the Secretary's dying, and you were brought back to childhood. I always dreamed about my childhood when I was sick. Funny how we see our mom and dad. I mean, we thought a lot about them when they died. When we think about ourselves or our friends dying we're naturally reminded of them. That's how I figure it. But I can't make heads or tails of their words, and I don't understand the part about the crosses. Maybe somebody else'll come up with the answer. The Vice President here has a great talent for interpreting events, though I can't say as I've always agreed with him."

"I'm glad you think I have a talent for something," Nixon rejoined with a smile. "I believe Senator Johnson is correct in seeing the fields as a symbol of death. I was particularly struck by the words your parents spoke, Mr. President, and by the shapes and colors of the crosses. Now the crosses, I admit, puzzle me, but the words I think I can interpret. Mrs. Eisenhower represented the desire you have for peace. I'll tell you why I say that. She sadly kept asking you to walk on farther and farther toward the horizon, where you find the yellow fields again. Mr. Eisenhower was telling you how to get there—by being firm with our enemies, by resisting the pressures to give in to the Communists, by refusing to the easy way out. It's significant, Mr. President, that you should have dreamed this while Secretary Dulles was dying. I think the dream was your inner self's way of telling you you have to keep faith with his ideals and principles."

"Now, Milton, how about you?" the President prodded his brother. Milton, the youngest of the Eisenhowers, had been regarded as the family intellectual. While the other brothers had

become businessmen, and Dwight David had become an army
officer, he had gone on to be a college professor and administrator,
rising eventually to the presidency of Johns Hopkins University.
Throughout their lives Dwight had consulted Milton about important matters, personal and public, and had often followed
his advice.

"I have to take issue with the Vice President," Milton said.
"I cannot imagine Dad justifying a hard line against one's enemies.
On the contrary, he went even further than Mom in his aversion
to war, in advocating magnanimity and charity. He rejected the
lex talionis, the eye for an eye, tooth for tooth, admonitions of
the Old Testament, and he often contrasted the rigors of the
Pentateuch to the mercies of the apostles. So that I place an
entirely different construction upon the dream.

"Yes, Mr. President, Mom was beckoning you toward a peaceful future. To that extent, Mr. Vice President, you're quite right.
What, then, did the crosses represent, with their various colors
and sizes? The answer is obvious to me. They represent the lives
of the men, women, and children of all races and nations who
have been killed in wars past and to come. Now, you will note
that no one else was present, just the three of you. Now Mom
and Dad were pacifists by conviction and religious faith. They
were saying to their son who seemed to go back on their faith,
who went to West Point, who became a military hero—they were
saying to him: Son, what shall it be? Are you a man of peace
or war, now that you have the power to bring about either?
As for Dad, he was trying to tell you—so I construe his words
—to be firm against those who would deflect you from the
pursuit of peace, who would keep you from walking on. He
was asking you to be strong in defense of right, so that the fields
of the world will not be turned into cemeteries. Mr. President, it
was a beautiful dream."

A long silence followed.

"To tell you the truth," the President said at last, clearing his
throat, "I cried a bit the first time I had the dream. Milton
beautifully expressed my own feelings about the dream. I appreciate your interpretation, Dick, but knowing my dad and mom
I was pretty well convinced that their words, the whole setting,

was a call for peace sort of coming up from myself, from the depths of my past.

"I think Foster's imminent death was the stimulus. In his last months, you know, Foster kept saying we've got to seek avenues of understanding with the Russians and Chinese, now that they're not going to expand very much any more. When Churchill and I went to visit him at the hospital a few weeks ago he repeated it. Poor Winston didn't understand him, I don't think, but he said over and over, yes, we must have peace, the young people must live and prosper—that sort of thing. Foster said if he could bring the world just one step closer to peace he would die content. I was very moved.

"Well, I have about two years left in this office, God willing, and I'm going to make the most of it struggling for peace, even if it upsets some of my friends, especially in the military. I'm going to be resolute about this."

Lyndon Johnson rose from his sofa and ambled over to the President.

"I have to congratulate you on what you just told us, Mr. President," he said, extending his hand. "I'm moved by this experience, and I'm with you all the way. I think I also speak for my colleagues in the Congress in both houses, on both sides of the aisle. You can count on my full cooperation."

Nodding and smiling, Nixon and Milton Eisenhower came over and shook the President's hand too. "I share your sentiments, Mr. President," Nixon said somberly.

"I do too," Milton added, mildly patting his brother on the shoulder. "I hope your dream, like the Pharaoh's, is a prophecy."

"If so," the President said jocularly, "then you've been my Joseph."

The President acted swiftly to "implement the dream" (as he put it). He instructed the State Department to approve of plans under which Soviet and American citizens, and political leaders, including heads of state, would visit each other's countries. He referred to the plan as "people to people diplomacy." "If the people and their governments can only get to know each other," he explained to Secretary of State Christian Herter, "the other problems will dissolve like morning mist." Accordingly, Soviet and American diplomats agreed that Khrushchev would visit the

United States and Eisenhower the Soviet Union sometime before the 1960 presidential election.

A "dry run" was attempted in the summer of 1959. The two deputy premiers of the Soviet Union, Anastas Mikoyan and Frol Kozlov, visited the United States on separate occasions. The American public did not receive them enthusiastically, but neither did it evince any demonstrable hostility toward them. The conduct of the groups they met—businessmen, professors, women, reporters—was gracious and correct.

They returned to the Soviet Union with identical impressions. Americans, they told Khrushchev, wanted to get to know the Soviet leaders better and desired nothing as much as peaceful coexistence. "They are interested in solving their economic and social problems," Mikoyan said. "They want no wars or conflicts. That's why Eisenhower is so popular."

"In that case," Khrushchev declared, "I'm going over there as soon as I can. Make arrangements for a two-week visit. I want to see for myself."

The arrangements were duly made, and in September Khrushchev flew to the United States. Weeks before, Eisenhower had asked the American people to be courteous to their guest. "This is an unprecedented event in our history," he pointed out in a brief television address, "and it may well turn out to be a turning point in our quest for peace. Whether we like him or what he stands for or not, I want every consideration to be extended to him. I know you won't let me down."

Khrushchev began his whirlwind tour of the country in New York, where the reception was cool and suspicious. New Yorkers acted as if a creature from outer space had flown into their midst, but it has also been said that they treat each other that way. Speaking before the United Nations, Khrushchev delivered a startling proposal: general and complete disarmament within four years. No one took the proposal seriously, least of all the American delegate to the UN, Henry Cabot Lodge, who dismissed it as "so much smarm."

From New York Khrushchev and his vast entourage went to California, where, as expected, the reception was more eventful. His first stop was Los Angeles. There he attended a gala dinner in his honor given by the mayor, Morris Pall, who in his welcoming remarks extolled the capitalist system, pointing to the magnificence of his city as proof of its virtues.

"I don't see what's so magnificent about your city," Khrushchev replied, shocking the guests, the cream of Los Angeles society. "And if it is magnificent what has capitalism got to do with it? We have nice big cities in the Soviet Union too. Come visit us sometime and see for yourselves. We have a saying in my country: 'Be proud but be silent.' Also: 'Don't hide your riches, but don't flaunt them either.'"

Los Angeles papers the next morning deplored the "rudeness" and "barbarity" of their city's guest. "If this is the new Communist man that the Russians always boast of," commented the Los Angeles *Messenger,* "the less we see of him the better."

In Hollywood, Khrushchev met a delegation of movie "moguls," led by Cleon Thermopoulos, the president of Twentieth Century Metro. "You see, Mr. Khrushchev," Thermopoulos said, "all of us started out poor. Many of us were immigrants from your country. I came from Corfu in rags when I was a boy. This is the land of opportunity. Here a man can succeed whatever his race, religion, nationality, or birth. We're proud to be Americans."

The other executives cheered.

Khrushchev shrugged. "America is great because you're rich? Is every immigrant a millionaire? I understand there are a lot of poor people still. Maybe for them it's not so great. I would honor you a little more if you, any of you, were a fighter for the oppressed, were an intellectual, a poet. All I see is that you're rich."

Shouting in Greek, Thermopoulos suddenly lunged at Khrushchev. But others quickly intervened, and, fortunately, no blows were struck.

Next, Khrushchev was taken to the Twentieth Century studio lots to witness the shooting of a film on Parisian café and music hall life. The particular scene Khrushchev was shown featured a cancan dance by scantily clad girls thrusting out their ample buttocks.

"Scatalogical and degenerate," he said, rising to leave. "It's an insult. This whorishness would not be permitted in the Soviet Union."

In retaliation for what they called his "disparaging statements about our city and its institutions," the proprietors of Disneyland cancelled his visit to that celebrated tourist attraction.

"I'm glad to leave this strange place," Khrushchev said, as he boarded the train that took him up the spectacular California coast to San Francisco.

In San Francisco he held conferences with business and labor leaders. He and the businessmen discussed the possibility of trade and the exchange of technical knowledge. "These are reasonable men," Khrushchev said, "and the Soviet Union looks forward to improving relations with them." One of the businessmen, Marvin Holmes, chairman of the board of World Business Machines, described their talk as "refreshing." "It may surprise you," Holmes told reporters afterward, "but we can learn much from each other. The Russian system of industrial and labor relations has much to recommend it. Remember, there are no strikes there, and profits are plowed right back into capital."

Khrushchev's conference with the union leaders was a little more tempestuous. They asked him about the rights of Soviet workers—their independence, their bargaining procedures, their organization. Their rights, he angrily replied, were guaranteed by the state and the Communist Party, both being one with the "proletariat." He went on to attack American unions as "instruments of the ruling class and collaborators in oppression." They asked him about Hungary. He told them to "mind their own affairs." "If you labor fakers can't swallow it or spit it out, why don't you choke on it and leave well enough alone."

"But you're the one who's going to choke on it," Walter Reuther, the articulate young president of the United Automobile Workers, shot back. "There'll be more East Berlins, more Hungaries, for you to choke on. Your own proletariat will give you the *coup de grâce*."

The meeting broke up in turmoil.

"It's ironic in the extreme," Henry Sforza of *The Argus* wrote the following day, "that the head of a self-professed workers' state should have gotten along so well with the top corporation executives of this country and so poorly with its labor leaders. There's a lesson to be learned here."

Khrushchev also stopped for a day in the American heartland, at the huge Iowa farm of Gar Laswell. Months before, the two men had discussed agricultural problems at length in Khrushchev's office. He had sought out Laswell, who had been touring the Soviet Union, because of his interest in adopting the American formula—i.e., the utilization of a staple crop like corn as pig feed—to help solve the Soviet Union's acute meat shortage. The only question was where corn could be grown in sufficient quantity in the Soviet Union. That was why Khrushchev's "virgin lands" policy was so important. If, he reasoned, the lands of Central Asia, which had just been opened up for agricultural settlement, could be plowed for wheat, those parts of Russia and the Ukraine where the wheat had hitherto been grown could be converted to corn and hog production.

Khrushchev thus brought his top agricultural specialists with him to Laswell's sprawling estate. "Why, this is larger even than the Spotkov collective farm," Khrushchev observed, staring in awe at the ocean of corn stalks.

The army of reporters crowded close as he and Laswell talked in their shirt-sleeves. Suddenly Laswell, a tall, powerfully built man in his sixties, shouted, "All right you creeps, scram, get the hell outa here. I want to talk to Mr. Khrushchev in peace." He picked up several ears of the corn lying on the ground and threw them at the reporters. Khrushchev gleefully threw them too. So did the rest of his entourage. A shower of corn fell on the reporters who ran in full retreat. Laswell and Khrushchev laughed and flung their arms around each other.

The Des Moines *Advertiser* wittily referred to the incident as "The War of Laswell's Ears." A bold *Pravda* headline read: "An Amusing Example of Soviet-American Friendship: Premier N. S. Khrushchev and Farmer Laswell Join Forces to Rout Unruly Correspondents."

The high point of Khrushchev's visit, of course, was his summit conference with President Eisenhower. It took place in the President's beautiful Maryland retreat, Camp David (named after his grandson), minutes from Washington. Though they spent most of their time surrounded by advisers, they managed to take long walks together in the quiet woods, accompanied only by their interpreters. The purpose of their talks, which lasted three days, was, as Eisenhower later described them, "simply to get acquainted man to man, explore the issues that divide us, and gain a little more confidence in our dealings with each other."

The most poignant moment of the Camp David summit came one night when, following a supper of baked fish, the two men exchanged photographs of their grandchildren.

"Why, Mr. Premier," Eisenhower said, "I think we owe it to these children to live in a better world than we found it. We must see what we can do to create a just and peaceful world. Otherwise, we've lived in vain."

"I dedicate my life to such a hope, Mr. President. We must try and try again to reach an understanding on the problems that both of us agreed yesterday are paramount: Berlin and disarmament. We shouldn't argue about those problems now, but we must do something before we leave office, before 1961. The United States and the Soviet must both yield a little. I swear to you, Mr. President, the Soviet Union is willing to make great concessions, concessions that will surprise you. We don't want West Berlin to lose its independence. Only it must stop being a sword in our belly, a refuge for hooligans and counterrevolutionaries. We're not afraid to have our arms and our bases inspected, not at all. Only you must also shut down your bases which ring our territory on every side."

"Our diplomats have been trying to thrash out those problems, Mr. Premier," Eisenhower replied, frowning deeply, "and you know how long and arduous those things are. Why certainly we must both concede points. Believe me, I'd make many concessions, but I've got to be sure. I recognize your difficulties, but you must recognize mine. I really don't know what to do about Berlin. We can't stop those refugees from coming in, and it's not easy for the West Germans to find jobs for them, homes, and the like. The source of the problem, really, is East Germany, but I don't want to discuss it. We've discussed it plenty. As for our bases, why I'd be the first to want to shut them down. They're a big expense, and they bring us a lot of trouble to boot. But unless we get some genuine disarmament going, I don't think the American public's going to tolerate eliminating them.

"In other words, Mr. Premier, what we've got are problems that have grown over the years like big oaks whose roots go deep into the ground. They're sort of institutionalized, and though we can begin to work on them, draw up an agenda, and so on, we're not going to solve them in a day, or a season."

"Well said, Mr. President. Yet we must start somewhere. We must seize the initiative, lest our grandchildren find the tree still higher and the roots still deeper. We have a good Ukrainian proverb: 'Tomorrow belongs to him who acts today.' We must act today, Mr. President."

"I couldn't agree with you more wholeheartedly. I'm having my Secretary of State and my disarmament man—they're both top level—analyze our problems exhaustively, using all the experts they can lay their hands on. I'm going to have their report by early next year. Which leads me to the second thing. Would you be agreeable to a formal meeting of ourselves, England, and France sometime next year? Maybe then we can come up with concrete bases of agreement. Our people can discuss meeting sites, and I trust we won't have the kind of trouble that faced us back in 'fifty-five. What do you say, Mr. Premier?"

"Yes, yes, by all means," Khrushchev said enthusiastically, raising high his glass of vodka and ice. "And I offer a toast for the success of next year's conference. Better yet, a toast to our grandchildren, to the grandchildren of the world."

"To a thousand years of peace," Eisenhower added.

The Camp David meeting was followed by a period of unprecedented tranquillity and good will in United States-Soviet relations. Absent was the name-calling, the polemics, the innuendoes, the Cold War rhetoric. When, on occasion, a dispute arose, as it did in Berlin and the Middle East, both sides applied "the spirit of Camp David" like a magic poultice to settle it.

Eisenhower, meanwhile, traveled to the ends of the earth bearing his message of peace and harmony. He was nearly seventy, and he had had two heart attacks and major stomach surgery in recent years. Yet his energies rarely flagged as he visited country after country, stopping only long enough to catch his breath—or allow his party to catch theirs. His objective, he said, was to "meet the people directly, face to face."

Wherever he went, in places familiar to him, such as Paris, London, Rome, Ulm, as well as unfamiliar—Kabul, Karachi, Bombay, Mandalay, Katmandu, Christ's Church, and Adelaide—

he received tumultuous receptions. So tumultuous that his hosts (not to mention the hundreds of secret service men he brought with him) often feared he would be swallowed up by the surging crowds that greeted him. But, like an expert swimmer, he always emerged smiling, his arms spread-eagled in triumph.

The spirit of Camp David, however, was short-lived. The Big Four had agreed to hold their summit conference in Paris in mid-May 1960. Two weeks before it was scheduled to begin the State Department Public Relations Officer, Robert Klosco, read a brief message to reporters. "The United States has reason to believe that a few days ago one of her unarmed planes, in the course of flying a routine meteorological mission, developed mechanical trouble, strayed over the territory of the Soviet Union, and crashed. The government of the United States deeply regrets the incident and hopes that it may be closed as expeditiously as possible."

But two days later Moscow Radio issued a contradictory account of the crash. "As usual, the U.S. government has lied. The plane was not on a meteorological flight. It was engaged in espionage. It was a U-2 high altitude plane taking pictures of the Soviet Union. It did not stray over Soviet territory. It was twelve hundred miles inside. And it did not crash because of mechanical failure. It was shot down by our gunners."

The State Department promptly denied the Soviet account. "We stick to our version of the facts," Klosco said. "This is a typical case of Communist propaganda."

An astonished world learned the following day that it was not "a typical case of Communist propaganda." Khrushchev himself dramatically announced before the Presidium that the plane's pilot, one Francis Gary Powers, had been captured and had "confessed everything." According to Khrushchev, Powers, working under contract to the "infamous" CIA, had been on a photographic reconnaissance flight high over the Soviet Union when it was struck by a "missile." Khrushchev promised that "the agent Powers" would be tried and punished as a spy. "The trial will reveal the sordid details."

Americans reacted angrily to Khrushchev's announcement. But, confounding everyone, Eisenhower admitted Khrushchev's charge of espionage. "I personally authorized the U-2 flights over the

Soviet Union," he said to an overflow news conference, "and I hereby declare that they shall be forthwith discontinued. I wish to emphasize that the responsibility lies not with the pilot, Francis Powers, but with me. I hope and pray he will be shown mercy."

Diplomats and political analysts were dumbstruck by Eisenhower's admission. When told of Eisenhower's statement Khrushchev closed his eyes and shook his head in disbelief. "Oh, that fool, that fool," he said to his son-in-law. "He's played right into Mao's hands, and now I'm caught between the fool and the knave."

The day before, Peking Radio had cited the U-2 flight as "conclusive proof of America's aggressive intentions. . . . Those who think it is possible to coexist peacefully with the imperialist bandits are learning the hard way. In the words of Chairman Mao: 'Take your eyes off the imperialist for one second, indeed a thousandth of a second, and he will rob you of them.'"

Appearing before the Presidium again, Khrushchev denounced Eisenhower as "two-faced and devious." "The Soviet Union doesn't want such a man to come here and enjoy our hospitality. He should stay home and play harmless games with little children."

Nonetheless, Eisenhower did save Powers' life. Ordinarily, Powers, like other CIA agents caught behind the Iron Curtain, would have been shot or put away for life. He was given an elaborate show trial in a huge auditorium and sentenced (it had all been prearranged) to ten years in "confinement."*

Khrushchev did not cancel the Paris conference, as many thought he would. "I want to let Eisenhower know what I think of him," he told Adjhubei, "and I want our perfidious Chinese comrades to know where we stand, too."

Minutes after the Big Four conference opened at the Lycée Palace Khrushchev seized the floor and launched into a tirade against those who "sanction spy missions into other countries" and then "compound their folly" by openly acknowledging their "complicity." "Mr. Eisenhower," he said sharply, "I once hoped we could have a meeting of the minds and settle the outstanding differences between our two nations. I trusted you. Now I see

* Two years later Powers was released and sent home in exchange for an imprisoned Soviet master spy.—N.F.M.

how wrong I was. Some of us thought you were a Prince Myshkin, a good-hearted, rather naïve man, yet one whom we could
go to the table with. Yes, maybe you are a Myshkin. I believe
that, looking at you now. But we can't go to the table with you.
It would be like talking to a kindergarten teacher. I'm convinced
of it now. You should teach kindergarten. I advise you to leave
affairs of state to those who are more worldly wise."

"This is shocking," British Prime Minister Macmillan exclaimed.
"Your conduct, Mr. Premier, is wholly out of order. In all my
years in politics and diplomacy—and I've had a good deal of
experience, let me tell you—I have never heard anything quite
like this. It's beyond apology."

"To you, Mr. Prime Minister, with all due respect to your
office, I say mind your business. You remind me of a court jester
protecting his king and master. Please don't play the referee with
me."

"Gentlemen, gentlemen," French President Charles de Gaulle
implored, "show some elementary decorum and dignity. This is
not a fish market. Premier Khrushchev, I'm truly surprised. I had
no idea you intended to turn this conference into an *opéra comique*. Surely this is not worthy of you. We might, for a moment,
lay our personal animosities aside. We have vital questions to discuss."

"I agree all the way with you, General de Gaulle," Eisenhower
stated emphatically. "And I'm not personally offended by your
remarks against me, Mr. Khrushchev. I've heard rougher things
said against me in my public life. My own feelings aren't at issue
here. If we can avoid the recriminations, whatever we think of
each other, why we might hold some fruitful discussions and even
come up with a settlement or two. By the way, this Myshkin,
whoever he is, can't be all bad."

"No, he's not bad," Khrushchev said grimly, "he's only an
idiot-saint. In other words, he has no business meddling in
politics. If the American people prefer Myshkins as presidents,
fine. Only keep them out of international affairs. There innocence
has no place. The Ukrainians have a valuable saying: 'Only the
very wise can afford to be innocent.'

"And Mr. de Gaulle, I don't like to be lectured to. I'm not a
child. The CIA, the U.S. government, committed a provocative

act. Who among you distinguished gentlemen would sit at the negotiating table with someone who only a few days before admitted his responsibility for espionage against your country? I demand a public apology from you, Mr. Eisenhower. I demand that those guilty of the horrendous act be punished.

"Will you comply with these demands?"

"Well no, of course not. I already gave my full statement on the matter. I consider it closed. Now let's get on with it. I'm losing my patience."

"Come, come, Premier Khrushchev," De Gaulle said, extending his arms, "your *amour propre* should not interfere with your duties as a statesman. I—"

"None of you understand," Khrushchev interrupted, stamping his foot. "Do you think I'm personally insulted? Do you have any idea what problems the U-2 flight has brought me? But I won't burden you. I was taught never to reason with a sow— nothing personal, gentlemen. So far as I'm concerned this conference is over. In fact it never began. Maybe in the future, when the United States has another President, we'll meet again. Good-bye." [. . .]*

Two weeks before leaving office Eisenhower delivered his farewell address to the nation. He was about to take leave not only of the presidency but of his public career, which had begun with his entry into West Point more than fifty years before. Never in his life had he labored so long, so carefully, over a speech as he did this one. It had been his sole preoccupation for a week, and it was said he had discarded thirty drafts and was still dissatisfied with it when he went before the television cameras.

"My purpose in speaking to you tonight," he said, reading directly from the text, "is not to congratulate myself for the accomplishments of my administration during the past eight years. My purpose, it would surprise you to learn, is to confess my failure.

"When I agreed to serve as President of this republic I thought I would be in a position to fulfill a lifelong dream—a dream which my parents passed on to me—of advancing the cause of peace. Terminating the Korean War was an important step along

* A page of Prescott's manuscript is missing here.—N.F.M.

the way. Then there was the thaw in the Cold War, the summit meetings, the Austrian Peace Treaty—these were important steps also. I became convinced that we, the United States and the Soviet Union, would soon move swiftly in overcoming the major source of our differences, the difference over disarmament. For what better guarantee of peace is there than the control of nuclear weapons and the missile systems created to convey them? But here I failed. We are no closer to disarmament today than we were eight years ago, and I am saddened beyond words at the prospect that the arms race will continue—nay, grow.

"It is my unhappy duty to report to you that it will grow. The nature of armaments has been revolutionized. When I graduated from West Point the tank had just been invented and the airplane had scant military significance. The army comprised the infantry, the artillery, and the cavalry, and military combat hardly involved the civilian population. Today, my fellow Americans, the military budget every year amounts to some thirty-five billions of dollars, equivalent to the goods and services produced by a large, rich nation such as France. That is because today military hardware requires the most complex scientific and technological apparatus imaginable, the use of the best brains in the country, the largest universities and industries—I needn't labor the point.

"As a result, a larger and larger share of the civilian population has been drawn into the production of war goods. Not only scientists, engineers, corporations, and universities, but labor unions and entire communities. They have all become dependent for their livelihoods and security on armaments. Millions of Americans have entered into unwitting partnership with what used to be called the merchants of death. Thousands of retired generals and admirals have been hired by corporations doing work with the Department of Defense. I myself was offered a position as a director of one of our largest corporations—I won't mention its name. It goes without saying I indignantly turned down the offer.

"America, then, confronts something unprecedented in her history. I refer to the emergence of a gigantic military-industrial complex, one which is increasing in size every year, every day, one which has a life of its own, independent of the society on which it battens and whose free institutions it threatens, an empire within our democratic republic. And it will continue to increase as long as the arms race goes on. I cannot stress strongly enough to you my feelings of apprehension about the future. I fear for the freedoms that have made us what we are. I fear we may win the Cold War but lose our souls."

"Measures must be taken to reverse this ominous course on which we are set. I am leaving office. It is not for me to initiate them. But I vow to do everything necessary, my health permitting, to help my successor bring the military-industrial complex under control. I may yet see my dream realized. I may yet see my efforts vindicated."

BOOK III

John F. Kennedy and the American Epoch

I

ELECTION

THE moment John Fitzgerald Kennedy entered the political lists as a congressional candidate in 1946 he impressed even the most seasoned observers in Boston. "Angel" O'Casey, a Sixth District ward heeler for forty years, commented at the time: "Young Kennedy is nonpareil. I've seen them all—Curley, Honeyfitts, the best of the Brahmin lot. None measures up to that lad. He has everything: looks, brains, money, a sense of humor, the social graces. Don't underestimate the social graces. If you don't have them in this democracy of ours you're stuck. The Brahmins, who command the heights, will let you go so far, no farther. If I were young I'd tie my string to his kite. He may go all the way."

Not only did Kennedy possess the attributes O'Casey mentioned. He also possessed a distinguished war record as a naval officer in the Pacific, and, above all, a distinguished family name. His father, Joseph Kennedy, was one of the richest men in the country; certainly he was the richest man of Irish extraction. The older Kennedy once had been quite close to President Franklin Roosevelt (he had served briefly as ambassador to Great Britain, and before that, as chairman of the Security and Exchange Commission), and was a mighty power in the Democratic Party.

Kennedy won his contest handily even though the Republicans swept the 1946 congressional elections in Massachusetts and in the country at large. Politicians took notice of the boyish-looking twenty-nine-year-old representative.

Immediately, Kennedy began to map his strategy for the future. He set his sights on the seat occupied by Republican Senator Henry Cabot Lodge. Lodge's family had sat in the Senate for generations, and it was said in Massachusetts that the Lodges enjoyed an historic right to that place. Some of Kennedy's advisers recommended that he wait twelve years, not six, before taking on Lodge; that in the meantime, he try for the governorship of Massachusetts or a high post in the Truman administration.

"Being governor of this state or an appointed official of the government," Kennedy argued, "are both graveyards. Rather than try for them I'd quit politics and go into something else, journalism or teaching. I think Lodge can be taken if we work hard enough, beginning now. Fortune is a woman, Machiavelli said, who yields her favors to the young and impetuous."

His father agreed with the plan and promised to provide an "unlimited war chest." "We'll settle some old scores together," Joe Kennedy said.

For the next six years, John F. Kennedy traveled throughout Massachusetts and spoke on thousands of occasions, before women's organizations, patriotic societies, ethnic groups, and gatherings of the Democratic Party faithful. Everywhere he conveyed the same impression of moderate idealism combined with native shrewdness and a keen sense of the political realities. Ideologically, he stood slightly left of dead center, though he dared not criticize—at times he even applauded—Senator Joseph McCarthy, who was nowhere more popular than in Massachusetts. In 1952, after receiving the senatorial nomination, Kennedy introduced a novel campaign technique. He would attend several teas and coffee klatsches every day in carefully selected homes. He was at his best in these intimate settings, and the women of Massachusetts gave their hearts to him, and, more important, their votes.

Meanwhile, Lodge, who took his re-election for granted, was spending too much time away from the state on national business, playing the role of Eisenhower's Warwick. He secured Eisenhower's election, but lost his own. Kennedy again bucked the heavy Republican tide, and he entered the United States Senate at the age of thirty-four.

He quickly gathered together a large staff of dedicated lieutenants, headed by his twenty-five-year-old brother Robert, and a twenty-eight-year-old Nebraskan, Theodore Sorensen. Their motto was, " '60 or bust."

Kennedy nearly won the 1956 Democratic vice presidential

nomination, losing by a hair to the famous Estes Kefauver of Tennessee. The Party bosses closely observed Kennedy's performance at the 1956 convention, and they liked what they saw. "He's the best item we've had since FDR," Abe Garvey of Illinois commented. Tammany Hall's Ludovico DeSemino added: "He's a star, a luminary, and there's no question he outshines everyone else." Kennedy went on to win the 1958 Senate election by the largest plurality in Massachusetts history, settling all doubts as to his vote-getting ability.

Shortly before the election a delicate operation had been performed on his back, which he had injured in the war. For a time it seemed he would not walk again. But slowly, painfully, he regained his feet, and after a year returned to a reasonably normal life. It was while recuperating in the hospital that he and several assistants wrote his sensational best-selling book, *Profiles in Courage,* a descriptive account of how down through the years a handful of senators had acted heroically, violating the canons of expediency and their own self-interest in the name of a higher principle. Kennedy left no doubt in the reader's mind that, given the choice, he would rather join their exalted company than reap the glories of the conventional politician. However, he pointed out in the preface, "America is the one place on earth where one can be both successful and courageous, a popular leader and a statesman."

Kennedy "kicked off" his campaign for the presidency in January 1960 when he invited a host of leading Democrats— labor union leaders, prominent businessmen, representatives of ethnic groups, and Northern Party chieftains—to his father's sumptuous estate in exclusive Moca Baton, Florida. Kennedy eloquently appealed for their earliest possible support, "before we Democrats begin flying at each other's throats." By doing so, he argued at some length, they would keep the Party from "dividing into hostile and self-destructive factions, thus giving the election to the Republicans by default. It would be a national calamity. Eight years of do-nothingism and decay are all this country can stand."

As usual, he was impressive, and after deliberating his guests were inclined to do as he asked. But they had two serious reservations. George Meany, the president of the AFL-CIO and one of the most astute men in American public life, aptly summed them up.

"Jack," Meany said, lighting a thick cigar, "we're all pretty much convinced that you're the best man of the lot. Probably, you'd make the best candidate. But a couple of things give us pause, and they'll come as no surprise to you. First, your youth. The people will admire you—who doesn't?—but will they vote for you against a really solid-looking older man? You know, you look even younger than your years. Don't blush, it's true. [Loud laughter at the table.]

"Second, and more significant, your Catholicism. We're not sure the people are ready for a Catholic President. We all remember how Al Smith was clobbered in '28. Americans aren't as anti-Catholic as they used to be, and maybe they accept Catholics as good Americans, but that doesn't mean they're going to allow one to sit in the White House. They'll see you as the Pope's emissary, trying to give government money to the Church, sending all their kids to parochial school. You may not know how deep these prejudices are, and they'll come boiling to the top if you're the candidate."

Kennedy's answer was brief and pointed. "There's nothing I can say to answer George's remarks. The only answer is not in words but in acts. I'm going to enter the primaries in Catholic and non-Catholic, perhaps anti-Catholic, states. If I lose or do poorly I'll bow out gracefully and support the winner with all the strength I have. Judge me by my deeds. That's all I ask of you."

One of Kennedy's rivals for the nomination was Senator Hubert H. Humphrey of Minnesota, a militant liberal from the time he was elected reform mayor of Minneapolis in the early 1940s. Elected to the Senate in 1948, he soon gained a reputation as an idealist who got things done, a Northern liberal who remained on good terms with the conservative oligarchs of the Senate.

Humphrey was one of the most rugged and forceful campaigners in American politics. Inexhaustibly energetic, he would —so it was alleged—deliver speeches for sixteen or seventeen hours at a stretch, talk in his sleep for six hours, and resume the next day fresh as a flower. Humphrey was popular among the same groups, especially organized labor and the urban ethnic blocs, whose support Kennedy solicited. And so, when Kennedy announced in January that he would enter the primaries he meant that he would take Humphrey head-on.

They met in two notable engagements: in West Virginia and Wisconsin. On the face of it both states should have belonged to the Humphrey camp. They were overwhelmingly Protestant, and they suffered from considerable unemployment, Humphrey's record on aiding workers having been particularly estimable. But Humphrey had only the scantiest financial backing, while Kennedy mustered an enormous campaign staff and spent limitless sums on radio, television, and newspaper advertisements. Humphrey strove mightily, crisscrossing each state in his bus, speaking in every village and hamlet, wherever he could find an audience.

It was not enough. He failed, losing both elections by wide margins. The main reason he failed was that he fought on Kennedy's terms, consuming his time and energy refuting Kennedy's charges, the most damaging of which was that he was too liberal and therefore could not win in November. Some of the Kennedy people went beyond the bounds of propriety and emphasized Kennedy's war record. The West Virginia airwaves, for example, were saturated with spot announcements such as the following: "What was Hubert H. Humphrey doing while John F. Kennedy nearly died rescuing his buddies in the navy? He was at home advancing his political career!"

As far as Kennedy's ambitions were concerned the essential fact was that he had won decisively just where it was thought he labored under the greatest handicaps. The men who had attended his Moca Baton party needed no further convincing, and they promptly "fell in line," offering him what he had asked in January—their purses and organizations. His nomination was assured.

Kennedy's remaining opponent, however, stubbornly refused to acknowledge defeat. He was Senate Majority leader Lyndon Baines Johnson of Texas. Johnson was a tall, heavy-set hulk of a man who had risen from rural poverty to wealth and power, the owner of radio stations, ranches, and assorted properties. In Texas he was called "the king of the brokers" for his consummate skill in appeasing that state's various and conflicting interests. He was at once the friend of the large corporations, primarily oil, and "the lowly, the poor, and the disadvantaged" (his own words)—the small farmers and migrant laborers, the Negroes, the Mexican-Americans, and the workers.

Elected majority leader only six years after going to the Senate, he demonstrated his genius for keeping his proud and contentious colleagues reasonably satisfied and harmonious. "Lyndon Johnson throws a sop to everyone," one of his senatorial colleagues noted, "and the liberals, the conservatives, and the popinjays—and there are many popinjays in this august body—go away contented. Only Lyndon could pull it off."

"It's only a matter of time," another senator asserted in 1958, "before he begins calling in his debts."

In 1960 he called in his debts. When he declared early that year that he would be "available as the candidate of *all* the people, East and West, North and South, all races, religions, ethnic and national groups, all classes and occupations, all ages and sexes," he already had the endorsement of the Democratic leaders of most of the Southern and Western states.

But Kennedy's nomination was a certainty well before the Democratic convention opened at the Los Angeles Horse Arena. Ex-President Truman, who supported Johnson, spoke at the Lotus Flower Hotel on the eve of the convention and delivered a blistering attack on "this inexperienced young man whose nomination will surely lead our Party to crushing defeat in the election." And a movement was generated to put up Adlai Stevenson's name on the theory that Kennedy and Johnson would cancel each other out. Nothing, however, could stop the Kennedy express, and he was easily nominated on the first ballot. Johnson's acquiescence made it unanimous.

The only suspenseful event at the convention was Kennedy's selection of the vice presidential candidate. He arrived at his choice during an all-night session with his advisers in his compound on the outskirts of the city. In determining that choice certain criteria had to met. He had to be a Protestant, a Westerner, preferably one with a rural and small-town background, mature, and fairly well-known.

Each of the men suggested were ruthlessly evaluated as to their strengths and weaknesses, their compatibility with Kennedy, and their capacity to be President. The most important criterion, of course, was voter appeal. "There's much euphoria here today, and I share it," Kennedy soberly reminded his advisers as they were about to get down to work, "but I'm not deceiving myself. This is an uphill fight all the way. I'm the underdog, no question of it, and I need someone who can help me."

At three A.M. Senator Abba Bluestone of Connecticut, one of Kennedy's earliest sponsors, brought up the name of Lyndon Johnson. "Lyndon meets our requirements to a 'T,'" Bluestone explained. "He's the only one mentioned here who can carry the South and West—at least a number of their states. He's the only one, Jack, who can add appreciably to the ticket. Nixon will pull all the stops in appealing to small-town middle America. He'll be the plain, homespun Protestant, the poor boy who made good on his own. I think Lyndon will run with you enthusiastically because he wants to get the hell out of Texas politics. He'll be grateful. He wants to be a national statesman."

Kennedy was lying on a sofa, smoking a cigar. He asked his brother Robert and Theodore Sorensen what they thought of Bluestone's suggestion.

"I can see Abba's point," Robert said, "but I disagree with him. For that matter, Jack, I disagree with you. I don't think a vice presidential candidate brings very much to a presidential election. What's important is to avoid having a man on the ticket who can hurt you. I think Johnson can hurt you. He might swing a state or two in the South and West—Arkansas and Wyoming, say—for a total of what, six or seven electoral votes? Let's say he brings you ten, twelve, fifteen, even twenty. But Johnson's not exactly popular up North. Illinois or Michigan alone is worth all the little states in the South you might win. You stand to lose more than you gain. Besides, I don't think you can trust him. He has his own fish to fry. If you win, Jack, you'll have an awful liability on your hands."

"I'd rather win with a liability," Kennedy replied grinning, "than lose with an asset. Ted?"

"I'm inclined to go along with Bobby, though I don't believe Johnson would hurt you in the North. With Nixon against you, Northern liberals, Negroes, and workers aren't going to be terribly put off by Johnson, who, I imagine, wouldn't be seen very much outside the South and West anyway during the campaign. Still,

I doubt he will help. I think we should look for someone who's less political, less of a wheeler-dealer, who's prominent but not controversial—a college president or general or something."

"There's one other consideration we should keep in mind, and it's not unimportant," Bluestone said. "The Vice President is a cipher, but the Senate Majority Leader is a great power, especially when his closest friend is the House Speaker. If, Bobby, Lyndon is what you say he is, wouldn't it be smarter to get him out of the Senate and put him in the administration, where he'd be out of harm's way? More than that, he'd be a help in passing legislation. The more I think of it the better Johnson looks."

By six A.M. the Kennedy circle had run out of energy, though Kennedy himself was as lively as ever. He called a recess until nine.

When his advisers returned and took their places around the table Kennedy insouciantly announced, "I've made a determination. It's going to be Lyndon. It came to me while I was shaving. In a flash I saw the whole election turning on Texas, Florida, the Carolinas, Georgia. Suppose, I thought, the election was close in most of these states? How can I swing them? Which Southerner has kept their loyalty without offending the North? And Abba, I agree with you too about getting Lyndon out of the Senate. If I won without him he'd be out to upstage me all the time. It would be a mess. My plan is to send him down South to campaign in the swamps and bayous and backwoods for all he's worth. He's a damn good campaigner—if he accepts the offer, that is."

Kennedy spoke these words with an ironic smile, for he knew that Johnson would accept unhesitatingly, though the acceptance would be accompanied by a show of soul-searching humility and profound concern for the momentous step he was being asked to take.

The scenario went according to plan. When Robert formally asked him if would accept the vice presidential nomination Johnson delayed answering for a whole minute, and then said he wanted to consult his friends and especially his wife, "Lady Bird," whom he often described as his "prime minister," or "chancellor," or "brain truster."

A half hour later he called Kennedy on the telephone. "I'm grateful that you've honored me by selecting me to be your running mate. I humbly accept, and vow here and now to stand alongside you and behind you in the campaign ahead and during your tenure as President of the United States. We will go forward together, leading a unified and powerful Party to victory. Thank you again."

The Republican candidate was Vice President Richard Milhouse Nixon. Ever since assuming his office in 1953 Nixon had been laying the groundwork for his nomination. It had been possible for him to do so because Eisenhower took little interest in the hurly-burly of party politics. Eisenhower, in fact, had hoped the Republican Party would produce a better choice than Nixon.

"Actually, Dick's a weak and indecisive man," he admitted in an off the record interview. "He's a good subaltern—tidy, neat, conscientious, but no decision-maker. He's continually having to prove himself, so that he's really troubled by himself rather than by the problem. I can't remember one suggestion he's offered that my administration's adopted. Dick's a nice fellow and a loyal worker. He's no leader."

Nixon, however, did not share this estimate of himself, nor did the hundreds of Republican Party delegates from the South and West whose support he had sedulously, painstakingly cultivated over the years. According to the tally sheet kept by his wife, Pat, Nixon in the course of his eight years as Vice President had attended a total of four thousand Party breakfasts, luncheons, dinners, and suppers, and had delivered a total of sixty-five hundred talks, varying in length from a few minutes to more than an hour. The reporters who wearily accompanied him on these trips referred to him as "the compleat Babbitt," or "Mr. Reader's Digest," because of his unerring ability to reflect the fears, pieties, and shibboleths of middle America.

As he had done in the primary campaign against Humphrey, so in the presidential campaign against Nixon, Kennedy took the offensive and defined the terms of the contest. Kennedy criticized the Eisenhower administration—rarely Eisenhower himself—for "failing to get America moving," for "allowing the country to fall into a deep torpor," for "consigning America to second-rate status." He cited the adminstration's failure to beat the Soviet Union in the space race, and, worse, in the arms race. He alarmed the electorate by asserting that "a missile gap" existed between the Soviet Union and the United States. "So long as our enemies have more long-range missiles than we," Kennedy stated, "we will be at their mercy. Their missiles are bigger and shoot farther than ours. I say this is intolerable."

Nixon emphatically denied the charge and pointed out that the United States already possessed enough bombs and missiles to incinerate the Soviet Union, and the rest of mankind thrown in for good measure, several times over.

Nevertheless, the phrase "missile gap," with all its fearful connotations, stuck in the public mind.

Kennedy also charged that the past eight years had been the worst for the economy since the 1930s. "We've had three recessions since 1953, an average rate of unemployment approaching seven per cent, and an average rise in the gross national product of only two and a half per cent. Our economy is stagnating while Russia's is leaping ahead. If this continues the United States will shrink to a second-class power within a generation. For by then Russia's gross national product will have swelled and risen far beyond ours."

Kennedy's campaign turned on one main argument—that the nation needed a President who could revitalize it, marshal its energies, and restore its place as undisputed world leader.

Kennedy proved a much more effective campaigner than Nixon. Despite the grueling, racking schedule, day after day, week after week, Kennedy maintained his equilibrium and humor. As he went along he seemed even to gather strength from the crowds he addressed.

Nixon, by contrast, showed his fatigue in a number of ways: by his embarrassing slips of the tongue, often saying the exact opposite of what he intended—e.g., lose instead of win, bad instead of good, wrong instead of right, Democratic instead of Republican, Communist totalitarian instead of freedom-loving, etc.—and by his frequent outbursts of distemper, which caused him to reprove reporters, members of his staff, whole crowds of people.

Still, Nixon would have won the election, thanks to the persistent anti-Catholic sentiment in the country, especially in the West and South and among small townspeople. He lost because he committed one catastrophic error: he consented to debate Kennedy on television. Before the campaign started Kennedy flung down the challenge. "Let us go forth to enlighten the people just as Lincoln and Douglas did in 1858. Let us discuss the issues in the cut and thrust of debate, just as they did. Where they were heard and seen by thousands only, every American will hear and see us." Nixon's most trusted friends— fellow Californians Murray Cholent, Herbert Gross, and Robert Shrike—advised him to turn down the offer.

"You're an incumbent, Dick," Cholent pointed out, "and he can go on the offensive. It's bad form to be on the defensive. And keep this in mind, too. Kennedy is very telegenic. He comes on like a movie star. Personality and charm is not exactly your forte. Reject the challenge, I say."

"Well," Nixon asked, "suppose he makes my refusal a campaign issue?"

"The public won't buy it," Gross said. "That's no damned issue. If he tries to make it one he'll become a laughingstock. People will say, is that his big issue? The best that can happen to us is if he does make it an issue."

"I understand what you guys are saying, but I just don't want it thought that I'm afraid to take him on, that I ran away from a fair fight. He thinks he stands to gain most from a TV debate. I think he's wrong. It's possible it might turn out to be the straw that broke the camel's back, and it will be done with weapons of his own choosing—"

"You're mixing your metaphors dreadfully, Dick," Shrike interrupted.

"I'm serious now," Nixon continued. "I'm confident that I can demolish him. I like debating. I won some championships at Whittier High, and I sometimes defended some awfully bad causes, like nationalizing big business."

"Don't let your enemies hear of it," Shrike said with a laugh. "They'll accuse you of being a fellow traveler."

"Anyway," Nixon said decisively, "my mind's made up. I'm going to accept the challenge. Let's work out the arrangements with his people."

Nixon's error was to assume that watching debaters perform on camera was no different from seeing them in person, at a distance. The close-ups on camera pitilessly magnify every personal defect. Kennedy had few defects, Nixon many. Kennedy was handsome, cool, self-possessed. In the first debate Nixon was palpably nervous, for he sweated and his make-up ran, giving his face an unshaven and sinister look. For the second debate he wore many layers of facial powder; but they were too heavy, and his face was a mask. For the third debate, rouge, eye shadow, and lipstick were added.

In the last three weeks of the campaign Nixon recovered some of the losses he suffered during the period of the debates. Had the election taken place only a few days later than it did he certainly would have won it. As it was, he lost by the narrowest margin since the Cleveland-Blaine election of 1884: some 100,000 votes out of 68.8 million cast.

One need not go far afield to find the reasons for Kennedy's victory. First was the yeoman work in the South performed by Lyndon Johnson. Without Johnson some fifty electoral votes might have gone to Nixon, or at any rate been withheld from Kennedy. Second was the support of Negroes, who made the difference in at least six large Northern states. And last was the ingenuity of Chicago's Mayor Daley who found enough Democratic ballots in the Cook County polling machines (always the last counted) to give Kennedy Illinois' twenty-six electoral votes.

The election was electrifyingly close, but what is important in politics is the possession of power, not the fact that the possessor nearly failed to obtain it. And as Kennedy would soon demonstrate, possession itself confers great popularity. [. . .]

2

GRANDEUR

AT his vacation retreat in Moca Beach, Florida, in the two and a half month interval between his election and the inauguration, Kennedy conferred for long hours with friends and aides and Democratic leaders on the men who were to join his "team."

He defined his standards for them: "I follow Jefferson in seeking an aristocracy of talent and virtue. I want the best men for the jobs they have to do, irrespective of their political affiliations. I want dedicated administrators and civil servants, not tired bureaucrats, lobbyists, and spoilsmen. I want the sort of esprit de corps that Teddy and Franklin Roosevelt inspired in their administrations. And as you all know the only way to ensure that we have this aristocracy of talent is by selecting the absolutely best men for *all* the top positions. It would be no good if we have first-rate men at the summit and hacks and mediocrities at the center and base. Our goal is virtue in depth."

The cabinet he chose unquestionably met his rigorous standards, all but two department heads having distinguished themselves outside of politics. The Secretary of State was Dean Rusk, a long-time State Department functionary before becoming president of the Rockefeller Foundation. Kennedy was impressed by Rusk's conception of his task. It was, Rusk said, "to apprise the President of the country's international obligations and to accept and carry out the President's decisions faithfully and expeditiously. The Secretary of State should execute policy, not make it."

"Rusk is no Foster Dulles," Kennedy said to his brother Robert, "and that's his best recommendation."

As Secretary of Defense Kennedy appointed Robert Mac-Namara, the president of the Ford Motor Company and a Republican, whose genius as an executive was legendary. Detroit knew him as "the automaton," or "the robot," acknowledging his incredible efficiency, his capacity for finding the most rational means to effect a given end.

"Give Bob a goal," Ezekiel Ford said, with a touch of acerbity, "and he'll break down walls, climb mountains, cross oceans, and no one else will do these things so well and so quickly. But ask him what the goals he should pursue and he's a helpless babe."

For Attorney General Kennedy selected his thirty-five-year-old brother, Robert. Some people at the time cried nepotism, but anyone who knew or worked with Robert Kennedy testified to his skill, intelligence, and energy. He had requested the Department of Justice because, as he put it, "nothing needs reform more urgently today than the administration of justice."

As a sop to the Adlai Stevenson contingent of the Party ("magpies and furies," Kennedy called them), Stevenson himself was made ambassador to the United Nations. "His eloquent voice will speak for the United States in the council of nations," Kennedy said, announcing the appointment. "His idealism, his wit, and his wisdom will inspire the other nations of the world as it has inspired ours. I further vow that Adlai Stevenson will be not merely a voice but a power. He will sit in on cabinet meetings and participate in policy decisions." [. . .]*

An army of college professors, administrators, businessmen, and bankers occupied the middle levels of the federal bureaucracy.

A number of Wall Street firms and some universities were virtually ransacked of their best personnel. Harvard (of which Kennedy was an alumnus) suffered the greatest loss, and for a while the trustees considered shutting it down for a semester.

Joining Kennedy's huge White House staff were special advisers on books, plays, painting, poetry, sculpture, music, and athletics. Kennedy appointed a special intellectual in residence,

* A section of Prescott's manuscript is missing.—N.F.M.

Professor Arthur Schlesinger, Jr., of Harvard, the author of widely read books demonstrating that the Democratic Party since its inception in the 1790s "has been the historic repository of America's liberal tradition, its well-traveled middle path between its ideals and its possibilities." Schlesinger and the others [. . .]*

Inauguration day, January 20, 1961, was blustery, grey, and bitterly cold. The hundreds of distinguished guests sitting on the platform and the thousands of people standing below trembled in discomfort beneath their multitudinous layers of clothing. Kennedy, however, wore neither coat nor hat and waited imperturbably as the ceremony took its lengthy course.

After swearing to uphold the Constitution, Kennedy read the speech that he, Sorensen, his brother, Robert, and Schlesinger had spent a month preparing. They had carefully studied the greatest inaugural addresses of the past—Washington's, Jefferson's, Jackson's, Pierce's Lincoln's, Harrison's, Wilson's, and Franklin Roosevelt's—as models. And, indeed, Kennedy's would one day be favorably compared to theirs. [. . .]

A day after his inauguration, the applause still ringing in his ears, Kennedy held a conference in the large and sumptuous Warren Gamaliel Harding Room of the White House with his top officials, his personal aides and the department heads and their chief assistants.

"The point of this meeting, gentlemen," Kennedy explained, "is to familiarize you with the major policies that this administration will undertake in the next four, perhaps the next eight years. I've chosen the broadest possible forum for discussion and criticism. Each of you, regardless of your rank in the bureaucratic hierarchy, is an equal here, and I urge you to speak up if you have anything on your minds. I've had a number of you work on drawing up policy statements on your particular areas of concern, and in due course I'll ask you to present them to the rest of us.

"But before we get started let me impress upon you the seriousness of what we're trying to do here. We're going to lay the foundations of national endeavor abroad and at home not only for this administration, but for decades to come, whoever succeeds us. We're at the point of termination and initiation. After

* Prescott's text trails off into gibberish here.—N.F.M.

so many years of stagnation and foot-dragging we've got to move ahead rapidly. We've got to have our own leap forward, to borrow Chairman Mao's phrase. This is our historic mandate. What comes out of this meeting, and I'm not exaggerating now, will shape the country's future.

"Bob MacNamara will start the ball rolling and tell us about our defense posture and related matters. Bob?"

MacNamara, of course, had done his homework. In a little less than a month he had mastered the infinitely complex set of Defense Department operations and procedures, a feat matched by none of his predecessors. He was able to do it because his brain was like an enormous computer, storing everything he came across and instantaneously feeding him whatever information he needed.

"Our main concern," he said, in his quick, decisive manner, "is to make certain that the United States is strong enough to beat back any attack while visiting total punishment on the aggressor, and protect its vital interests in the world. Let me hasten to say, this country is in fairly good shape, militarily.

"To be specific, we suffer from no missile gap. Don't be alarmed. I'm not contradicting the President. I've already discussed it with him. You see our intelligence reports had erroneously informed us that the Soviet Union had 1,000 ICBMs to our 750. We've since learned that their total is closer to 250. More important, we now know that their rate of production is much lower than ours. At the present rate we should have eight to ten times their number by 1965. Now this doesn't even include Polaris submarines, where our advantage will soon be overwhelming. In short, they're no match for us.

"But the paradox is this. If we move too far ahead of them and widen this missile gap in reverse, what will they do? All our experience tells us that they're either going to try to catch up to us—an expensive proposition—or develop something new that would enable them to bypass this whole phase of the arms race. By something new, gentlemen, I mean an anti-missile missile, or some such defensive weapon that can nullify our entire stockpile.

"I therefore propose we make this offer to the Russians. We'll let them reach a near parity with us in ICBMs, provided they agree not to work on an anti-missile missile. If they refuse then we'll have no alternative but to escalate the arms race ourselves and build our own anti-missile missile. That would mean an extra two or three billions a year, maybe more, for years to come. Then, after that plateau's been reached, one of us will discover—it's inevitable—a missile that can penetrate the anti-missile missile network. And so, another more costly phase of the arms race will begin, and so on and on.

"On the arms race I make two concrete recommendations: that we beef up our defenses, and this would involve an extra four or five billions a year, and that we seek grounds for negotiation so that the present plateau will be the last.

"Let me elaborate on the first recommendation. After the election the President asked General Taylor and Professor Walt Rostow of MIT to draw up a report on how our armed forces might be better equipped to fight small wars. At this point in the arms race large-scale wars between the superpowers are out of the question. Such wars are no longer viable instruments of foreign policy. The national interest isn't exactly served if we destroy all of Russia while Russia destroys only half of the United States. More and more we're faced with civil wars and limited acts of aggression perpetrated by small countries. These aggressors are usually encouraged by a great power.

"The Taylor-Rostow report, which is still incomplete, though the President and I have seen the preliminary draft, is going to suggest, and I heartily concur with it, that we place greater emphasis on counterinsurgency warfare. We must set up special mobile units that can be sent overnight into a country to put down illegitimate uprisings. In other words, we're going to get away from the doctrine of massive retaliation and the game of brinkmanship. They just don't work. There's no reason why, if faced with trouble in, say, Vietnam or Iran, our options should be limited to either doing nothing and seeing them go under, or unleashing atom bombs. We should prepare for a third option—the use of counterinsurgent techniques. We've got to be surgeons, not butchers. That's all I have, Mr. President, gentlemen."

Undersecretary of State Chester Bowles, an ex-governor of Connecticut and a well-known liberal, raised his hand. Kennedy called on him.

"Mr. President, I'm a little troubled about the Taylor-Rostow report, about counterinsurgency. On the face of it, as Secretary

MacNamara explained it, it bears an ominous resemblance to the sort of thing that Metternich and the Congress of Vienna did in the nineteenth century. First we declare ourselves international policemen or firemen. Then we intervene to curb disorders or extinguish the flames. Always, we would find ourselves intervening on the side of reactionary rulers against rebellious popular groups. The very term counterinsurgency suggests this. After all, from a practical standpoint, what petty dictator won't ask us to help him suppress what he calls Communist rebels?

"I might add," Bowles continued, "that we shouldn't be so certain that counterinsurgent operations won't escalate into something bigger. Suppose we go into a country, and it turns out we haven't succeeded, that, in fact, the insurgents are hitting us pretty hard, and we're losing men and our positions are threatened. Do we pull out ignominiously, our tails between our legs? Or do we send more men in, and more men again? I don't think it would serve the United States well if our boys were one day to fight against guerrillas in Asia, Africa, or South America. The possibility is remote, I admit, but it *is* possible under the principle of counterinsurgency."

"When you put the issue this way, Chet," Kennedy replied, "we would all agree with you. The point is, the possibility is infinitesimally remote. Our objective under counterinsurgency is not to shore up reactionary governments. It's designed to allow the people to determine their own fortunes without fear of disruptive minorities. At all events, as Bob MacNamara said, we must seek ways of protecting our national interest short of major war. That, I believe, is what counterinsurgency's all about.

"Of course, if applied badly, it might not work. Any of us might make mistakes. Every situation has to be evaluated to take into account just the possibility you raise, Chet. But I don't think anyone will confuse us with the Congress of Vienna, or me with Metternich. Not unless Pope John and I agree to Catholicize the world. It'll be awhile before we work out that agreement." [Loud laughter in the room.]

"Next, let me introduce my science adviser, Professor Jarman Laser of MIT, who'll discuss the space program."

"Thank you, Mr. President. I will confine myself to two questions. First, whether the United States is capable of mounting a much larger effort than now exists. Second, what effects, beneficial and adverse, can be expected if such an effort is mounted. That the United States is capable of vastly expanding the space program is incontestable. I would go further. I would argue that the United States *must* expand the space program lest she suffer irreparable harm. Let me explain what I mean.

"The world is on the verge of a series of spectacular breakthroughs in technology. What we are about to witness is a quantum jump equivalent in its magnitude and consequences to the rise of agriculture in neolithic times and the industrial revolution of the modern era. Thanks to computers and cybernetics we will soon be in the position to introduce self-sustaining, self-correcting, self-improving systems of engineering.

"Does this boggle the imagination? It should. Does it sound like science fiction? In fact, it surpasses the wildest fantasies of the science fiction of our youth. What I am suggesting is that sooner or later we will have systems of production, distribution, and transportation that think, that solve problems independent of the men who operate them. Do not be frightened by the revolt of the robots. Their thinking will consist solely of problem-solving. Their job will be to come up with the best means of realizing the ends assigned to them. Man, not machines, will continue to occupy the kingdom of ends.

"But to enter this third and most critically important epoch in the evolution of technology, of man's control of his environment, the United States government must spend immense sums in research and in subsidizing those new industries that will apply the research to concrete problems. The federal government, then, must do two things. It must establish a scientific program tied closely to a compelling national objective, specifically the race to the moon. And, in administering that program, it must draw together all its essential components: the universities and research centers, the various space bureaus, the thousands of corporations that will make use of cybernetics, computers, nuclear physics, electronics, and whatever other innovations emerge in the future—and emerge they will. In time the whole of society will be locked into the new technology.

"Now, you might ask what the fuss is all about. Why the crash program, why the sense of urgency, why not allow the country to take its natural course? The reason, simply stated, is that we cannot fall behind in the development of the new technology. For to fall behind would have fatal consequences. The United States would become increasingly dependent on the societies that had pioneered in research. Or, more ominously, it would be at the mercy of its more advanced, more venturesome enemies. Measured against their gross product, their total wealth, the Soviet Union, Germany, and Japan, invest much more than we do in research and development. Let me remind you of one obvious fact. When such investments pay off they do so by generating geometric, not arithmetic, leaps, thereby freeing yet more funds for yet more research, and so forth.

"What I am saying, gentlemen, is that the choice now is to be first or to fall behind and perhaps eventually drop out of the technology race altogether. The space program is our opportunity to enlist the public's support in this terribly critical drive to seize the future.

"This excursus leads me back to the question at hand. Yes, we have the resources. Hundreds of thousands of scientists, engineers, technicians, and skilled workers can easily be brought into the burgeoning space program. The colleges and universities can be enlarged to accommodate three and four times their current population within the decade. And once the federal government initiates the program, underwrites it, and lays down definite guidelines, the private sector will rush in to reap the rewards. Billions will flow into the new industries. You will see how rapidly America will convert to the new technology, how the general standard of living will rise, how many opportunities will spring up, especially for the young, for there is no reason why every qualified youngster should not go to college. Equality of opportunity for every American would be one of the residual benefits of the space program. I think I have said enough. Thank you."

"Professor Laser," someone put in, "you said the space program might also have adverse affects, but you haven't mentioned them. What are they?"

"Well, the space race and the new technology might call forth some legitimate complaints—and I know the President is aware of them—that placing so much emphasis on sending rockets or ships into distant space would distort our priorities. Why not spend the money on our problems here on earth, some will say. My answer to that is that it will, on the contrary, help solve some of those problems, as I have indicated. Besides, it has never been proved to my satisfaction that the absence of one program necessarily leads to the adoption of another. If, for example, less money goes to the military, more money will not automatically go to housing, medical care, foreign aid. The people will instead lower their taxes and spend the money on themselves, on consumer goods. So with the space program. It will rise or fall on its own merits. It will not be at the expense of something else."

"That," the President said, rising from his rocking chair, "was a breathtaking, brilliant presentation. You've defined the choices before us very clearly.

"Let me say here that we've already reached a determination on the space program. When we deliver our recommendation to the Congress we'll declare that America's goal is to reach the moon first, and we'll set 1970 as our timetable. We'll really turn it into a race. Our being behind now makes it all the more interesting. Competition will be the spur. If the Russians lose, and I'm confident they will, they won't boast about the glories of Communism so much, and Khrushchev won't threaten to bury us any more. Our victory in the race will give us a big moral lift, too. I think the American people can be induced to look at space the same way the English once looked at overseas exploration and empire.

"Now I'd like to introduce Philip Mallose, a young aide whom I met several years ago when I spoke to some Harvard seniors in the political science department. Phil Mallose was very critical of U.S. policy in Latin America, berating me and others in Congress for their indifference, and he predicted that unless we did something quickly the continent is going to explode, not at once, but piecemeal. He thought Cuba would be the first to go. Hardly anyone had heard of Castro then.

"I was impressed with Phil, kept in touch with him, and finally brought him into the government against his will, for he would rather be on the outside as a critic. Who wouldn't? Anyway, he came in and has been working with some people in the State Department on a plan for Latin America. Surprisingly, he's gotten along quite well with the insiders, and I have a feeling he's beginning to sell out. Here he'll present the general outlines of what this administration intends to do. Phil?"

"Thank you, Mr. President. I'm flattered you think me worthy of selling out. Every man, I suppose, has his price, and I hope you don't think mine was too low [laughter].

"Gentlemen, I'm sure you're familiar with the conditions of life in nearly every country in Latin America: grinding poverty, illiteracy, disease, and the demoralization of the masses on the one hand. And a tiny ruling class of landowners, industrialists, and military officers, on the other. This model is, I admit, quite broad and somewhat simplistic, for there are all kinds of variations and qualifications as we go from one country to another. But the model holds for our purposes here.

"Except briefly during Franklin D. Roosevelt's administration, American diplomacy has been acceptance—and consequently approval—of the status quo. Our military aid has been considerable, our economic aid negligible. American weapons and advisers have gone to such paragons of democracy and decency as Batista, Trujillo, Samoza, Stroessner, Rojas Pinilla, and Jiminez, among others. When, on occasion, we have intervened, it has been on the side of the tyrants, including some named above—we created Trujillo and Samoza—or, recently, to turn out a leftist regime in Guatemala, plunging that poor country into continuous turmoil ever since.

"What, then, should our policy be? Obviously, we can't go in and establish liberal democracies. We can't make every Latin American country into a Uruguay. What we can do, what it is imperative we do, is attempt to create the social conditions from which liberal democracy would in time emerge. Who among us here believes that Cuba went Communist because Castro and his men were Communist agents? Even if they were, the fact would remain that Cuba went Communist because Batista and the social oligarchy he collaborated with—an oligarchy, incidentally, consisting of many Americans—had driven the people to the wall. And so it would be if Castros arose elsewhere in

Latin America, where, if anything, the differences in wealth and status are even more grotesquely extreme than they were in Cuba. Latin America contains two hundred million people, and it has one of the most rapid population increases in the world. The poverty and maldistribution of wealth is growing, not diminishing. And the example of Cuba is now before it. Will the Latin American peoples go on enduring their miserable lot much longer? The time is very late. The United States must act at once, without delay.

"I and several members of the State Department have been working on a plan to establish development projects throughout Latin America—schools, factories, clinics, housing, etc.—with the cooperation of the governments concerned. These projects would be non-political. Their aim will be to bring about a transformation of the economic base in the hope that the political superstructure would change correspondingly and without violence. Our hope is to bring about a middle-class society in the place of the oligarchic despotism that presently characterizes most Latin American countries.

"Such a plan, moreover, would give the United States a lever to promote the changes we favor and encourage popular, peaceful, democratic movements. We are proposing that the United States offer a long-term commitment of aid, amounting to some twenty billion dollars in ten years—a modest sum in view of the catastrophic problems and dangers that confront us. We propose also that this program be established on an independent footing, that it be answerable solely to the President, not to the bureaucracies. If it succeeds it will, I repeat, be only a start, a turning of the tide. Thank you."

"Well," Kennedy said, smiling, "you certainly laid it on the line, and I, and I think the rest of us here, agree with you. Only the amount of money you recommend may be too much for the Congress to swallow, especially after it's asked to swallow so many other bitter pills. But I'll do my part to get as much as we can.

"My brother Robert and I have discussed the matter somewhat, and we've tentatively decided on a name for the Latin American aid program. We would call it the Friendship in Progress Program. How does that strike you?"

No one objected except Secretary of State Rusk. "On the whole," Rusk said diffidently, "I like the name very much. I'm afraid, however, Mr. President, the word friendship might be too idealistic, too soft for the tough-minded boys in Congress. That much money, they will say, shouldn't be distributed to friends but to allies or partners. As far as they're concerned a costly program is justified if it brings us real security. The program has to sound tougher, I think."

"Your point's well taken, Dean," Kennedy replied. "Why not Alliance for Progress, then? Does anyone object to that name? OK, the Alliance for Progress it'll be.

"Now the last item on our agenda today is economic policy, and discussing it with us will be the chairman of the Council of Economic Advisers, Walter W. W. Heller, whom we dragooned from Minnesota U., where he once lived the contemplative life, writing textbooks for unhappy undergraduates. Walter?"

"Thank you, Mr. President. I see, sir, that you have been taken in by the myth of the professoriate. Someday, you must come down to academia, and you will see how decidedly *un*contemplative it is.

"Mr. President, gentlemen, I need not detail the shortcomings of our economy. Mr. President, I think you performed an extremely valuable service in your campaign last fall by informing the public of the meaning of economic stagnation. If during the Eisenhower years the economy had been functioning at a reasonably prosperous level, the gross national product rising by three and a half to four per cent a year—a modest rate—this nation would have been richer by a total of some sixty to seventy billion dollars. That is a quantity of wealth lost forever.

"Today, one out of thirteen able-bodied citizens is out of work. Consider what that means in terms of unrealized potential. Here is another instance of unrealized potential: our industries are operating at sixty to seventy per cent of capacity. The question is, what is wrong, what is at fault?

"The main fault, I maintain, lies in the public's misconception of government. This country has grown up in the Jeffersonian belief that the government must be as thrifty and parsimonious as a yeoman farmer or a storekeeper, borrowing little, owing little, or better, nothing, his budget balanced, thanks to low outlays. That, in essence, was the philosophy of the last administration. But, like it or not, we live in an advanced technological society, as Professor Laser brilliantly pointed out, where nearly everything is produced for the national or world market. Things don't work out according to the ancient Jeffersonian formula.

"Consider this situation. The economy falters for one reason or another. Taxes decrease because the national product has decreased. Factd with a deficit the government cuts back its expenses so as to balance the budget. The withdrawal of government outlays intensifies the recession, taxes fall further behind expectations, the debt grows correspondingly. That is pretty much what happened in the 1958–60 recession, the worst since the 1930s. To make matters worse, prices no longer fall when business drops. The big companies, which monopolize the market, simply produce less and maintain prices at the old levels.

"What I am saying, gentlemen, is this. To ensure that the gross national product, the goose that lays all our golden eggs, keeps growing by four to five per cent a year, the federal government must intervene in the economy. The economy is too important to be left to businessmen. The government must resort to deficit spending. It must be willing to provide incentives to industry and labor. It must stimulate the forces of consumption. In short, when tax receipts are too low, tax less. This must be accompanied by an increase in federal expenditures, a further stimulus. When both are done simultaneously, strategically, selectively—for the incentives must be applied to the most productive and vital industries and the expenditures applied to those most in need—there is no reason why within two or three years the gross national product should not grow to four per cent per annum and the unemployment rate drop to below five per cent.

"And when in the future the prosperity causes the economy to overheat, the government can then take countermeasures: higher taxes, decreased outlays, higher interest rates, and the like. The point is this. The government must become an active partner in managing the economy so that we can enjoy an even and continuous growth of goods and services.

"This leads me to the second consideration. If gross national production rises by fifteen billion a year, as we can anticipate, that would mean three to four billions in federal tax revenue which can be used to deal with some of our urgent problems: slums, poverty, job training, schools, social security, medical care, and the rest. And since gross production grows by arithmetic ratios—the first year, fifteen billion, the second year, eighteen, the third, twenty-two, etc.—tax revenues rising with it, so more and more can be allocated for social services. All of the country's needs can be met by the relentless expansion of the economy, and this administration will see to it that its expansion will be relentless. Thank you."

"Thank you, that was fine," Kennedy said. "Yes, prosperity is the keystone of the arch of our domestic policy. Without prosperity nothing is possible. John, do you have a comment?"

Kennedy recognized Professor John Kenneth Galbraith, a prominent Harvard economist and wit, soon to be appointed ambassador to India. "I don't want to sound like a scold and a moralizer, though I know you'll think me one," Galbraith said in his amusingly ironic way, "but I'm a little troubled by an assumption my old friend Walt Heller made.

"I wonder why he assumes so blithely that the increased tax revenues flowing from a prosperous economy will be spent for social services. My own desiccated instincts tell me that Congress won't be all that happy about money being spent for the poor, many of them black, for urban transportation, housing, and so forth. Human desires, you know, are infinite in their capacity, and in our society they're more infinite than anywhere else. Consumption is like sex. Stimulate it and you want more. You may be satisfied, but you won't be satiated.

"What I'm suggesting is this. The private sector, when sufficiently enlarged, will overwhelm the public sector. Even more than now we'll have a society consecrated to accumulating quantities of goods rather than a society seeking the good life. I don't want to sound like an Aristotle or a Jeremiah, though I won't be insulted if you compare me to them, but I think we should be aware of the other side of prosperity—prosperity untempered by a concern for the more important values of man and society. The gross national product is far from being the supreme good."

"John, you can't scold us often enough," Kennedy said, grinning, "and as far as I'm concerned you are both an Aristotle and a Jeremiah, a polymath and a prophet. But John, don't you think the issue you raise is one that should more properly disturb us in the future? The task now is to get the economy moving again, to put men and industries to work. That, of course, is a quantitative matter. When we've achieved prosperity we can turn to the problem of the quality of life, the problems of recreation, leisure, spirit, intellect.

"Your other reservation is more concrete. Will the Congress go along with a program of social reform? That's going to be hard because the Congress is just about evenly divided. Conservative Republicans and Democrats can stop us in our tracks. I have no illusions about the difficulties ahead. So what I've got to do, what all of us here have got to do, is to begin mobilizing public opinion on our side, especially on domestic policies. In foreign affairs, in our military policies, in the space race, I'm fairly confident the Congress can be moved. We must build up a constituency. It may take time, and it may require overcoming any number of obstacles. But if we know what we want—and the talks here give us a damned good idea of what we should want—we can get public approval. The Congress will follow.

"Before the year's up these policy positions that you heard will be distilled and refined and sent to the Hill for enactment. I'll do my part to bring the issues to the people. Woodrow Wilson had an evenly balanced Congress too, and he got his reforms through by using the presidency as a vehicle of persuasion. That's what I intend to do. Above all, I'm determined to get America moving again, to restore her position in the world, restore her sense of destiny. Winston Churchill said, 'A great people occupies center stage in the dramas of history.'"

By and large Kennedy managed to obtain what he wanted from Congress, at least in the major policy areas explored during the White House conference of January 21, 1961. Counterinsurgent military units were formed; the space program was significantly expanded and the nation committed to a moon landing by 1970; the Alliance for Progress was created under a semiautonomous agency and launched with great fanfare and panoply; and prosperity did eventually come to America, a prosperity without equal in its history, a prosperity, moreover, that favored precisely those industries and technologies discussed at the conference.

Not even Kennedy's severest critics could deny that he had made good his promise to get America moving again.

3

COLD WAR REDIVIVUS

IN early April 1961 Premier Khrushchev unexpectedly appeared at the annual party thrown by the American embassy in Moscow for the diplomatic community. "Your President is a very popular young man—he's popular in my country also—and may God shower him with favors," he said to the American ambassador, Thomas A. Llewelyn. "We believe he's serious about negotiating differences with us, and I may say—and you can tell him this—I look forward to seeing him soon. A meeting of the minds will be useful, don't you think?

"But I've heard rumors, only rumors, that the United States may be planning an invasion of Cuba. That would be a grave error. I hope for everyone's sake they're untrue."

"I am sure they are," Llewelyn said. "I will, of course, communicate your wishes to President Kennedy."

A week later the two leaders informally agreed to meet in Vienna in early June, following Kennedy's scheduled visit to Western Europe.

The very day Khrushchev spoke to Llewelyn in Moscow Kennedy was conferring with his National Security Council at the office of the Joint Chiefs of Staff in the Pentagon's majestic "inner ward." Attending, along with the Chiefs, were Secretary of State Rusk, Secretary of Defense MacNamara, Secretary of the Treasury Douglas Dillon, Attorney General Kennedy, CIA Director Allen Dulles, Senator J. William Fulbright of Arkansas, chairman of the Foreign Relations Committee, and presidential aides MacGeorge Bundy, Arthur Schlesinger, Jr., Walt Rostow, and two long-respected authorities on Latin America, Professor

B. B. A——— of Columbia University, and L. D. G———,*
a business administrator.

"Gentlemen," Kennedy said gravely, tilting back his rocking
chair, "you know what brings us here. The situation in Cuba
has reached a crisis point, and we—I—must come to a determination one way or another. Without further ado I'll have
Mr. Allen Dulles explain the situation to you."

Dulles had aged since his brother's death two years before.
Wizened and stooped, his pipe stuck firmly in his mouth, the
CIA director looked more than ever like the gentle headmaster
of a New England boy's school.

"All of you are familiar, I'm sure, with events in Cuba
and our relations with the Castro regime. As of now the United
States has practically no relations with the regime. Our business
there is being transacted through the Swiss embassy. Now as
far back as 1956 our operatives in Cuba warned the State
Department that Castro—then fighting for his life in the mountains—could not be trusted, that he was no mere reformer, as
the press in this country depicted him.

"I'm not suggesting that Batista wasn't bad, only that Castro
wasn't the most desirable alternative from our point of view.
And so when he seized power a little more than two years ago
my people weren't surprised when he turned out to be a Marxist-
Leninist and when he pretty rapidly joined the Soviet camp.
There was a great hue and cry in this country, but we—and I
claim this with no special sense of pride—we had foreseen
these developments.

"Well, in March of last year the CIA set up a military training
program for the Cuban exiles who wished to enroll in it. We
opened up camps in Florida, and, with the approval of their
governments, Guatemala and Nicaragua. Now our reason for
mounting this training program was simply to prepare for the
time when the Cuban people would rise up against Castro.
Vice President Nixon's memorandum specified that—and I quote
him now—the United States should provide assistance to those
Cubans who wish to return to their homeland to aid in the
struggle for Cuban freedom. The United States did not fight

* Why Prescott gave the initials rather than the names of these men
is a mystery.—N.F.M.

a war to rid Cuba of one tyranny so that, sixty years later, she would fall victim to another.

"We currently have some fifteen thousand Cuban exiles, all young and eager, under arms and in various stages of training and proficiency. So far as they are concerned I would say, yes, they, or most of them, are ready to go in and fight. They are well led and know what to do.

"Mr. President, I would urge that they go in within two to three weeks. The moment is critical. The guerrillas in the Escombrey Mountains and elsewhere are strong and await the signal to come down. The cities will rise up simultaneously. Our operatives there tell me that discontent is rife, though it must remain invisible for fear of the secret police, who are ubiquitous.

"The police apparatus, I should add, is Castro's one major achievement so far. Colonel Senyov of Russian intelligence—whom I got to know in the last war, a very able man—has been instructing the Castro people on how to organize an effective secret police force.

"Here, then, is what I urge, Mr. President. The exiles must land in Cuba before the month is out. The United States must lend them air and naval cover so that they can secure a beachhead and commence the march inland toward Havana. As they do so, another force will march down from the mountains. Uprisings, meanwhile, will take place in the army and in the cities. The chances of success are excellent. It'll be like the landing of William of Orange in England in 1688."

"Thank you, Mr. Dulles," the President said. "Are there any comments?"

B. B. A———— spoke. "I agree entirely with Mr. Dulles's analysis and recommendation. All I want to know is this. What kind of government will replace Castro? I think we'll have some responsibility in choosing it, or seeing to it that it's one compatible with our interests."

"The administration has given the matter considerable thought," said MacGeorge Bundy, who addressed his listeners in the sharp, abrupt manner that he had acquired during his years as a dean of students in four Ivy League colleges. "We'll settle for nothing less than a liberal democratic government, one that guarantees free elections and civil liberties. We're not as stuck as our predecessors were on returning the nationalized industries to American firms. We'll insist only on reasonable compensation."

"That's exactly right," Rusk added. "And Mr. Dulles, your men have weeded out the most notorious of the Batista followers from the training program, haven't they?"

"So far as I know, Mr. Secretary, they have, yes. But sometimes it's difficult, and we've found that the people who worked for Batista have proved the most experienced in handling arms, in giving commands, and the like. The top echelons of the exile army are, I believe, anti-Batista."

"What we have, then," Arthur Schlesinger, Jr., said, investing the discussion with larger significance, "is the vital center, the democratic way between totalitarian extremes among the exiles. And when they assume power they will maintain the vital center as their controlling ideology."

"Why, yes, I would say so," Dulles agreed.

"Before we go any further in this colloquy I have a few questions, Mr. President," said Senator Fulbright, who had been listening with his eyes half closed, his head resting on his hand. Kennedy had expected Fulbright to raise some questions. In Washington circles, Fulbright was known as the "invincible skeptic" because of his tendency to disbelieve official reports. ("Ninety-nine per cent of what the government tells us on foreign policy," he once said, "is either unintentional distortion or wish-fulfillment.")

Fulbright was also known as the "old republican" because of his fear, expressed in numerous speeches and articles, that America's role in world affairs might bring down its republican institutions. "When democracies become empires," he had written in an article in *International Relations,* "they become their own opposites; they lose their freedom and degenerate into the worst kinds of despotism—the despotism of the dictator and the mob at home and the rapacious aggressor abroad. Empires as degenerate democracies are set on an irreversible course of expansion and repression, and they end up in a flaming holocaust of revolution, civil war, disintegration. Does the United States imagine she is exempt from the rules of history?"

Kennedy had asked Fulbright to attend the Security Council meeting on Cuba for personal and political reasons. He liked the ex-scholar and law school dean, and he wanted maximum con-gressional support for his foreign policy.

"Now Mr. Dulles, I wonder how you can be so certain that the Cuban people, or a sizable number of them, are ready to rise up against Castro. I've read some of the European press, and their correspondents—and they're pretty reliable and ob-jective—insist that he's popular. They cite the fact that he's armed hundreds of thousands of common people, since he be-lieves the United States is going to attack him. Our papers have been calling him a lunatic for saying that. These days the lunatics seem to be the only ones who can anticipate the future.

"In other words, Mr. Dulles, I wonder if your operatives down there are telling you and the President what you want to hear rather than what's really going on. I'd like to know from Mr. Rusk what the situation is. Is Castro that unpopular? Is he oppressing the people, as we've been told? Now, I don't care for Castro worth a dime. I'd like to see him deposed tomorrow. But I'm not the Cuban people. I hear—and I admit I don't have well-paid, highly professional operatives—I hear that they like what he's doing. They aren't especially offended that he's a Marxist-Leninist, works with the Communists, and gets help from the Russians.

"And I might add here, while I'm being the devil's advo-cate—someone should be—that in his relations with us Castro hasn't been completely in the wrong. We've been at least partly guilty, partly responsible for alienating him over the past two years. I'm not going to mention what we've been doing to Cuba in the last fifty, though that can't be omitted from the picture either.

"Finally—I'll be done in a minute, I can see you're all straining at the bit to devour me—let me ask you this. Suppose after the exiles go in, and there is a general rising, suppose a full-scale conflict breaks out between the pro- and anti-Castro forces. Will the United States enter that war? What I'm supposing, hypothetically, is that this thing may get bogged down and drag us into it. That would be a pretty nasty situation. I'm sure, Mr. President, you've thought about that eventuality.

"Now, remember, I'm not arguing a case here so much as raising questions. But, for the record, so there's no misunderstanding, let me say I'm dead set against any invasion, and I think the training camps should be shut down. Thank you for your patience in hearing me out."

Dulles was the first to reply. "Senator, your questions are very pertinent. But I have complete confidence in our men. I have gone over their reports very carefully, you can be sure of that. They are based on the most scrupulous acquisition and analysis of the facts. As for the rest, they are policy matters and are outside my purview."

Rusk spoke next. "Senator, the political analysts in the department have arrived at mixed conclusions. Castro does seem popular with the peasants and some workers, but he's definitely out of favor with the middle class, which is the largest in Latin America. He's getting rid of the middle class by forcing them to leave the country. His active opponents he puts in prison. He—"

"Let me interrupt you, Mr. Secretary," Fulbright rejoined. "Do you think a landing will trigger a general rising? Do you think the insurgents in the mountains are a real danger? Can you tell us one way or the other?"

"I, well, no, I can't say with certainty," Rusk answered hesitantly. "Again our reports are mixed. I, too, have the utmost confidence in the CIA. Personally, I have some doubts about a mass uprising. Then again, a lot more people might join the anti-Castro movement once there's an invasion."

"In other words," Fulbright said, "you're willing to take your chance on a bloodbath there."

"Well, Senator, I believe the risk is worth taking anyway. Civil wars aren't children's games. A people should be willing to fight for their freedom."

Walt Whitman Rostow, a widely respected and brilliantly persuasive expert on economic development, broke in.

"Well said, Mr. Secretary—if I may contribute my own mite to the discussion. My position is this. We are presented with an accomplished fact. Cuba is today a satellite of the Soviet Union, operating in full freedom in the Caribbean and Latin America. When the Soviet Union faced the prospect of having a neutralist regime—not an anti-Soviet regime, mind you—she crushed that regime with impunity. The world was shocked, horrified, as it should have been, and then it forgot. Here we have something much worse. We have an anti-American regime, ninety miles from our shores, securing arms and materiel from our opponent, its ambition to subvert the whole hemisphere, from the Rio Grande to Tierra del Fuego.

"I'm not absolving American big business and the previous administration from their guilt in having helped bring this situation to its present pass. But this is what we confront, here and now. After all, none of us asked to be born into the twentieth century, when the United States emerged as a world power. Yet here we are, responsible at this moment for the nation's fate. The rest—and I say this with all due respect to you, Senator, whom I have admired ever since you were elected to Congress—the rest involves abstract issues of moral right and justice which simply do not apply in this situation."

"I'm humbled by your admiration for me, Mr. Rostow," Fulbright replied, "and I might say I've admired your books, though I found nothing in them that would prepare me for the argument you're advancing now.

"As I understand it, you're saying—in this particular instance, to be sure—that might is everything, right nothing. Or, to put it more exactly, right is the exercise of *American* might. If that's so, what's all the fuss about in the Cold War? The only difference between Russia and us is that they're Russians and have their interests and we're Americans and have ours. If that's what we genuinely think, fine. Only the American people should be told that they've been living—and dying for—a lie for the last fifteen years. We're just another powerful nation seeking to lord it over the weak and over those who stand in our way.

"Now I can argue against the thesis that might is right, our country right or wrong, and so forth—it's what Plato's *Republic* is all about. I just want to be sure that's the thesis you gentlemen have. Mr. Rostow, you put your finger right on the problem. I don't see how your position allows you to say a word of criticism against the Russian invasions of East Berlin and Hungary, or against China's massacres in Tibet. Might makes right."

"Senator, I think you're being carried away by your eloquence and by your skill as a debater," L. D. G——— said sonorously.

"Walt Rostow, as usual, was too logical, too lucid. I don't think at all that he was implying might makes right—."

"He didn't have to imply it," Fulbright shot back, "it was the whole thrust of his argument."

"Well, Senator, I have to disagree with you. What Walt was saying, if I understood him correctly—and I've had the pleasure of knowing him for twenty years, incidentally—was that power imposes certain obligations. Might serves to temper or condition right, to concretize it. Anybody will be right if he removes himself from the marketplace, if he's powerless. It's more difficult if he's in the thick of things, if he has all kinds of responsibilities. When the United States was a small, isolated country, sure, we could make all those great pronouncements about the rights of man. The Monroe Doctrine would have been remembered as pure swagger if another country, England, hadn't enforced it. She exerted the might. We took credit for the right.

"Well, we're a mighty power today, and, as Walt said, we have no choice but to act like one. Past generations worked and bled to hand down the legacy of power to us. Our task, I think, is to draw a balance between our ideals of right and the burdens that our position in the universe compel us to assume. Russia doesn't bother to draw a balance because her ideals are entirely subordinate to the claims of her power."

"My God," Fulbright said wearily, "what a tissue of platitudes. If I had time I'd try to pick your argument apart piece by piece. Have you ever bothered to argue with a Communist? It might be a valuable experience. Do you think he'd admit that Russia's ideals are subordinate to its power, but that the United States draws a balance between them? Substitute some of the terms and facts and a Soviet apologist would say the same thing you said, Mr. G———. That's how he'd explain away every crime committed by Russia since 1917, you know, the purges, the slaughter of the farmers, Berlin, Hungary, Finland, and so on. The same can be said of Nazi Germany, Fascist Italy, and so on. I'm rather shocked by this colloquy, to tell the truth."

"Let me remind you, Senator Fulbright, this is not a classroom, and we're not studying the *Republic* under your tutelage," B. B. A———, himself a professor of public law and government, said sternly. "I'd like to point out that at this very moment Castro has thousands of his agents in Latin America, fomenting trouble wherever they can find it or stir it up. Many times he's stated his intentions to 'bring the United States down.' His sidekick, Che Guevara, who's even more fanatical, promises to kindle brush fires throughout this hemisphere. Even the cities of the United States, he says, aren't immune. I quote a story in yesterday's press: 'In his speech to the Youth League Señor Guevara likened the United States to "a powder keg." "In the slums, among the black people, the workers, the poor, discontent borders on revolution," he said. "We Cubans will work with our revolutionary comrades in the United States. The overthrow of capitalism is the death of imperialism."'"

"In other words, Mr. A———," Fulbright said, looking down over his glasses, "as an expert on South America you judge Castro a clear and present threat to our safety. You think Castro's agents will produce revolutions in South America and in this country as well. You take Guevara's rhetoric to be deeds and policies. I'm rather astonished that a man of your sobriety and wisdom could succumb to the prevailing hysteria. Haven't we become obsessive about this little man who rules a little island? I'm afraid what we've done is accept him at *his* valuation. In making a colossus out of him we hardly do ourselves credit as a balanced and cool-headed people. How will we act if we come up against a truly great country? I tremble when I reflect on it."

"May I break in here for a moment?" Army Chief of Staff Hiram Horvitzer, the soft-spoken chairman of the Joint Chiefs of Staff, asked. "Senator, I'd like to return to one of the problems you raised a while back. You wondered what we would do if the Cuban operation succeeded partially, if it got bogged down in a protracted civil war. Would we join the anti-Castro army or watch from the sidelines? Well, to pose the question this way is to answer it. I'm for throwing everything we have into it at the outset and get it over with as quickly as possible. We should prevent a civil war. Our paratroopers and mobile units could be ready within twenty-four hours."

The other members of the Joint Chiefs nodded their heads vigorously.

"And the Russians should be told very plainly to keep their noses out of it," Admiral George H. Anderson, Jr., added.

"I disagree with the Chiefs," Robert Kennedy said in a rasping voice. "Let's keep in mind the reasons for the invasion. It's to support the efforts of Cuban insurgents. We want Castro out because he's a tyrant over his own people and an ideological menace to the rest of Latin America. Send in an American army and Castro would become a great hero to the Latin Americans. Imagine the outpouring of anti-Americanism? The Alliance for Progress would be finished. It would take years to repair the damage. The operation has to be surgically clean, and it has to be carried out by the Cubans themselves."

In brief statements MacNamara and Dillon agreed with Robert Kennedy.

"But what if the invaders fail in their objective?" General Horvitzer persisted.

"That's possible," Robert replied, "but Mr. Dulles led me to believe that they won't fail. If we thought there was a good chance of failure then we wouldn't be here and there wouldn't be an invasion. Am I correct in assuming this, Mr. President?"

"Yes," Kennedy said. "That's why I said at the beginning that the moment is critical and that I must make a determination right now. As Mr. Dulles pointed out, unless the invasion is launched within the next few weeks the moment will be lost. And if there are no further comments, I'll explain why I've decided to go ahead with the operation.

"I've done so after taking into account all your objections, Bill. In the first place we've got to demonstrate to the Cuban people that we're solidly behind them, in deeds no less than in words. Second, we've got to demonstrate to Castro and the Soviets our determination to uphold the Monroe Doctrine. The Soviets are not going to gain a foothold in this hemisphere, not while I have anything to say about our policy. Third, it will serve notice to Latin American governments that they can count on us in resisting their own Castroite movements. It will discourage the revolutionists and bolster the moderates and liberals. Fourth, it will strengthen my own hand when I go to Europe next month and talk with De Gaulle and Khrushchev. One of our chief problems in dealing with them is that our country has lost so much of its prestige in the last five years, while Russia's prestige has risen.

"These are the reasons that prompt me to order the invasion to proceed as scheduled.

"Now I want it to be absolutely clear that it is to be a limited operation. We'll give the invaders as much naval and air support as they need to secure the beachhead. But from then on they're mostly on their own. Not a single American soldier is going to be involved. That's definite and irreversible, and the exile army knows it. If there is a protracted conflict we'll provide aid to the rebels but no troops. The exiles know this too.

"And, oh yes, one more thing. Arthur, I want you to compose a white paper on the U.S. position toward Cuba. Have it ready for release within three weeks. You know what to include—how Castro betrayed the revolution by going over to the Communists and the Soviet Union, how we wished him success at first and then turned away in disgust, how he deliberately brought on the conflict, provoked the confrontation, and so forth. Conclude by emphasizing that the United States desires a true democracy in Cuba and will do everything to ensure its viability, that we deplore Batistaism on the right and Castroism on the left, and that what we want is liberal democracy, the vital center. You're very good at putting these things together. The white paper will present our case to the world.

"All right, that's all I have now. The meeting is adjourned."

That the United States was preparing some kind of action against Castro was scarcely a secret. Talk of an imminent invasion filled the air in Washington and other capitals. Detailed reports on the CIA training camps were published in a number of journals. Every day the Castro government warned the Cuban people to expect the worst—that is, a full-scale American assault. Soviet, Czech, and East German arms, from tanks to rifles, were brought into Cuba, and the militia, reputedly half a million strong, was placed on standby alert.

At his April 12 news conference Kennedy emphatically denied that the United States would intervene in Cuba. "Our policy is hands off," he declared, "and if Castro leaves us alone, we'll leave him alone. No group of exiles will be dispatched from U.S. territory to recover their homeland. The only place in

Cuba that American military personnel will ever go while I'm President is the Guantánamo Naval Base."

Minutes before the press conference, however, Kennedy had asked the editors and bureau chiefs of several leading newspapers to suppress reports recently filed by their correspondents on CIA-directed invasion plans. "I'm not saying such plans are in the works," Kennedy told them in a strictly off-the-record conference. "It's only that our security would be impaired if these stories are published. You might consider this interference with freedom of the press, and in a sense it is. But such freedoms have to be balanced against the security needs of this country, and the need, possibly, to save lives. I'm not at liberty to say any more."

The operation began on April 15, when CIA planes flying from Florida, bombed Cuban airfields. Their mission was to destroy the nine propeller-driven bombers of the Cuban air force. But the Cubans, anticipating just such an attack, had hidden their planes, and none was touched. The American government claimed that the attack had been made by Cuban planes flown by defecting pilots of the Cuban air force.

This was the explanation presented to the world by Adlai Stevenson, ambassador to the United Nations, after the Cuban ambassador, Achille Boa, had accused the United States of bombing Cuba preparatory to an invasion, and had gone on to demand a plenary session of the Assembly to take up the charge of aggression. Stevenson, who knew nothing about the impending invasion, indignantly denied everything.

"I'm tired of these outrageous, utterly defamatory accusations," Stevenson said. "Let the wind rise to more than five knots an hour over sunny Havana, and Señor Boa will blame the United States. Do you suffer from poor sugar crops? Blame the United States. Admit it, sir, you and your leader see hobgoblins and demons and fiery devils, all dressed up as Uncle Sam, all emanating from the same source—your own heated and quite distempered brains."

Then, pointing to blown-up photographs, Stevenson proved to the other delegates of the Security Council that the planes, which were marked with Cuban insignia, could not have been American.

"Not that I expect irrefutable facts to change the Cuban ambassador's mind."

"I always thought Mr. Stevenson was an honorable man,"
Boa replied with a sneer, "one of the few left in the American
government. I now see I am wrong. Or maybe Mr. Stevenson
himself has been deceived."

Two days after the bombing and strafing attack, sixteen
hundred "freedom fighters" assembled near a fleet of small
boats in a concealed cove somewhere on the coast of Nicaragua.
Their commander read a message from the President. "God
speed. May your efforts to free your people meet with rapid
success. Our hearts and hopes go with you. The United States
is one with you."

Their spirits were high as they approached the Bay of Pigs
(Bahía des Cochinos) on the southern coast of Cuba. Meanwhile, a hundred transmitters from Florida, Central America,
and the Caribbean were informing the Cuban people that their
liberation was at hand. "The war of national freedom is on!
Rise up, Cubans, against your tyrant and his lackeys! Join
the patriots who have landed on your shores! Redeem beloved
Cuba!"

The invasion was a fiasco from the start. Having landed, the
"patriots" found themselves in an impenetrable, snake-infested
swamp. "We have moved in, but can we move out?" Major
Fuego lamented.

When a company of local militia arrived they did not embrace
the invaders but shot at them. More militia arrived, and the
fighting intensified. Their food and ammunition nearly exhausted,
the invaders pleaded for American assistance—for more supplies,
more men, above all, for air support. Nothing was forthcoming.
By the time Castro's army laboriously make its way down to
the Bay of Pigs, the invaders—those who had not fled, drowned,
or been shot—twelve hundred in all, were ready to surrender.

On April 20, before a wildly cheering crowd in Havana's
Hidalgo Square, Castro announced that the invasion had been
"liquidated" and "the running dogs of American imperialism"
dealt a "death blow."

It was Kennedy, however, who had decided that the invasion

should be "liquidated." Told on the morning of April 18 that no general uprising, or sign of one, had taken place in Cuba, he concluded that the situation was hopeless. Later that day he peremptorily turned down the invaders' plea for help. He told Dulles: "I wish I could save them, but I'm not going to be euchred into a war fought in the mountains and swamps of Cuba. Close it out and pick up as many of the broken pieces as you can."

The recriminations began to fly as soon as the public learned of the fiasco. One columnist held Stevenson responsible, alleging that Stevenson called the President in the middle of the night to demand that the invasion be halted and American support for it withdrawn or he would resign as ambassador to the United Nations. Another columnist claimed that Kennedy was about to send in planes and ships and technical personnel, but a telegram from Khrushchev threatening "retaliatory action" stopped him "cold in his tracks." Others blamed the CIA for "botching up the operation." Still others blamed the Cuban émigrés for their "incompetence and bickering."

Kennedy moved swiftly to calm the tempest of public opinion. He conferred separately with the most highly respected statesmen in the country, including ex-Presidents Hoover and Eisenhower, General Douglas MacArthur, Richard Nixon, twelve governors, the heads of several of the largest corporations, and the minority leaders of both houses of Congress, explaining to each of them why the invasion failed and why he refused to commit American troops. Each of them promised their support during the "crisis."

Kennedy also went on the air to tell the American people that he and he alone was responsible for what had happened. "The President," he said, "makes the executive decisions of our government, and he, consequently, bears the blame for them when they go badly, just as he receives the credit for them when they go well. If you must find fault for the defeat at the Bay of Pigs, find it with me, no one else."

But the public did not blame him. On the contrary, as columnist Monroe Asch wrote later, "The genius of John F. Kennedy is his capacity to turn adversity to good account. Almost any other President would have suffered gravely for the

error he committed, the seriousness of which should not be
minimized. But, if anything, his popularity has grown since
the Bay of Pigs. The attitude of the man in the street is:
'Anyone can make a mistake. It takes a man to own up to
it.' "

Privately, Kennedy was "boiling mad," as one newspaper described it. "You know why it's my fault?" he asked his brother and
his closest military aide, General Maxwell Taylor. "Because I
trusted the experts. I should have followed my intuitions. When
Bill Fulbright spoke out that day he echoed my feelings. That's
the truth. The trouble is, I wanted to be told what Dulles and Rusk
and the others told me. My hopes, not my intelligence, dictated
my action. Remember what Dad used to say to us: give twice as
much consideration to your enemy's argument as to your friend's.
Well, I forgot that piece of advice.

"And I'm goddamned mad at the CIA too. What the hell are
they getting so much money for? This much I'm going to insist on
now, that they stick to gathering facts, not recommending policy.
If we don't chop them down a notch or two they'll be running the
foreign affairs of this country.

"Now, Max, I would like you to head up a special investigation
to look into the whole Cuban business, what went wrong, and so
on, from top to bottom. And I'd like you to suggest changes in the
CIA, such as the one I've mentioned. I'd appreciate it if you
could have the report by the end of the year. Dulles'll be out by
then. First the U-2, then this. Something's rotten in our intelligence system."

Kennedy did not forget the invaders who had been captured
in the Bay of Pigs. He explicitly warned Castro that the United
States would not "tolerate" their execution. "If Castro chooses to
treat them as traitors rather than prisoners of war then he, and
unfortunately the Cuban people too, will suffer the consequences."

Castro denounced Kennedy's "idle threats." "Our revolutionary
tribunals," Castro declared defiantly, "will mete out revolutionary
justice." But in the course of an eight-hour May Day speech before a million people, he said the twelve hundred prisoners might
prove useful to the revolution. "In prison they are an expense and
an encumbrance. Dead they are worthless. Alive they might be

exchanged for tractors and equipment. How much are these pathetic mercenaries worth to the imperialists? A tractor for a traitor—that is not extravagant."

Kennedy immediately took up the offer. After much haggling and recrimination the Cuban and American governments eventually came to terms on the precise fee. The prisoners were at last ransomed and returned to the United States, thus closing the last chapter in the invasion of the Bay of Pigs.

4

PARIS AND VIENNA

A FEW days after Castro announced the surrender of the invasion force Khrushchev met with his two trusted associates, Deputy Premier Anastas Mikoyan and his son-in-law (and now *Pravda* editor as well) Alexei Adjhubei, in the Kremlin "vault," the name given to the Party Secretary's lead-and-concrete-enclosed basement office. Lately, Khrushchev had been holding his important conferences there.

"Don't be alarmed, comrades," he said, leaning forward on his chair, his arms resting on the huge steel table in the center of the room, "there's no emergency. In fact some good luck has fallen in our lap. As a child I learned that fortune comes to those who need it most—if they are ready. Let me explain.

"An hour ago Comrades Chou and Liu denounced us before the Peking Peasants and Workers' Council. Here's an excerpt from Chou's speech. 'The imperialists are on the run. The defeat of the criminal mercenaries in Cuba exposes the U.S. aggressors as paper tigers. Paper tigers scare the weak. Paper tigers collapse when challenged by the strong. Yet among us are many weak comrades who cower and hide when the paper tiger raises its tail. They are the opportunists and revisionists who preach such despicable nonsense as peaceful coexistence and disarmament.'

"And so on and on and on. Blah, blah, blah.

"The handwriting is on the wall," Khrushchev continued. "Mao's preparing for an open break with us. He's already dividing our camp. The slant-eyed bastards are stirring up trouble everywhere. Tomorrow Kadar will order the whole yellow mission to leave Budapest. Encouraged by Mao, our Albanian friends—they're half human, you know—are thumbing their dirty noses at us, swaggering like the hooligans they are. If I had my way I'd make short work of those goatherds. Whenever I meet Hoxha I smell manure. At the next Congress I'm going to read him out of the movement.

"And what about the vultures in our own back yard? So far they haven't *done* anything. They're talking, concocting rumors about me, falsifications. But I'm watching them. Agrinov's men found the following note in the desk drawer of a Party official who works in this building, right under our noses. You see, written across the top it says, 'Type and run off on machine.' Let me read it to you.

" 'We Party members should not allow ourselves to be deceived. Why is agricultural production lagging? Why the shortage of wheat, butter, eggs, meat? You are led to believe that it is due to the incompetence and corruption of officials in the Ministry of Agriculture. You are told that their removal and arrest (eighteen so far) and replacement by better people will solve the problem. Nonsense! They can be replaced by eighteen, twenty-five, fifty of the best people in the Soviet Union, all of them Lenins, and the agricultural problems will still be unsolved. The reason is that the incompetence and wrong-headedness is located closer to the top, among the comrades who set policy but are immune from blame. Naturally, they blame others. Wait for further information on the great agricultural disaster of the 1960s. You will be shocked.'

"Memoranda like this are circulating in many places. I have an idea where most of them originate."

"Why don't you have them arrested, Father?" Adjhubei asked indignantly.

"You think I should go after Kosygin, Ustinov, Novikov, and Ignatov? What do you advise, Anastas Ignatz?"

"I say you should give them enough rope," Mikoyan said. "It's good to know who and where they are. Let a hundred flowers grow. As long as they're no threat and obey orders, I say leave them alone. Only watch them like a falcon and strike when you have to."

"Right. Very good. Besides, I need them now. A purge would wreck the agricultural and industrial programs. It would kill the reforms. If they try sabotage I'll deal with them sternly. They know Agrinov's watching them. That should be enough. 'The knout is better seen than applied.'"

"I understand what you are saying, Father," Adjhubei said, "but I don't understand what you meant when you said good luck has suddenly fallen in your lap."

"I was getting to that. From what I've just told you it follows as spring follows winter that what we, the government, need now is a healthy show of strength against the United States. When Mao tried to challenge the United States over Quemoy and Matsu he looked like a fool. The paper mouse lost to the paper tiger. But we will act like a real bear. I'm going to bring the Berlin question to a head when I meet Kennedy in Vienna. He's going to think a wall fell on him. I'll throw the fear of God into the Americans. The time's ripe for it.

"That's where our good luck comes in. The Cuban adventure's sent Kennedy reeling. Personally, I think he's mostly bravura, a mock hero who wilts in the heat. My April 17th telegram made him sweat—Balabanski swears to it.

"If I win over Berlin, over Germany, I'll be able to deal with our comrades here and in China. With a stronger hand I'll be able to knock some sense into their thick skulls. 'Persuasion,' my old father taught me, 'is a heavy fist.'"

"Yes, of course, I agree with you," Adjhubei said, "but remember, Father, there are many maniacs in America. They would attack Kennedy for being a coward. Who knows what they might do? He might try to prove to everybody, to himself, that he's a man. After his defeat in Cuba he might want the chance to 'stand up to the Communists,' as they say in America. That's good politics there."

"Don't you think I've thought of that?" Khrushchev answered sharply. "All right, Kennedy has problems. So do I. Should I be careful not to embarrass him even if it hurts me? Why didn't he worry about embarrassing *me* when he sent those pirates into Cuba? The trouble with Americans is that they think they're invincible. If they are maniacs it's because they know nothing about the real world, which is full of setbacks and disappointments. When they fight the Indians or Mexicans or Spanish they strut like Prometheans. Limits? They don't know what it means.

Well, it's about time they learned the meaning of limits the hard way. The world is not their sugar field.

"Soon I'll tell them a secret. I'll tell them I have bombs that can sink the whole continent of North America. Not even the worst of the maniacs will fail to draw lessons from that fact. Our Chinese comrades will draw profitable lessons also. Mao will piss against the wind. The Soviet Union will again show everyone who and what she is. The time is propitious. World public opinion" [. . .]*

To Kennedy, Paris was no mere stopover on the way to Vienna. Of late he had been receiving alarming reports from his State Department analysts on the deterioration of United States-French relations. The most recent report, in the form of a personal letter, came from the ambassador to France, Winslow Andrew Barton, a close friend of Kennedy's ever since prep school days.

"From what I could piece together (not always easy; Paris sometimes feels like an enemy camp) De Gaulle has his course of action worked out for the next ten years or so. He expects to live well into his eighties. 'If Adenauer can do it, so can I,' he is reported to have said. He is completing the first phase of his long-range plan. When Algeria becomes independent he will have rid France of her colonial inheritance. Of course, the generals and the extreme right, who put him in power to preserve that inheritance and, in the process, destroy democracy (succeeding where the Dreyfus Affair failed), now seek his destruction. But the French people, tired of foreign colonial wars, are behind him overwhelmingly. And he is a brilliant strategist, moving his pieces at his own pace, slowly here, swiftly there, like Napolean at Austerlitz. I believe he will prevail over the generals and the right.

"The second phase might be called the epoch of French grandeur. It may sound wild to you, Mr. President, but De Gaulle imagines himself a second Charlemagne. He regards it as no accident that his name, too, is Charles. Here again, he will employ any means to gain his ends. He will change directions overnight, contradict himself, disavow promises, anything.

"What is his objective? As far as I can tell it is to raise France to the status of paramount power on the European continent,

* Two pages of Prescott's manuscript are lost.—N.F.M.

and the European continent, it may interest you to learn, he defines as that area of 'Western Christendom,' Catholic, Protestant, and Orthodox, embracing the entire area from the English Channel to the Ural Mountains.

"De Gaulle thinks that two essential conditions must be met before he can accomplish this objective. First, France must be completely unified and obedient to his will. He has set forth a system of paternalistic justice designed to overcome class, regional, and ethnic divisions and so bring about the desired unity and solidarity. Second, he must keep Europe safe for the Europeans. That is to say, anyone who threatens to upset his calculations must be removed from the scene or prevented from entering it. He will not let Britain enter the Common Market in the event Britain requests admission. He will one day try to kick the United States out of Europe, his hope being, in fact, to dissolve NATO altogether. But he does not want us out yet—not until we have compelled Russia to retreat from East Germany, Poland and the other satellites.

"That is why De Gaulle and Adenauer are so closely allied at the moment. Adenauer's tough anti-Communist posture, his refusal to make any concessions to the East Germans and Russians, suits De Gaulle's plan fine—now. For De Gaulle's plan is to stop the United States and the Soviet Union from reaching an agreement of any sort at Europe's expense. In other words, De Gaulle assumes that if the two superpowers withdraw France will fill the vacuum. France will establish her own hegemony over an independent Europe, the equal in every way of the two giants lying at her eastern and western flanks.

"In some ways, I should add, he sees the United States—or the Anglo-Saxons, for he thinks the British our servitors; at best, our racial kinsmen—as a greater long-term threat to his ambitions than the Soviet Union. He is convinced that if Europe does emerge, under his tutelage, as a third force in the world, the Soviet Union would, in time, come apart at the seams. The Soviet Union, he maintains, is inherently unstable. It keeps its separate nationalities together mainly by force, and by the conviction that it commands respect and deference. Once that conviction disappears, force alone would be an insufficient 'integument'—one of his favorite words—to keep Soviet society from dissolving into its component units: White Russia, the Ukraine, the Baltic countries, Georgia, Uzbekistan, Azerbaijan, etc. These would then be welcomed into the third-force bloc, or greater Christian Europe, presided over by France and, if he lives, Charlemagne the Second.

"Do you think this is fictitious, Mr. President? Let me assure you it is not. I have spoken to enough people, some of them well placed (see accompanying packet), to persuade me beyond a shadow of a doubt that French grandeur, spelled out in the foregoing terms, is De Gaulle's life goal, the fixed basis of his policies, foreign and domestic. I hope, Mr. President, that the views expressed here will help you anticipate some of the issues that may arise in your upcoming talks with him."

When Kennedy read the ambassador's letter he told Rusk he would need "a hell of a long time to ponder its frightening implications." A week before leaving for Paris he received an "in depth" briefing from a battery of State Department experts on European affairs [. . .]

To the French public the Kennedys' visit was comparable, in the words of *La Terre,* to "the liberation of Paris or Lindbergh's landing." Every magazine carried feature stories on the young Kennedys, in particular "Jackie," the President's handsome, rather exotic-looking wife. The obsession with "Jackie" prompted Kennedy to state at the airport, in his best deadpan style, that he had come to France as "Mrs. Kennedy's escort," that Mrs. Kennedy wanted to "drop in on the President and Mme. de Gaulle, do some shopping, and visit some museums, operas, and ballets."

While the windswept audience laughed at these remarks—all of France would the next day—De Gaulle, who stood at Kennedy's side, gave no hint of a smile. Looking down at Kennedy with raised eyebrows from his full height of six feet, six inches, De Gaulle seemed even more disdainful and reproving than usual.

The Kennedys' three-day stay in Paris was full of pomp and ceremony and fuss. Wherever they went they were besieged by regiments of eager photographers and reporters. Practically, this was the sum and substance of their visit to Paris. On several occasions Kennedy sought to engage De Gaulle in private discussions. Only once did De Gaulle permit himself a brief exchange of political views. It took place on the evening the De Gaulles and the Kennedys returned to the Élysée Palace after seeing a spectacular Paris Ballet production of *Les Sylphides* at the Opéra Comique. While their wives talked in the elegant Cardinal Mazarin Room the two men sipped cognac in the Clemenceau Library.

Kennedy asked: "Do you think, M. le Président, that there's any substance to reports of serious differences between our countries, or rather governments?"

De Gaulle smiled. "La Bruyere, one of our great moralists and men of wisdom, wrote: 'Genuine friends will bring to light their most trivial differences. Masters and slaves will conceal the truth from each other.' Being friends we have differences, of course, and we owe it to each other openly and freely to reveal them."

"Yes, you're absolutely right," Kennedy said, "and speaking for the United States I can truthfully say I'm not aware of any serious differences with France. I therefore infer from what you've just said that such differences or grievances as do exist are on France's side."

"Well, Mr. President, you are the best judge of whether the United States has any grievances against France, whether, as yokefellows, we are pulling together. As your yokefellow my complaint is less over what you are doing than over your intentions for the future. I shall speak in earnest with you. France entertains no apprehensions for herself. She is capable of caring for her interests and, if it came to it, defending herself against an aggressor, for, at an extremity, she can bring into play the most sophisticated weapons. France is, however, apprehensive about the *possible* conduct—and, believe me, Mr. President, I lay the heaviest stress on the word *possible*—of her great and true ally, the United States.

"France is committed categorically to the position taken by Chancellor Adenauer that no compromise with the Soviet Union can be made over East Germany and Berlin. What France certainly would find intolerable—I tell you this, Mr. President, as a point of information—what she would find intolerable is an arrangement between the United States and the Soviet Union that would sacrifice the independence and integrity of West Berlin, and, at the same time, acknowledge the legitimacy of the East German regime.

"Now, Mr. President, I am not suggesting that you wish to enter into such an arrangement. France's apprehensions have grown because of remarks that certain traveling statesmen in your Party have recently dropped. Some of your senators—their names escape me—have come out in favor of negotiations on Berlin, and—"

"Mansfield and Fulbright."

"Yes, they, and they have led a number of people in our Foreign Office to wonder if, perhaps, they were speaking for you."

"No, President de Gaulle, they spoke for themselves. It's the President of the United States who alone makes foreign policy. I've heard nothing about any arrangements with the Soviets on Berlin and East Germany. Frankly, I don't know what Khrushchev and I will talk about at Vienna. This much I will say, quite candidly. There's no reason why outstanding differences between the Soviet Union and the States cannot be discussed. In full consultation, of course, with all of the NATO allies and West Germany.

"There's no thought, no possibility whatever, of internationalizing Berlin on Soviet terms. I'm rather surprised that such apprehensions can be entertained in responsible quarters. The United States will neither abandon Western Europe nor make deals behind its back, both of which propositions obviously underlay the fears of your Foreign Office people. What is eminently negotiable with the Soviet Union is a scaling-down of the arms race. That's what's primarily on our minds, and I hope Premier Khrushchev is amenable when I see him in Vienna."

"Certainly, certainly, Mr. President, disarmament is an admirable hope. But I trust you realize that France cannot be bound by any disarmament terms to which she has not given her explicit approval. The nations who possess Priapus missiles and hydrogen bombs have every right, indeed obligation, to impose limits upon themselves through mutual agreement. They have no right to impose them on other nations. To freeze armaments at a given level would leave those who have not yet acquired them at the mercy of those who have."

"But M. le Président," Kennedy said, staring intently into De

Gaulle's heavy-lidded eyes set in pools of dark grey, "that's an invitation to extend the arms race indefinitely. I don't really understand why a small country would want nuclear arms. After all—"

"Pardon me, Mr. President," De Gaulle interrupted, stiffening his back, "by small country do you mean any country other than the United States and the Soviet Union?"

"I mean—"

Just then Mme. de Gaulle, followed by Mrs. Kennedy, opened the door unannounced and strode into the room.

"Charles," Mme. de Gaulle said brusquely, "I think the Kennedys are tired. They have a heavy schedule ahead of them. Why don't you let them retire for the night?"

Riding back to the American embassy, Kennedy asked his wife: "Do you think she broke in on me by prearrangement? I have a feeling the general instructed her to barge in that way."

"You may be right, dear. I noticed her constantly looking at her watch as she sipped her Hennessey. Then she suddenly got up and said we must both be exhausted, poor dears, and she would tell the President, who's a tyrant of a talker, to release you."

"That cagey old bastard," Kennedy said, pursing his lips.

The Kennedys arrived at the Vienna airport in a cold driving June rain. They were met by a huge Austrian delegation, a sea of black umbrellas. "I assure you, Mr. President, the people of Vienna are more hospitable than the weather," Austrian President Adolf Sharf quipped.

"I'm sure of that," Kennedy replied. "I also hope the political climate ahead is more hospitable than the weather."

In fact, the first day of their meeting Kennedy and Khrushchev got along "quite famously," as Kennedy's press secretary, Pierre Salinger, phrased it. The two men exchanged witticisms as they drew up an agenda for the next day's conference.

That evening, during the state dinner held in their honor at the presidential palace, once the home of the Esterhazy family, Khrushchev toasted "the virile and handsome youth of America, personified by President and Mrs. Kennedy." Kennedy replied with a toast to "Premier Khrushchev's future accomplishments. May many more ribbons and medals be added to those already pinned to his chest." Grinning, Khrushchev proposed that the United States "establish a peace medal, too, preferably one like ours, a laurel wreath surrounding the bust of Lenin." Kennedy came back with a proposal that the United Nations should strike a peace medal, "one with a dove on it, awarded to any statesman in the world who advances the cause of peace." Khrushchev laughingly pleaded for a halt in "the verbal war of peace medals." Kennedy agreed, saying that if wars had to break out he for one "would prefer a verbal war of peace medals to any other."

The Kennedys and Khrushchevs then went off to see Beethoven's *Fidelio* at the majestic Vienna State Opera House. Throughout the performance they talked convivially, and when the evening ended the two men affirmed their intention to hold a "productive" meeting.

"Did you notice how affable and friendly he was?" Kennedy asked Jacqueline as they prepared for bed. "I doubt that he's going to give us much trouble over Berlin. I think I know why. He's having too much trouble with China. He may not want to antagonize us, not now anyway."

"I rather like him," Jacqueline said. "And Mrs. Khrushchev is such a simple and unassuming woman. They're not as uppity as the De Gaulles. You have the feeling you can trust the Khrushchevs."

"Well, Jackie, they're working class, you know. They speak bluntly, to the point. They don't hide behind manners, strategies, and disguises, like the De Gaulles."

"Maybe you're right. Anyway, they're nice people."

That night Khrushchev gave his impressions of Kennedy to Alexei Adjhubei. "He's a rather nice boy. Only he shouldn't have gone into politics. He should have taken care of his father's millions and spent his time with the parasites of his class. He would be better off going to night clubs and parties than handling affairs of state. He strikes me as being adventurous but weak, his wishes leading him to begin things he can't finish once he sees how difficult they are.

"He reminds me of Artychev. Artychev brought me into the Communist Party right after the Revolution. He rose like a rocket in the Party. Lenin himself congratulated him on his work with youth. Artychev was a great personality: tall, handsome, well-

educated. He had a way with girls, and he won them all. He spoke
beautifully too. But then he changed. He drank, his thoughts
wandered, he was inefficient. It was soon clear why. He couldn't
make decisions. He couldn't bring himself to reward some and
punish others. He couldn't flatter his inferiors or hurt his equals.
Finally—he was regional boss at the time, it was '27—finally, he
broke down completely and was replaced by Suvorin, a tough
bastard if there ever was one. Artychev just couldn't hold power.
He was too weak, too good maybe. I'll grant that."

"What happened to him, Father?"

"Who knows? I never saw him again. He disappeared completely. When I was with young Kennedy tonight I thought I
was seeing Artychev again. Too bad, because I have to give
Kennedy a roasting tomorrow, a roasting like he's never had.
What can I do? We're not playing a child's game. I have too
much at stake to wear kid gloves. He should have pursued another vocation."

The conference was held on the morning of June 5 in the
Grand Ballroom of the Scharnhorst Castle overlooking the green
Danube. Kennedy, Rusk, MacNamara and the other Americans
were already seated at the long oak table when Khrushchev and
his aides solemnly walked in and took their places. Khrushchev
nodded slightly to Kennedy and asked to begin the proceedings.
He read from a grey pad.

"The Soviet Union wishes to resolve the Berlin and German
questions once and for all. Too long now have the Soviet Union
and the German Democratic Republic put up with the provocations and injustices that have mounted daily since the Hitlerite
aggressors were defeated and Germany occupied. For the past
sixteen years the Western sectors, now the so-called German
Federal Republic, have followed a policy of imperialism and
revanchism under the protective guise of the occupation statutes.
The leaders of the Federal Republic, supported by the United
States, Great Britain, and France, still claim that all of prewar
Germany, including the lands ceded to Poland, belongs to them.
Since they cannot have what they want, they have declared the
German Democratic Republic to be non-existent, a fiction, a
phantom. But the German Democratic Republic is a nation of
twenty million people and exercises sovereign rights.

"Yet its sovereignty is violated by the presence of an alien entity in its midst, an entity, moreover, which the revanchist Adenauer clique insists is part of its domain, in direct contravention of the occupation statutes. West Berlin is a center of espionage and propaganda. It stirs up discontent. It is an instrument in the evil designs of the West German revanchists. This situation is untenable. The Soviet Union and its allies have been patient long enough. The Soviet Union, accordingly, proposes the following:

"First. Berlin must become a unified international city, under UN administration, with troops of the Soviet Union, the United States, Great Britain, and France still present in token numbers.

"Second. All countries that fought against the Hitlerite aggressors will meet late this year in Moscow to draw up a peace treaty with the German Democratic Republic and the German Federal Republic. If the Western countries refuse to take part in such a conference the Soviet Union, by the first of next year, will unilaterally sign a treaty with the German Democratic Republic, recognizing it as fully sovereign in all matters, including control of the access routes to and from Berlin. The Western countries will have to work out their own arrangements on Berlin with the German Democratic Republic. The Soviet Union will no longer be involved, the occupation statutes having been nullified by the treaty."

Khrushchev pushed the pad aside and looked at Kennedy with a scowl. "This is not an ultimatum, Mr. President. It's to let you know that the Soviet Union intends to wipe the German question from the ledger. I trust the United States will realize that the above solution is in its best interests also. Such a peace treaty would consummate the great wartime alliance between our countries."

Khrushchev had momentarily stunned Kennedy. Kennedy would later say that he saw "a different man sitting there, reading that ultimatum to me. If there was a Jekyll and Hyde act, I was witnessing it. When I recovered—it was as though I'd been slapped in the face—I was mad as hell."

Except for the crimson that crept into his face, however, Kennedy concealed his anger admirably. He seemed calm and in complete possession of himself.

"Mr. Khrushchev, I'm not about to trade insults with you. That's not why I'm here. I listened to what you just read and I'd like to ask you a practical question. Let's assume it's January 1st and you've given the East Germans responsibility for guarding the routes to Berlin. Do you think the East Germans would try to stop an American military convoy on its way there?"

"Why should they stop you unless you refuse to recognize their sovereignty? It's their country. When our diplomats go to the UN in New York they have to deal with American police, who aren't models of politeness and courtesy, even though the UN, like your West Berlin, is independent of the surrounding state. The Vatican's another example."

"The analogies are specious, Mr. Khrushchev. There's no military agreement between occupying powers that covers the UN or the Vatican. The occupation statutes take precedence over any laws passed by the Germans themselves. In the absence of any modification of those statutes, or any general peace treaty, the United States will continue to hold the Soviet Union to the terms of the 1945 agreement at Potsdam. You can do whatever you want with East Germany as long as those terms aren't impaired. Mr. Khrushchev, the United States does not and will not deal in any way with the East Germans, no matter what they say, no matter who authorizes them, if they try to block the trains and highways to and from West Berlin."

"I see," Khrushchev retorted, his eyes having narrowed into tiny black apertures, "now let me ask you a direct question. If stopped by the forces of the Democratic Republic, will your military open fire and try to bull their way through?"

Kennedy's face was an intense red. "I'm sure the American army will do its duty. It will meet force with force."

"Do you think, my good man, that such a showdown will be confined to Americans and Germans? Do you know that the Democratic Republic is a member of the Warsaw Pact, and any aggression against the Democratic Republic is an act of aggression against the Soviet Union and five other states?"

"Let me correct you again, Mr. Khrushchev. The act of aggression will have been made by the Soviet Union. If the Soviet Union and its satellites choose to expand the conflict they have created they will suffer the consequences."

"And you and your lackeys, Mr. Kennedy, you will be free of the consequences of your choice? You realize that the Soviet Union and the Warsaw Pact members have the means not only to protect their territories, but to carry the war into the aggressor's territory. The Adenauer revanchists won't be pleased if such a war is fought on their soil."

"Hitler and Stalin, who were more terrible and awe-inspiring than you, Mr. Khrushchev, used to threaten us with this kind of language. We weren't intimidated by them, and we aren't intimidated by you. We'll do our duty and honor our commitments. Keep that in mind. And in case you've forgotten, remember this: the United States will fight its wars in places and with weapons of its own choosing."

"I needn't sit here and listen to you compare me with Hitler. That's the grossest impertinence. I thought you said you didn't want to trade insults, and now you call me a Hitler. And please don't tell me what I should remember and what I shouldn't." Khrushchev was alternately wagging his forefinger and pounding his fist on the table.

"Do you dare threaten atomic war?" he continued. "Is that what you mean by fighting with weapons of your choosing? Listen, you can threaten all you please in this castle, at this table. But when you had to act a few weeks ago you weren't so bold. You played the bandit, but failed as a man and leader. Even bandits must show courage. And now you will do something that will humiliate you a second time. You'll be laughed off the stage of history. Think twice, think ten times before you say or do something you'll regret.

"Now let me tell you something *you'll* remember. The Soviet Union has in her arsenal bombs that can blow up Washington or any other city in the United States. We'll have some tests late in the year to prove it. I'm not threatening, I'm informing you of a fact. Don't think you have the advantage over us in nuclear arms. We'll give you two, five, ten blows for each of yours. The people of the Soviet Union, all Communists, will pay any price, if it's war you want, to rid the world of the imperialist scourge. Read your own history books, young man. Since 1917 every war has increased the size of the Communist movement. The next war, should you provoke it, will obliterate capitalism from the face of the earth—every millionaire and his patrimony. That's what *you* should remember."

"Thank you for a pleasant little chat," Kennedy said, standing up, smiling coldly. "You testify to the success of the Soviet Union in producing the new Communist man. Courteous, temperate, fair-minded, rational, humane, and civilized. Let me thank you also for helping us clarify our position toward East Germany and the Soviet Union. We were prepared to negotiate in good faith. You saved us from making a terrible mistake."

"It was a pleasure to talk to you," Khrushchev replied mockingly. "I'm glad to be of service. Call on me if you need any further help."

The reporters, crowded into the anteroom of the Grand Ballroom, perceived at once that the conference had been a disaster.

"The tension is so thick here at the Scharnhorst Castle you could cut it with a knife," one columnist wrote. "The two delegations emerged from the truncated conference as though escaping from a fire. 'The dialogue ran hot and heavy and nearly turned into fisticuffs,' said one American delegate, an experienced diplomat. He could not recall anything quite like it even in 'the gamy days of Molotov and Vyshinsky.'"

The reporters' impression was confirmed by Kennedy's cryptic statement at the airport, delivered in the driving rain (which had not let up for a minute during his stay in Vienna), as he was about to board the presidential jet to London.

"The talks were useful. Premier Khrushchev and I took each other's measure. We had a fruitful exchange of views and opinions, and I think we understand each other a little better now. Mrs. Kennedy and I enjoyed our visit and hope to return someday when the sun comes out."

5

BERLIN

THE moment he returned to Washington Kennedy called former Secretary of State Dean Acheson—since his retirement in 1953 a prominent lawyer, essayist, and short story writer—and asked him to come at once to the White House.

Kennedy described what had transpired in Vienna.

"Mr. President," Acheson said after a pause, "this is the most serious situation since the Berlin airlift. I think, in fact, it's more serious. Once Khrushchev sets things in motion—the peace treaty with East Germany—there'll be no turning back. We and they will be on an inescapable collision course."

"Yes, that's why I asked you to come down, Dean. Would you head up a task force—I'll give you anyone you want—to develop some concrete suggestions before the end of next week? We can't afford to delay this thing one second longer than we have to."

While the Acheson task force deliberated in strictest secrecy the world became aware of the magnitude of the crisis. Khrushchev launched scathingly vituperative attacks on the United States, West Germany, and the NATO alliance. "The West has exactly six months and fourteen days to accept the facts of life," he told the Dzerzhinsky Military Academy on June 16. "We know the fate of those who refuse to accept the facts of life."

Kennedy, however, would not be drawn into public discussions of the Soviet ultimatum. The United States, he declared again and again at his news conferences, "will do its duty and honor its commitments," and he promised to report to the nation "shortly" on what he intended to do.

"A chill now envelops this beautiful city," wrote Maxwell Bone, the highly respected Washington correspondent for the

London Review, "the mood contrasting strangely with the radiant spring warmth, the glistening white buildings, and the deliciously fragrant cherry blossoms that line the boulevards. It's all sadly reminiscent of that fateful spring of 1941: the diplomatic frenzy, the portentousness of minor events, the unspoken, pervasive fear."

When Kennedy received "the Acheson Report" he distributed copies of it (each labeled "maximum top secret: to be read only on President's approval") to the members of the National Security Council and Joint Chiefs of Staff, with the request that it be "pondered" carefully in preparation for a "full dress" conference in mid-July.

Entitled "Blunting the Soviet Threat," the report advised the President to "assume the worst: i.e., that Premier Khrushchev will carry out his threat, sign a separate treaty with East Germany, and relinquish control of the Berlin access routes to an illegitimate authority." The showdown, the report held, would inevitably involve Soviet and NATO troops. "In the event, the United States, as leader of the alliance, must not shrink from the consequences, namely a conventional-type land war fought in Europe. . . . A nuclear exchange is highly improbable, for the United States is more than adequately prepared for such an exchange, and the Soviet Union is unlikely to venture where she is weakest."

"The Soviet army," the report continued, "can be checked and therefore defeated—not an inch need be conceded to it—provided the United States government undertakes decisive and far-reaching measures."

It then recommended what those measures should be: doubling the size of the United States army, instituting "an accelerated training program for recruits," placing the entire reserve force of six millions on alert, sending as many new divisions to Germany "as necessary within the next six months," warning the airline, train, steamship, and bus companies that "they might be pressed into military service at a moment's notice," and preparing to enact broad controls over the economy to prevent inflation and shortages. "Thanks to the discipline learned in World War II and the Korean War there should be no severe dislocations in this country when it goes on a semiwar footing."

"Let it be emphasized," the Acheson Report concluded, "the

primary objective of partial mobilization, as herein urged, is to *avoid* a military conflict. In the view of the author the only way it can be avoided is by acting as if it *will* occur. The author believes very strongly in the philosophy of 'as if'—a philosophy which relies not on miracles or unforeseen consequences but on a carefully thought-out calculus of probabilities and on the assumption that the most adverse of those probabilities will materialize. In short, he contends that in preparing for the military confrontation ahead the United States stands the best chance of abolishing its probability."

The administration judiciously leaked some of the report's recommendations to the press. Ten days later an authoritative poll sampled public opinion on the subject of Berlin. When asked if they would "approve or disapprove if the government places the nation on a semiwartime basis," 73 per cent of the respondents said they would approve, 15 per cent were undecided, and only 12 per cent flatly said they would disapprove. When asked if they were "prepared to go to war with Russia to preserve the freedom of West Berlin," a much greater proportion—88 per cent—said they would.

Kennedy was gratified by the nation's support of a "tough stance," but he kept his counsel, admitting only that he was studying the problem "intensively" and would make a "determination" in due course.

He hoped that Khrushchev would back off from his threat and so render a "determination" unnecessary. Instead, Khrushchev announced that the Soviet Union would significantly increase its military budget and the size of its armed forces, especially its East German garrison. "The Socialist camp," he said, "shall meet the aggressors head on. Against the war preparations of the U.S. imperialist clique we will redouble our efforts, and redouble them again if necessary. Let them start something! After burying them we will do them the honor of writing their epitaph."

In mid-July the long-awaited conference on the Acheson report took place in the John Quincy Adams Room of the White House. The twenty members of the National Security Council, the four members of the Joint Chiefs and their deputies, plus numerous cabinet subsecretaries, presidential assistants, and various experts on Central Europe and the Soviet Union, sixty-five people in all, crowded into the room, which Jacqueline Kennedy had recently refurnished and redecorated in warm yellows, reds, and beiges ("like a New England autumn landscape," she said, during a television tour of the White House).

"Gentlemen," Kennedy said, after calling the assembled multitude to order, "I would have convened you earlier, but I was waiting for Khrushchev to reply. Now that he has replied we can go ahead. In a sense, Khrushchev has simplified our work, making this meeting an anti-climax.

"Gentlemen, I see no choice but to accept the report of the Acheson task force, substantially if not entirely. If Khrushchev's bluffing, I say let's call it. If he's serious we must hold fast and go as far as he goes. It's not Berlin alone that weighs in the balance. It's the free world. It's America's credibility as a leader of the free world and as a great power in her own right. To destroy that credibility, that leadership, at least for a long time, is the reason Khrushchev has generated the crisis we face today.

"That's why I agree with Dean Acheson—I quote from his brilliant article in last month's *International Report and Survey*— and Dean, don't be alarmed, the publisher has granted me permission to quote you [much laughter in the room, heightened when Acheson shouted, "But I own the copyright"]: 'In its continuing conflict with the United States, the Soviet Union seeks not so much to win minor tactical successes as to inflict deep wounds that will diminish American prestige in the world. The process is subtle and long-term. For the Soviets know perhaps better than we that power in international affairs is not measured by abstract counters—the number of weapons, the amount of wealth, the size of the population, etc.—but by what a nation can do, whether its will is obeyed, if it appears to be the master rather than the slave of the future.'

"You'll agree, gentlemen, that these words—written long ago, I understand—apply to the current situation. Were we to yield to Khrushchev, the United States would, I say, suffer precisely the kind of wound to which Mr. Acheson refers. We wouldn't be buried, but it would determine the context of our relations for the next decade or so at the very least. And to be honest, I wouldn't deserve to be re-elected in 1964. But I'm not concerned about myself. I'm concerned about my responsibilities. I'm willing to let the judgments of history take care of themselves.

"The issue, then, is settled, and I must apologize to you for turning this meeting into a referendum on a decision already made rather than a symposium to ascertain what the decision should be. I feel I've no choice but to adopt the Acheson Report's recommendations. Before I go ahead, however, let me ask if anyone here thinks I ought *not* to adopt them? No one? All right, the question is whether I ought to adopt them as written, in toto, or in modified form. Attorney General Kennedy?"

"Mr. President, I have one point. The report speaks of 'partial mobilization.' But if you followed its recommendations I think it would be more accurate to call it full mobilization. The difference, I believe, is very important. Because if it's our intention to prevent a confrontation from coming about then I don't think we should make the confrontation inevitable or put ourselves in an embarrassing hole should Khrushchev back off. Yet those are the options that full mobilization would force upon us.

"Suppose we've drafted a million men, imposed all manner of controls, and so on. Then, late in the year, as the deadline nears, the crisis ends. What then? Suddenly relax the controls, discharge the troops, confess that we've overreacted? People might get the idea that this administration, this President, is off balance and tends to hysteria."

"Bobby," the President said, "you've done something dangerous yourself. You've taken on Dean Acheson. Prepare for the worst. Dean?"

"Thank you, Mr. President. It may surprise all of you beyond belief, especially you, Robert, that I agree with you. Or rather I would agree with you if I could accept your premise, that what we, my task force, recommended amounts to full mobilization. Most of you here are old enough to remember the Second World War [laughter]—no offense meant, Robert—when we, of course, did have full mobilization. Nothing like that control over society, over the private sector, that degree of regimentation, is envisioned in the report. The only controls would be over those aspects of out national life deemed vital to the precise operation at hand. Now if a real war should develop that would be a different ball game.

"In any event—to change the figure reprehensibly—the fat is in the fire, and I'm convinced it will remain there quite a while. The Soviet Union may back off. I certainly hope so. If it does, the threat of another confrontation will arise again, probably sooner than later. What I'm saying here is that we gird ourselves for future crises similar to the one we're now experiencing, possibly with antagonists other than the Soviet Union. The increase in the army's size, the addition to our European forces, the development of mobile infantry and armored units trained to fight anywhere in the world in an instant—these should become a permanent feature of our military posture.

"What I'm proposing, Mr. President, is merely an expansion of your counterinsurgency plan. The present crisis gives us the opportunity, the propitious occasion we need, to put it into effect."

Robert Kennedy, who sat directly across from Acheson, was quick to reply. "I do remember price controls during the last war. I remember how hard it was for my mother to find a crib for me. [Laughter.] And, Dean, I understand it was really rough when Lincoln was President. Maybe some day you'll tell us your personal experiences at the time. [More laughter.]

"It's obvious that our differences are pretty deep. You regard confrontations as a permanent feature of American foreign relations. That's a self-fulfilling prophecy, in my opinion. If we go along with your reasoning we'll be in the Cold War forever. I say the crisis we're now in may be related to temporary circumstances —the refugee problem, Khrushchev's failures at home, China, many things. Too often we're enslaved to 'the long run.' In the long run we're all dead. Besides, people attribute to the future the goals they now have. If you ask me, Russia's long-run interest lies in securing closer relations with the United States and the West."

"If so," Acheson countered, his eyes glowing under thick grey brows, "let them pay the price. We shouldn't render up our friendship for nothing."

"As it is they've gotten too much for nothing," Admiral Anderson added.

"May I say something?" General Horvitzer asked softly. "In my humble opinion this interesting discussion is academic. What I think we should be discussing here, if I may be so bold, Mr. President, is what we should do when, not if, I repeat *when* the

Russians attack. We should be discussing what to do in anticipation of the great build-up that we are sure as Shiloh going to have after the first of the year."

"Well, General," the President retorted, "I think we can take the appropriate steps when we have to. This meeting today is not concerned with our response to a full-scale land war."

"But may I respectfully say, Mr. President," Air Force General Curtis M. LeMay interposed, "if we don't get down to the nitty-gritty, as Hiram suggests, we may find ourselves unprepared when push comes to shove. In fact, we've been shoved already."

"I deny that it's come to that," MacGeorge Bundy said sharply. "To prepare for war now creates new conditions, new tensions, and there's no reason to do that unless we're bent on bringing matters to a head once and for all. We can act swiftly if we're really pushed."

After hearing several more comments supporting one or another of the views already expressed Kennedy adjourned the meeting until 10 P.M. Then, he said, he would announce his "final determination."

The meeting resumed promptly at ten. "I'd like to read this brief statement to you," Kennedy said, leaning back in his rocking chair. " 'Having consulted the Joint Chiefs and logistics personnel in the Pentagon since this morning, I am satisfied that we now possess the means (a) to double or triple the size of our armed forces in a period of months, and (b) to send six or seven fully equipped and trained divisions to Germany right away, should trouble start. This state of readiness precludes the need for the partial mobilization recommended by the Acheson Report, at least for the time being. As we noted this morning it may become necessary to carry out, or exceed, those recommendations. But then we would be in a state of war.

" 'At the moment my objective is twofold: (1) to let the other side know we mean business and will not be deterred, and (2) to alert the American people primarily and our allies secondarily to the possibility of a war ahead. A partial mobilization would bring the imminence of war home to them right now. Instead, I want to plant the seed in the public mind, so that when the pushing and shoving does begin, Americans will do what is asked of them I will schedule my speech to the nation for about a week from today. I will make it as persuasive as possible to kinsman, friend, and foe.

" 'Finally a word on the concrete details of the build-up. I envision an immediate increment in our military of some 250,000 men, most of it for the army. More will be requested from the Congress as need dictates. The cost of the build-up, which will, incidentally, bring our armed forces to their highest levels since the Korean War, is estimated at three to four billions. I think it can be borne, despite the budget deficit, without asking for new taxes. Indeed, the Council of Economic Advisers informs me that the added outlays will give a further boost to the economy. The cost of living will rise slightly, but it will be more than offset by the growth in productivity. No controls are indicated. The airlines and other transportation media will give us their full cooperation. It will not be necessary to impress them into service.' "

Kennedy stopped reading and looked up. Rocking gently back and forth, he continued: "I arrived at my decision after mulling over everything that was said here this morning. Let me say that I agreed with you, Dean, and with the generals, as well as with Bobby. The decisive consideration for me is timing and conditioning. Our objectives are the same: to prevent a war while yielding nothing to Khrushchev. I think, Dean, that when our armed forces fill out to full strength under the plan I've outlined we'll be the equal of the Russians and the Chinese, yes, both of them, in our capacity to fight on the land, anywhere. And we'll be quick, mobile, and very powerful. That's why I don't think we need to keep a large standing army. As Bob MacNamara's put it, one mechanized mobile company, transported by superjet, is worth a conventional division. Khrushchev knows that too."

Before delivering his July 25 speech Kennedy had informed the NATO allies and the leaders of Congress of its contents. The response was uniformly favorable. West Germany's Chancellor, Konrad Adenauer, was especially pleased. From his Lake Como retreat, the eighty-eight-year-old doyen of world statesmen sent a secret message to the White House. "Your tough position is our passport to peace. You can be certain now that all will be well." And De Gaulle [. . .]*

---

* Prescott breaks off here with a note to himself: "Consult deM. and Lord H."—N.F.M.

Even Kennedy's opponents had to grant that his speech was impressive. To his television audience of 100 million—the highest Standson rating ever recorded—he appeared completely equable and self-possessed, despite the melancholy news he conveyed.

He explained in patient detail why Berlin was threatened and why it was imperative that "we honor our commitments to its brave and beleaguered citizens." If the past taught anything, he pointed out, it taught that peace and freedom could not be obtained cheaply, without "risks and sacrifices." Once again, he declared, the people of the United States must prepare for battle, and he went on to specify what he would request of Congress and the public.

Several times in his speech he went out of his way to stress his desire for peace and conciliation and to commend the people and soldiers of the Soviet Union for their extraordinary heroism in World War II. Nonetheless, he added, the United States was ready to fight if need be.

Two days later, on July 27, Khrushchev conferred with his associates at his Crimean summer home to decide on the Soviet Union's "riposte" to the American build-up. He, Mikoyan, Adjhubei, and East German Party boss Walter Ulbricht talked in the tree-shaded patio of the lilac garden overlooking the Black Sea.

"I am afraid, Comrade Secretary," Ulbricht said, his voice as wooden as his face, "that as far as the Democratic Republic is concerned the crisis has begun. We cannot wait until January 1st of next year or even until November 1st of this. Last month our people deserted to West Berlin at the rate of fifteen hundred a day. This month the rate is four thousand a day. They are not peasants or workers. They are professionals and young people. Our population is declining by leaps. We have lost millions already. The West German aggressors outnumber us three to one. At this rate we will lose yet another million by January first. This morning one of my most important ministers and six of his assistants went over the border, the pig. How obsequious, how German he was to me. That's neither here nor there. The life blood of our nation is draining out. What shall I do? My hands are tied."

"What do you want *me* to do?" Khrushchev asked grimly.

"I want your permission to close the frontier between our

section of Berlin and theirs. I want to construct a tourniquet to stop the flow of blood."

"What tourniquet, comrade? Will you build a fence, a wall?"

"A fence or wall is exactly what I have in mind, Comrade Secretary."

"Is that legal?" Adjhubei asked. "How can you divide the city that way?"

"It is perfectly legal under the occupation statutes," Ulbricht replied. "We have gone over the laws carefully. The wall would, of course, be on our side. Maybe a double wall enclosing an area of no man's land. It would be impregnable."

"A beautiful image of Communism," Mikoyan said with an ironic smile. "I can see the West making a great propaganda display of it. They would say, here's how Communists build the new society."

"Do you think we don't know that, Comrade Mikoyan?" Ulbricht said, a trace of animation in his voice. "But we're bleeding to death. Why must we make such unusual sacrifices? The Soviet Union and the other peoples' democracies regulate the movement of their citizens. Only we lack that power. We send a youth to school for twenty years, train him to be an expert engineer, and he goes over to our enemies, your enemies. A fine plate of herring! It's criminal. No, we cannot allow it, not one day, one minute longer. Excuse me, comrades, for my outburst."

"I haven't ever seen you so wrought up, comrade," Khrushchev said consolingly, patting Ulbricht's arm. "You're right. No one here disagrees with you. You may be surprised to know that we've been discussing the refugee problem, and we thought about a wall too. Mikoyan, however, had reservations. So did Alexei. That's why they seem so negative.

"But I'm not so negative. Since we're old comrades I'll be open with you. I'll lay my knife on the table. To tell you the truth I'm not so alarmed as you about your loss of blood. It might do your country some good to build from the foundations up, as Castro's doing. A little bloodletting of this sort isn't unhealthy. And so if I'm for sealing off the two sectors of Berlin it's because I have reasons of my own. I'll explain as briefly as I can.

"Reason number one is that a wall would settle the German question for a long time. It's been a thorn in our side. It doesn't kill us and we can't pull it out. All right then, let them have West Berlin. Let them choke on it. Let the Westerners go in and out all they want. Only no Communist, no refugee, no East German will ever set foot in it again.

"Not only that, the division in Germany becomes permanent. You're smiling, Comrade Ulbricht. *You* see what I'm driving at. You've won after all. Beria's gone, Malenkov's gone. It's all yours now. East Germany's yours. You played the game like a master. Only be grateful that the scoundrel Adenauer was on your side. Are you sure he's not your brother? I've never seen better cooperation. You can have your wall. West Berlin's no longer an issue. Right?"

"Right!"

"And the crisis over access routes, the quarrel between the United States and us is irrelevant. Right?"

"Right!"

"That leads me to reason number two. When the wall goes up it'll catch the West by surprise. It'll also scare them. They'll think we've escalated the conflict. But they won't do anything. How can they? The wall's legal. More important, to our enemies here and in China it'll seem that we're cracking the whip, taking the initiative, raining down one blow after another. Maybe Mao will shut up, that yellow mother ———. No, I'm going to restrain myself. But I won't be through with them yet. A few days after they've digested the news of the wall I'll suddenly announce new tests of our big bombs and rockets. This time I'll crack the whip hard, and everybody'll jump, especially our charming comrades in Peking and here, in our Presidium.

"This will set the stage for the final act. I'll move the deadline back indefinitely. Next year I'll let it lapse completely. By then who's going to remember that Kennedy played the rough little boy? We'll have what we want without a confrontation. Berlin, Germany—they'll be solved, though the West won't know that. You see how beautifully the wheels mesh? Germany'll be out of the way for good, and we'll have made our enemies cringe with fear into the bargain. Right, Comrade Ulbricht?"

"Right!"

"Now let's eat."

By and large events worked out as Khrushchev predicted.

In mid-August 1961 the frontier between East and West Berlin was sealed. Within weeks the wall had been erected, and the flow of refugees was turned off as though, indeed, a tourniquet had been applied.

Caught by surprise, the West responded with a show of massive indignation, condemning the wall as "a moral and social travesty of inhumanity scarcely paralleled in modern history," in the language of Vice President Lyndon Johnson, who made a hurried visit to Berlin as Kennedy's personal emissary. At one point Kennedy, stung by his right-wing critics, who were demanding action and accusing him of pusillanimity, did entertain the possibility of breaking down the wall. But the mayor of West Berlin himself, Willy Brandt, reminded Kennedy of the obvious and "tragic" fact that if the East Germans did not put up a wall they would "find some other, more hideous means of keeping back the refugees."

When, at the end of August during an angry diatribe, Khrushchev revealed that the Soviet Union would test her "megaton" hydrogen bombs in October, the world was plunged into a state of deep foreboding. The destructive effects on humanity—on generations to come—from the radiation released into the atmosphere, though great in themselves, were incidental to the primary fear of an impending nuclear war.

Kennedy called the projected tests "insane." The Soviet Union, he pointed out, "already possesses the wherewithal to deliver a second-strike retaliatory blow." He discounted the "utility" of a very large megaton bomb as a first-strike weapon, "since, as the Soviet leaders know full well we can wipe out every one of their cities. I don't know what's going on in their minds." Inevitably, the United States resumed testing also. Kennedy held out until September, when he announced that the United States would conduct small underground tests late in the year.

As promised, the Soviet Union in October exploded fifty megaton hydrogen bombs (each equivalent to fifty million tons of TNT) in Central Asia, leaving craters several miles in diameter and hundreds of feet deep. The heat and radiation alone would have destroyed any city in the world. Khrushchev boasted of yet bigger bombs, including "one hundred megatoners" and one that could "shift the direction of the earth on its axis." These, he said reassuringly, would not be tested "for the time being."

But the tension, which had been rising since early June, suddenly snapped five months later, when Khrushchev let it be known through diplomatic channels that he was moving the deadline for a peace treaty with East Germany well into 1962 and perhaps beyond. "It would be silly to have confrontations," he told a British visitor. "If it will help to negotiate a settlement of the Berlin problem we'll remove our sword of Damocles."

Privately, word was circulated that the Soviet Union had abandoned altogether its intention of signing the treaty.

On Christmas Day Kennedy invited Soviet Ambassador L. V. Sansinov to the White House for an eggnog. "I congratulate Premier Khrushchev on his statesmanship," the President said, raising the cup to his lips.

"In behalf of Premier Khrushchev," the ambassador replied, "I accept your congratulations."

6

INDOCHINA

ONE evening early in February 1961 Kennedy invited several members of his policy-making circle—his brother, Secretaries Rusk and MacNamara, and aides Sorensen and Bundy—to the Admiral Mahan Library of the White House for an informal "seminar" on Indochina.

"As you know," Kennedy said, rocking his chair gently, "we're going to make some hard decisions on Indochina in the near future. For that reason I've invited Professor John Smith,* one of our leading authorities on the subject, to fill in the background for us. Thanks for coming down, Professor. Why don't you start right off and tell us what the problem is that confronts us there today."

"Thank you for inviting me, Mr. President. Your question is complex. Actually, there are three major or supervening problems: South Vietnam, Laos, and Cambodia. Along with Communist North Vietnam these three countries, until 1954, constituted French Indochina. You are familiar, of course, with the Geneva settlement of that year. Under its terms South and North Vietnam became separate states until 1956, at which time an internationally supervised general election was to be held to unify the country. Laos and Cambodia were declared independent and neutral. The general election, as we know, was never held."

"May I interrupt, Mr. Smith?" Robert Kennedy asked. "Why wasn't the election held?"

"Because, Mr. Kennedy, the United States—that is, Secretary

---

* Inexplicably, Prescott crossed out the professor's name, leaving a blank. Since this professor figures so prominently in the pages that follow I have taken the liberty of calling him John Smith.—N.F.M.

of State Dulles—opposed it on the ground that the North Vietnamese would win and so communize the whole country."

"I'd like to pursue the matter a bit," Robert Kennedy continued. "Do you think if the election had been a fair one Ho Chi Minh would have won? If so, why?"

"Well, that's difficult to answer. According to Mr. Dulles and the State Department, the election could not have been fair because of Communist terrorism in the South. In my opinion, Ho Chi Minh would have won under any circumstances. It is also my opinion—I was in South Vietnam at the time and visited ten of the provincial capitals—there was relatively little terrorism going on. The reason was simple: the Communists felt so confident of victory they did not have to oppose the election."

"I have to take issue with you there, Mr. Smith," Dean Rusk interrupted. "The reports that reached the State Department from the Control Commission, from impartial observers—not that I question your impartiality—and from our own intelligence, tell a much different story. The South was plagued with terrorism. The Vietminh, who had fought so long against the French, were still active in the villages. Moreover, the North had shot or imprisoned its opposition—non-Communist nationalists. It would have been a one-sided election, confined mostly to the South."

"Much of what you say is true, Mr. Secretary, I grant you," Smith said, nodding his head. "But it should be remembered that Ho and the Vietminh had fought the French for ten years, and before that the Japanese, whereas most of the South Vietnamese leaders had collaborated first with the Japanese, then with the French. In agreeing to free elections at Geneva Ho was not going to surrender by ballot what he had won by bullets. And the French went along with this. The French were convinced that all of Vietnam would inevitably fall to Ho, and they allowed for a two-year period of grace to give the pro-French in the South time to leave the country.

"As for terrorism in the South, that is a matter of opinion. It should be kept in mind that the Communist insurgents had fought in those villages against the French, and they were not about to surrender them to government officials sent by President Ngo Diem.

"Now I am not arguing here against the United States decision to prevent the election from taking place in 1956. I am only suggesting that if one had taken place, fair or foul, all of Vietnam would have come under Ho Chi Minh's rule. Whatever his motive, right or wrong, wise or unwise, Mr. Dulles violated the Geneva accord, though, to be sure, the United States had not signed it."

"May I suggest gentlemen," President Kennedy asked, "that we set aside the question of the election. We have an accomplished fact on our hands. There are two Vietnams now. Let's begin there. Please go on, Mr. Smith."

"Yes. But it should be clearly understood that the North Vietnamese do not acknowledge the legitimacy of the South Vietnamese government and are committed to its destruction."

"Let me break in here," MacNamara said. "Do you mean that the North intends to invade the South? Is the North infiltrating the South? Is the North responsible for the troubles in the South now? I ask these questions because I haven't yet gotten a clear answer. Central Intelligence is ambiguous. And, Dean, State hasn't given me a definite answer either."

"Well, Bob," Rusk said with a restrained smile, "maybe you haven't asked the right people."

"I admit it," MacNamara said, laughing loudly. "It's the story of my life. It took me a month before I found out where the toilets are in the Pentagon."

"No, seriously, Bob," Rusk said, "if you had asked me I could have told you that the North has a regular pipeline to the South. They needn't invade. By sea and over the Ho Chi Minh trail through eastern Laos and Cambodia the North supplies men and materiel on a large scale to the guerrillas. There's plenty of evidence for it."

"Oh I know that," MacNamara replied, "but that's not what I meant. I want to know what quantity of men and materiel and what impact the North has on the conflict in the South. In other words, is it a conflict mainly between the North and the South?"

"You put your finger on the heart of the issue," Smith rejoined. "According to my studies—I could refer you to my arcane scholarly publications, but I inflict those only on my students—the conflict in South Vietnam is civil in character. It is South Vietnamese versus South Vietnamese. The Vietcong guerrillas are recruited from the villages and hamlets. There are thousands of such villages, and a good proportion of them, maybe most, are under Vietcong control. Or, if not in control, subject to Vietcong requisitions of food and sanctuary."

"Why are there so many Vietcong?" Robert Kennedy asked.

"The answer, to put it as succinctly as I can, Mr. Kennedy, is that more and more peasants are resisting the Saigon government of President Diem. This was not always the case. Until about 1958 or so Diem encountered little hard opposition because he by and large left them alone, and in some instances protected them from the ravenous landlords and planters. But for a variety of reasons Diem has submitted to the landlords and planters and to his own greedy bureaucrats. As a result the age-old conflict between the villages and the mandarins has flared up again. The number of Vietcong, as you know, has risen dramatically in the last two years, and will doubtlessly rise still further in the years ahead.

"I say that because a vicious cycle has been set in motion. As Diem meets armed resistance in the villages, he goes yet further in attempting to put it down. So he alienates the peasants even more. So the number of guerrillas grows. And so the North Vietnamese send down arms and advisers. The conflict, I repeat, is a civil one. The North, in my opinion, would not intervene in the absence of a civil conflict. It did not intervene from 1954 to 1960.

"I would like to say one more thing about the Diem regime. It is hopelessly enmeshed in corruption and nepotism. That is a matter of public knowledge. Diem's and his wife's families occupy the key positions in the government and Church.

"The Church, I might add, is another sore point. South Vietnam is ninety per cent Buddhist. And many of the Catholics are new-comers, who emigrated from the North in 1954. One of the more ominous signs is the increasingly active opposition of the Buddhist monks and the students to the Diem regime."

"May I offer a layman's comment?" Bundy asked. "I think your characterization of the situation is too gloomy. It's a fact, isn't it, that the Vietcong amount to no more than five to ten thousand? Isn't it a fact, too, that the government has been fairly successful in containing the guerrillas? Doesn't it inflict high casualties on

them? And don't you think a more determined prosecution of
the fight by government forces would effectively destroy the
Vietcong, much as the British destroyed the Malayan guerrillas?"

"Now, George," the President said, grinning, "Mr. Smith isn't
a student who was caught cheating on an exam. Beneath his
curmudgeonly manner, Mr. Smith, George is a warm and loving
man."

"I know that, Mr. President. I appreciate Mr. Bundy's manner,
and I like the give and take of sharp debate. Dialectics is the path
to the truth. As for his questions, the answers are, first, yes, the
Vietcong are now only several thousand, but their numbers are
burgeoning, and will continue to burgeon as long as the government goes after them. The vicious cycle I referred to is thus
accelerated. And, second, yes, it seems the government forces
are taking a high toll of guerrillas. But frankly I don't trust the
government's version. Vietnamese officers on the field will naturally inflate the body count to prove that they have fought or have
been courageous. Also, a high percentage of the bodies that are
counted are, I would guess, village inhabitants, including old
people, women, and children. Both sides are quite brutal. And
third, the analogy with Malaya does not apply at all in my
opinion. The Malayan guerrillas were mostly Chinese, mostly
city dwellers, fighting in a jungle inhabited by hostile Malays.
The Malays may have hated the British, but they hated the
Chinese even more. In South Vietnam many of the villages
may dislike the Vietcong, but they *despise* the mandarins of
Saigon."

"Mr. Smith, your explanation is extremely persuasive and
lucid, and I think we've really learned something here," Kennedy
said. "At least I have. I won't speak for the others. Before we
break up—we have a little time left—could you tell us something
about Laos and Cambodia?"

"Yes, Mr. President. About Cambodia little need be said.
Prince Noradom Sihanouk has managed to keep Cambodia free
of conflict during this whole time of troubles. His family had
ruled under French authority. He took over in 1941 and cooper-
ated with the Japanese, who also left Cambodia pretty much
alone. During the Vietminh uprising against the French he again

kept Cambodia nominally neutral. It is still neutral, and its neutrality is guaranteed by the Geneva Treaty.

"Sihanouk's policy has been clear. He gravitates toward the paramount power in the region, effecting accommodations that preserve the peace and independence of his country. Today he gravitates toward Communist China and North Vietnam. And they leave Cambodia alone. As you know, there is no love lost between the Cambodians and the Vietnamese. The South Vietnamese even today covet Cambodian territory and offshore islands. That is another reason Sihanouk is friendly to the North. He is very shrewd, and is liked by his people, who, incidentally, have a deep aversion to war.

"Laos, on the other hand, is in grave trouble because it is not really a unified country. It is mountainous, jungle-infested, still primitive in many areas, and much of it borders on North Vietnam. It is riven into numerous factions, some of them derived from tribal, ethnic, and regional differences that run very deep. My prognosis of that situation is gloomy indeed, Mr. President. The faction that the United States supports, or rather sponsors, is the government or Vientiane faction headed by Prince Boun Oum. But Boun Oum doesn't stand a chance against the North Vietnamese-supported Pathet Lao faction headed by Prince Souvanavong. The only way to stop the Pathet Lao is by sending large contingents of foreign troops. That would not work in the long run because the North Vietnamese would then intervene on a correspondingly large scale. Our intelligence and special service personnel have tried to create an army out of Boun Oum's motley following. It is like trying to churn butter out of water. Our policy in Laos is a failure through and through."

"Yes, I know that," the President said. "Dean, what do think of Mr. Smith's diagnosis?"

"I agree with him, on the whole. To bail out the Vientiane government we would have to make a tremendous commitment. Laos is an awfully forbidding place. However, Mr. Smith hasn't mentioned the third faction, the neutralists."

"Yes," Smith said, "the neutralists, led by Prince Souvanna Phouma, Souvanavong's half brother, are temporarily aligned with the Pathet Lao, Souvanna Phouma having been ousted by Boun Oum—that is, by the CIA—two years ago. Not that the brothers exactly love each other. In fact, they are, or would be, natural enemies, since, without American aid Boun Oum would count for very little. At any rate, the neutralist faction is the only one that can bring the war in Laos to a close, and that will happen only when the United States dumps Boun Oum and reaches an agreement with the North Vietnamese to restore Souvanna Phouma to power. If the war continues, Mr. President, the Pathet Lao are bound to win. The key is North Vietnam. Of course, all our problems in Indochina will disappear if North Vietnam disappears."

"Mr. Smith," Kennedy said, rising from his rocking chair and extending his hand, "I can't thank you enough for coming down and talking with us. It will help us greatly to formulate our Indochina policy in the weeks ahead."

Laos was Kennedy's most pressing problem. The Pathet Lao were rapidly advancing into government territory and nothing barred their way. Accordingly, Kennedy called in Averell Harriman, one of the wealthiest men in the country and one of the most experienced diplomats, having been wartime ambassador to the Soviet Union, among the other important tasks he had assumed in the past thirty years. Harriman's task now was to "sound out" the Soviet Union on reasserting Laotian neturality under the terms of the Geneva Treaty.

The Soviet Union was surprisingly agreeable and promised to consult with "some of the other interested parties" on the possibility of a settlement. By "interested parties" was of course meant North Vietnam.

Ho Chi Minh's motive in prosecuting the war in Laos was, he claimed, "defensive." He would not allow the Vientiane government to encroach on the regions properly belonging to the neutralists and the Pathet Lao. In a sense, Ho was telling the truth. He had no interest in occupying all, or most, of Laos, which was as forbidding to him—"uncivilized" he called it—as it was to any other outsider. His interest was to maintain control, through the Pathet Lao, of that segment of Laos adjoining North Vietnam. He was therefore amenable to a settlement that would mark off "the spheres" proper to each of the three factions.

Empowered by Ho to reach such a settlement, the Soviet Union (as co-chairman of the Geneva convention) entered into negotiations with the Western signatories to the accord—i.e., Great Britain and France—along with the United States. The "formula" they arrived at after much tacking and veering specified that the three factions would govern Laos jointly under the "stewardship" of the neutralists.

The difficulty, however, was that the factions had to give their consent to the agreement.

The three princes met repeatedly, first in Switzerland, then in Cambodia, then in a succession of Laotian capitals. Each of the conferences lasted for days, during which time there was much feasting, fornicating, and entertainment. "The only thing that ever comes out of these delicious excursions," a Reuters correspondent observed, "is a sated appetite. When their appetites return the princes hold another conference."

Early in October 1961, on the very last day of a sumptuous two-week meeting at Hin Hun Hump on the banks of the beautiful river Lik, Prince Boun Oum at last agreed that Souvanna Phouma should be the premier of Laos. The remaining question was how the various ministries of the new government should be divided. Again Boun Oum balked, demanding a majority of the important posts. Naturally, this was unacceptable to the neutralists and the Pathet Lao. It seemed that all of the laborious work of the past year would be for nought.

It was at this parlous moment that Harriman intervened directly, prevailing upon Kennedy to "apply maximum pressure" on the "obstreperous" Boun Oum. When Kennedy, responding to Harriman's entreaties, threatened to cut off all military and economic support to Vientiane the prince meekly came to terms with his rivals. In June 1962 the "Agreement of the Three Princes" was formally ratified by the fourteen-nation committee of the Geneva Conference.

President Kennedy threw a lavish White House supper in Harriman's honor. "I propose a toast," Kennedy said as everyone rose and held up his glass of champagne. "Our gratitude to this good and great American who has wrought a miracle, perhaps the beginning of the peace we have sought for Southeast Asia."

But a resolution of the Vietnam conflict seemed further away than ever, even as the United States was becoming more and more deeply mired in it.

One day early in April 1961 Kennedy called Rusk, MacNamara, and Bundy to his office. He showed them a report he had just received from Allen Dulles. "Last month I asked the CIA to provide me with a thorough evaluation of the situation in Vietnam. My question was how good a job the Saigon government was doing in combating the guerrillas. The report I got this morning from Dulles bears out Mr. Smith's analysis. I quote the report:

"'It is estimated that as many as three quarters of the villages and hamlets in South Vietnam are in Vietcong hands. These villages and hamlets fall into three categories: hard-core Vietcong; sympathetic, though unenthusiastic; and tributary—those forced to yield money, food, clothing, etc.'

"I quote further: 'The Saigon government has been completely ineffective in dealing with the problem. Its civil guard offers scarcely any protection to the officials it sends into the provinces. As a result, the officials are assassinated with impunity. Accordingly, the inhabitants of the rural areas feel they have no choice but to go along with the Vietcong.'

"There it is, men. I've read you the gist of the report, which will be at your desks in a couple of hours. What do you think?"

"It's a tough decision, Mr. President," MacNamara said curtly. "If Professor Smith is right then any further involvement in South Vietnam would only worsen matters."

"But I think we should keep certain facts in mind," Rusk said. "If we don't help the Saigon government right away, the Communists everywhere will take heart. The guerrillas couldn't last very long—and I know Mr. Smith's argument very well—they couldn't grow and flourish if it weren't for the help they receive from Hanoi. What we must do, I maintain, is convince Hanoi in the most unmistakable language of our determination to preserve democracy in South Vietnam, imperfect as it may be. Ours isn't perfect either."

"I agree emphatically with Secretary Rusk," Bundy said. "Democracy has to develop slowly, often in conflict. The War of the Roses, the Puritan Revolution, the Glorious Revolution—these civil conflicts preceded the rise of true parliamentary government in England. Preceding French democracy were the civil wars of the sixteenth century, the absolutism of Louis XIV, the French Revolution, the revolutions of 1830, 1848, and the

Paris Commune of 1871. We had a violent revolution and a pretty bloody civil war too. Granted Diem is authoritarian. We shouldn't be so purist, given our Western history. Democracy, when it comes to South Vietnam, will be forged in the smithy of the struggle now in progress. I think the United States should persevere and help Diem as much as possible."

"I'm not disputing you guys," MacNamara said, smiling slightly. "To argue with George, I'd have to memorize a hundred history textbooks as a start—"

"One night's work for you, Bob."

"Give me two nights. I just want to know the costs and the consequences. What kind of assistance? Suppose the situation goes on deteriorating. Do we ship over our troops? If so, how many? How far, at that point, are we prepared to go? What worries me is getting drawn step by step into the sticky business. Then, once in, we'll find that the South Vietnamese are dependent on us. We'd be paying the bills while Diem, or whoever's in charge, will play the piper."

"All right, now let me ask you this," Kennedy said. "What would it mean if South Vietnam fell to the Communists?"

"Mr. President," Rusk said gravely, his brows knotted above his eyes, "that would be an unmitigated disaster. If Laos goes Communist it would be serious, but not catastrophic. South Vietnam is a rich country, a prize in every respect. It has sixteen million people, large cities. Together, the two Vietnams, no matter who rules them, would constitute a powerful country indeed. I can't stress strongly enough South Vietnam's importance for the rest of Southeast Asia. It's really the lynchpin of that whole region. If it goes Communist, the other states—Malaysia, Thailand, Laos and Cambodia, perhaps Burma—will come under its domination. SEATO would disintegrate. The full faith and moral credit of the United States in the world would disappear. Who knows what might happen then. The Communists would be emboldened to try their luck elsewhere—in Latin America, Africa, Europe. We'd be a paper tiger, and everybody would know it."

"May I add something, Mr. President?" Bundy asked. "Your critics would like nothing more than to blame you for losing Vietnam, just as they blamed Truman and Acheson for losing

China. The Communists-in-government accusations would be revived. We would have a new age of McCarthyism."

"It's evident, then," Kennedy said, after pausing reflectively, "that our options in South Vietnam are tough ones, to say the least. We're stuck with Diem, like him or not. We've got to use what's available. Vietnam's our main line of defense against Communism in Asia, and we've already invested too much there to blow it. We'll have to plan ways of strengthening the army and civil guard. We'll try to get Diem to introduce more freedoms, cut down on the corruption, bring about democracy. Our goal is to get the Vietnamese people to defend themselves. But they have to want to defend themselves. Meanwhile, let's send more intelligence and technical and training personnel over there. Next week I'll send Lyndon there. Maybe Hanoi and Peking will get the message that we mean business."

In early May, Vice President Johnson visited America's friends and allies in Southeast Asia. It was a whirlwind trip conducted on the style of a Texas political campaign. Johnson would go to a country, and, after a hasty briefing by State Department officers, praise its political leaders in the most fulsome terms. President Diem he hailed as a "mighty and valiant foe of tyranny."

"The free world," Johnson said, "owes President Diem and the Diem family an eternal debt of gratitude, and the history of our time will record for all posterity how they advanced the cause of human liberty. The United States stands with them and beside them in South Vietnam's struggle for democracy and justice and peace."

Johnson's rhetoric and electioneering style was largely a pose. His mission was to convince the Asian Communists that the United States would "honor its commitments if all hell broke loose"—Kennedy's parting words to him. Actually, however, Johnson was distressed by what he saw in Saigon. Reporting directly to Kennedy on his return, he described the city as a nest of gambling, corruption, and prostitution where, despite the "overwhelming presence of the police the Vietcong operate openly." Diem and Mrs. Diem he characterized as arrogant and ungrateful.

"Mr. President, they told me the United States needed them more than they needed the United States. They said they were under a lot of pressure from neutralists to reach an agreement with Hanoi and the Vietcong. They said they would resist that pressure as long as the United States gave them unlimited aid with no strings attached. I raised the question of democracy. They told me that the politics of South Vietnam was South Vietnam's business, and besides the Vietnamese people don't have the same notion of democracy as we do. They kept saying, you Americans don't know us.

"When I asked them how a guerrilla movement could spring up the way it has if they know their people so well, they quoted an old Vietnamese proverb, which I memorized. 'Unsheath your sword and slay your enemies, and you will command great respect.' The point of that proverb, Mr. President, is that if the United States gives them enough they'll slay their enemies and get the support of the people. That may be, but Diem is a stubborn son of a bitch. We have some coyote on our hands."

Kennedy promptly dispatched a team of experts to Saigon to evaluate conditions and make concrete, "actionable" recommendations. It was led by Professor B. L. S——,* a geopolitician specializing in Southeast Asian area studies.

A month later Professor S—— presented his report to the President and the National Security Council. The meeting was held in the Theodore Roosevelt Room, against a backdrop of stuffed animals, exotic skins, medieval swords, and guns going back to the French and Indian War.

Holding the pages of his report close to his thick glasses, S—— read slowly and deliberately.

"Mr. President, gentlemen, my conclusions are based on extensive travels and conversations by my team in the course of the month we spent in South Vietnam. Our specific objective was to draw up a long-range plan for defeating the Vietcong guerrillas. We discovered that before a long-range plan of development and rehabilitation can be entertained a short-range strategy must be undertaken. South Vietnam must be saved before it can be helped. Our team, consequently, has come up with an eighteen-month crash program whose successful implementation will, we believe, lay solid groundwork for the long-range stability of South Vietnam. This program would be carried out by the

* Prescott again, for no discernible reason, gave the professor's initials, not his name.—N.F.M.

present regime and would be financed and otherwise assisted by the United States. It would involve no interference in South Vietnam's political affairs, a subject on which President Diem is inordinately sensitive. We have not yet fully reckoned the economic cost, which, in any case would be infinitely less expensive than a drawn-out war subsidized by the United States.

"The program embraces two features. The first is economic. The South Vietnamese should receive grants enabling them to increase agricultural yields and to become as industrially self-sufficient as possible, though this goal is a long way off. Dams, highways, canals, research centers, and universities should be built or improved throughout the country. At the same time, the long-promised measures to distribute land to the peasants should be launched at once. One of the causes of unrest has been the patently usurious rates of interest that landlords, in partnership with banks, have charged. The government rather than the landlords and banks should lend money. The United States should underwrite much of the cost of land distribution and the low interest loans.

"The second feature is military. The Vietcong are entrenched in the villages and hamlets, especially in the Central Highlands and the rich Mekong River Delta. We propose that the government embark on a rational and methodical campaign to root out and destroy the guerrillas. How this can be done is outlined in detail in the pages below. It can be summarized here briefly.

"The government should begin to set up large military and economic centers—we call them agrovilles—in all the rural regions. These agrovilles would be impregnable, self-sustaining bases—much like the forts we once had in the Old West—from which armed forays into the surrounding countryside could be initiated. Linked to the agrovilles would be a widening chain of strategic hamlets—peasant communities from which the Vietcong have been routed and which remain patrolled by native inhabitants or by the civil guard. Those villages and hamlets that are incorrigibly Communist, that cannot be pacified or locked into the agroville chain, must be destroyed and their inhabitants sent to detention camps or resettled on new land.

"These, Mr. President, are the recommendations I and my team offer. We are firmly convinced that if they are implemented, barring unforeseen contingencies, the civil war in South Vietnam can be liquidated, or effectively curtailed, by 1963–64."

"Thank you, Mr. S————. We'll study your recommendations. Are there any comments or questions? The Attorney General?"

"Yes, I have some questions," Robert Kennedy said. "How many peasants are there in South Vietnam, Mr. S————?"

"Twelve or thirteen million."

"How many villages and hamlets?"

"Between eight and ten thousand."

"In other words, Mr. S————, the agroville and strategic hamlet idea would be quite an undertaking, wouldn't it? According to our intelligence estimates up to three-fourths of the peasants are subject to Vietcong control. That would mean the government would have to move in against some nine million peasants over quite a large land area. Isn't that so?"

"Yes, Mr. Kennedy, though it would not be so extensive as you assume. Much of the population under Vietcong control has no choice. If offered a choice they would go over to the government side."

"Yes," Robert persisted, "but do you think the agroville and strategic hamlet campaign would be popular? Wouldn't it alienate thousands upon thousands of peasants? And what about those whose villages would be destroyed, who would be resettled? They wouldn't be very happy."

"Of course not, Mr. Kennedy, but it is really a matter of how you balance things. We believe that the strategic hamlet program would win over more peasants than it would lose, especially if accompanied by the social and economic reforms we have recommended. The risk is worth taking, if you think South Vietnam's freedom worth preserving."

"Theoretically, your report's very persuasive, Dr. S————," MacNamara said, having read and assimilated it during S————'s talk. "Several months ago, however, Professor Smith—"

"Oh yes. John Smith is an old and dear friend of mine. We have had our diff—"

"May I continue?" MacNamara asked curtly. "He warned us about a vicious cycle that would be generated if the life of the South Vietnamese villages was disrupted. He contended—and I'm sure you're familiar with his thesis—that the peasants would never permit the Saigon mandarins to send in their men and would join the Vietcong en masse if they were."

"Of course I am familiar with Smith's thesis," S——— replied. "And to a limited extent he is correct. The thesis is an old one. It did not originate with Smith. But this should be clear. The traditional mandarins were always alien and exploitative. They were tax collectors, bureaucrats, and the like. The Diem government, if it represents the will of the people, provides adequate protection, and guarantees the economic well-being of the villages, as my report envisages, would not be mandarins at all, except to the hard-core Vietcong. Furthermore—"

MacNamara broke in again. "But we know that the Diem regime is authoritarian and rather close to the landlords and planters. Your own report says so. The peasants distrust him. How's he going to get them to suddenly trust him when he sets up the agrovilles and strategic hamlets?"

"Well, Mr. Secretary," S——— rejoined, "in my opinion he is not as distrusted as is alleged, particularly by John Smith and those who share his views. The villages, I maintain, can be actively brought over to the government's side if it can be demonstrated to them that the government is strong against both the Communists and the special interests."

"Thank you again, Mr. S———," President Kennedy said, looking at his watch. "Let's break for a long lunch and discuss the report further this afternoon."

At three the members of the National Security Council returned to the Teddy Roosevelt Room. "Before we begin," Kennedy said, "I should tell you that I spoke to Professor Smith at his summer place in Vermont. I summarized S———'s report and asked him to comment on it. He said he predicted that that's what the report would find. He warned me not to implement an agroville-strategic hamlet program, which was, he insisted, an invitation to suicide. He was as certain of that, he said, as he was of anything on this earth. Above all, he warned me not to get drawn into South Vietnamese affairs. Asia, he claimed, is a seductress, a siren, and I would be advised to deal with her the same way Ulysses did. He regarded Diem as hopelessly discredited, and dismissed the contention that Diem could win the trust of the people as 'arrant nonsense.'

"I asked Smith what he suggests I do. He offered the following suggestions, though he didn't think I would care for them: We should attempt to secure a political settlement with the North Vietnamese and the Vietcong. Our objective in such a settlement would be to neutralize South Vietnam, hopefully all of Vietnam, with unification as the ultimate step. But to secure neutralization we would have to jettison Diem, work with various neutralists and nationalists, and be prepared to accept Vietcong participation in a future coalition government. Smith admitted that neutralization, or a political settlement on those lines, would be hazardous, and said if I wanted he could set forth the hazards for me in ample detail. He put it this way: Further militarization of the conflict must end in defeat, the magnitude of the defeat being proportionate to the extent of the commitment. A political settlement, at worst, stands a fifty-fifty chance of success.

"That, gentlemen, is Professor Smith's rebuttal of S———'s report. What do you think of it?"

Walt Whitman Rostow was the first to comment. "I've known John Smith for a long, long time. He's a sweet guy, and I respect him greatly. But I wouldn't want to entrust my life, liberty, and happiness to his safekeeping.

"We now have a very imperfect government in Saigon. At least it's in our camp, and as such represents an insuperable obstacle to Chinese Communist hegemony in Southeast Asia. That, Mr. President, is the issue as I perceive it. It's naïve in the extreme to imagine that the North Vietnamese would be content with neutralization. Neutralization is only possible where the contending forces in a country are roughly equal. Without our presence as a counterweight to Peking and Hanoi, how in heaven's name can South Vietnam remain neutral, no matter what's agreed to on paper, no matter how many international agencies and control commissions validate the agreement. I would reverse John Smith's arithmetic. We're certain to lose if we pursue the *ignis fatuus* of neutralization. We stand a darned good chance of containing China if we adopt S———'s recommendations."

"Hear, hear," Bundy declared, thumping the table.

"I think I speak for my colleagues," General Horvitzer said, "when I say we in the armed forces completely agree with Mr. Rostow."

"Does anyone here defend the neutralization of South Vietnam? Bob, do you?"

There was a stir in the room when MacNamara raised his hand to speak.

"Oh no, not all, Mr. President," he said, smiling. "I only want to say that we should face up to the consequences of the decision. I wholeheartedly accept Walt's argument. He's brilliant, as usual, and more important, he's right. But we should realize this: The Diem government is not going to be able to carry out the agroville and strategic hamlet program. In fact, if Diem is given responsibility for it, he'll botch it up and play right into the hands of the enemy. Then we'll have that cycle that Smith explained. I favor sending our own men over there to administer the program, if, Mr. President, you decide to adopt it."

"Well," Kennedy said, leaning back in his rocking chair, "I've thought a lot about it and, as I've said before, we have no choice but to adopt S———'s recommendations. If we committed ourselves to neutralization we might as well say good-bye to SEATO. We'd also be telling all our friends throughout the world, you see, I—the United States—know how to play the game of *machtpolitik,* the politics of power. Sure, we have friends and allies, but if to divide the world into great spheres of interest we have to sacrifice some of them, too bad, tough shit, we sacrifice them. Neutralization means acknowledging Communist China as the dominant power in Southeast Asia.

"That's not going to happen while I'm President. Unfortunately, we'll be getting involved more and more in South Vietnam's problems. I'll do whatever I have to to get the South Vietnamese to do their own fighting. I don't want Americans to fight Asians in Asia —not unless I absolutely must."

"I'm with you a hundred per cent there, Mr. President," General George L. Decker said. "Sooner or later we'll send our elite outfits and mobile infantry units there. South Vietnam will prove a valuable training ground, considering what's going on in the rest of the world."

"General Decker, the American people will decide these matters," Robert Kennedy said impatiently. "They might not like it if their boys are used that way, to teach them the art of counterinsurgency. We might also practice the art of using small nuclear weapons. They've never been deployed before."

"I'm not suggesting that," General Decker replied, "though if the necessity—"

"May I cut short this exchange?" the President broke in. "I'd like to think about the whole question some more. My main concern at this point is what kind of military assistance we should give South Vietnam so it can put these programs into effect. We'll come back to it soon. The Berlin thing is occupying all my time. If we had nothing but Vietnam on our minds life would be a bed of roses."

In October 1961 Kennedy sent General Maxwell Taylor, now the chairman of the Joint Chiefs and the President's most trusted adviser on military affairs, to South Vietnam for "a quick survey to see what needs to be done." During the week that Taylor and his party spent in Saigon the Vietcong insurgents attacked several cities and mauled some government units, while Saigon itself was so unruly President Diem imposed martial law on the city. Once Taylor was nearly caught by a mob of students. "Combat was easier than this," he said.

On his return home he reported at once to Kennedy. "I cannot impress upon you enough the gravity of the situation in South Vietnam," Taylor said in tones reflecting the urgency he felt. "The S——— report must be implemented without a moment's delay. In order to implement it the Diem government must mobilize the country's full resources of manpower and wealth. The army and civil guard must be increased to a total of a half million men, perhaps more in the future. Once it gets under way the strategic hamlets program must be accompanied by widespread economic and political reforms. The Saigon bureaucracy is top heavy. Administrative and political power must be decentralized. There must be maximum local self-government. Self-government and self-defense go hand in hand. Every peasant must feel he has a stake in South Vietnam. Then he can become a minuteman.

"All of this is to say, Mr. President, that the role of the United States must increase greatly. To build up the army we have got to send over many, many more technical and service personnel than we now have there. We have less than a thousand. We must raise that ten- or even twentyfold over the next year or two. Training facilities of all sorts must be constructed and staffed all over that God-forsaken land, and our men will have to run them. It will be quite a task, Mr. President. But unless we commence now, the entire operation will be lost. The Vietcong are growing, and they are receiving weapons and equipment from the North.

"Now if matters continue to deteriorate even after the Vietnamese have mobilized and have trained an army of their own, then, Mr. President, the United States will have to consider the next set of options, and they will be infinitely more serious ones. I'm afraid the cancer is spreading, and it may require more surgery than the South Vietnamese themselves may be able to administer."

"We'll see about that if and when the time comes," Kennedy replied after a long interval. His voice was heavy. "Anyway, we've got to move right now. I'll tell Bob MacNamara to start the ball rolling. By late next year I want ten thousand advisers in South Vietnam. Then we'll determine if more are needed. Every time I think about Vietnam now—I have to confess it, Max—I get a sickening feeling in the pit of my stomach. Do you think it'll turn out to be our nemesis? I see no end in sight."

"We must act with resolution and vigor, Mr. President. The freedom of South Vietnam is not the only thing at stake in this conflict. Courage, sir. You will see the light at the end of the tunnel."

"Yes. But I sometimes wonder."

7

THE EDGE OF ARMAGEDDON

IT was a dark, wintry morning in April 1962 when Mikoyan and Adjhubei arrived for the "emergency" conference in Khrushchev's "bunker" in the sub-sub-basement of the Communist Party Headquarters building on Borodin Square. Khrushchev seemed agitated, and he paced back and forth as he spoke. "I've asked you to come about an important matter."

"Berlin again?" Adjhubei asked.

"No, not Berlin, not Germany. I'm not worried about them. That herring's been salted and put away, though I'll let the West worry about it some more. No, it's much more important.

"There's an American spy in our midst. He's very high up. He knows everything, and he's shown them all our cards."

"You mean our space secrets?" Mikoyan asked.

"Worse, our atomic secrets. This fiend, whoever he is, has told them exactly what we have got and haven't got. The Americans now know how superior they are in missiles and bombs. We know what they have. It's an open secret with the Americans. We know where their bases are, their launching pads, their silos, everything. We know where their Polaris submarines are. But until recently they didn't know what we had, which is why they thought we had such a big lead over them.

"Now they know how much of a lead *they* have over *us*. Before this agent opened our books to them they were afraid of us. Fear is what restrains the Americans. They respect only power. Do you think Kennedy would have called off the invasion of Cuba if he wasn't afraid of our rockets?

"What the Americans don't know is that we now know what they've learned. Confusing, isn't it? Comrades, power politics *is* confusing. No wonder only a very few can play it well. The Americans think we'll go on trying to deceive them. Meanwhile their lead over us continues to grow. They'll laugh in their sleeves, thinking the deception's on us. Well, the deception's still on them because they don't know that we're on to their spying."

"It's a different kind of deception, though, Nikita Sergeyevitch," Mikoyan said, smiling enigmatically. "Once we led them to believe we were stronger. Now we lead them to believe that we don't know what they know, namely how much stronger they are. What good is this kind of deception?"

"I was just getting to that, Anastas Ignatz. Before I do let me ask both of you what you would do in my place. A wise leader will listen to anyone, even his son-in-law and his first deputy."

After a pause Adjhubei said: "Knowing what the Americans know forces us to move ahead on every front. We don't have the luxury of time any more. I say we must have a crash program to produce more and better rockets, more long-range planes, more missile-carrying subs. Everything else should be subordinate to that program."

"But that would push back our goal of Communism, wouldn't it?" Mikoyan asked in his customary rhetorical way. "And how many weapons do we need to convince the Americans that a nuclear war will not be in their interest? They have more cities and industries than we do. They're more vulnerable. It's enough for us to kill them only once. If they want to kill us ten times that's their business."

"Yes," Adjhubei replied, "but remember, if they think they have a big advantage over us they're apt to try something stupid believing we'll back down. I agree with you, Father, fear of our power is what restrains them."

"Theoretically you're right, of course," Mikoyan said with a perfunctory sweep of his hand, dismissing the argument as too obvious to pursue, "but they're not maniacs yet. If we were dealing with a Hitler it would be a different thing. I see no American Hitlers on the horizon."

"There are plenty of madmen in America," Adjhubei persisted. "The Birch Society, the Klux Klan, Texas millionaires, generals, the lumpen class—America has these in abundance.

People thought Hitler was a nobody when his putsch failed in the 1920s."

"Have there been any attempts at putsches in America?" Mikoyan asked slyly. "Do the reactionaries and neo-fascists have any organized following or sympathy among the masses, as Hitler had, even in his early days?"

"Enough, comrades," Khrushchev shouted as he paced the floor, his hands in his jacket pockets. "The problem's difficult, isn't it? Making life and death decisions is like pulling out your own teeth. But you have to pull them out.

"Listen, Alexei, what would happen if we launch a crash program? The United States would immediately launch its own. Another big boost for the capitalists. Mikoyan is right. Our consumer industries would be starved to death. What would become of Communism? Oh yes, the capitalists would be happy. Dulles used to think that the arms race would ruin us. No, it hasn't ruined us, but another big escalation, each missile system costing billions of rubles, might make trouble. My enemies would descend on me like a pack of wolves. I can't make a single move without thinking about them. They plot in every corner. You see, they would say, Khrushchev's lying. His promise of Communism by 1980 is a pipe dream. He's giving the masses opium, a new religion. No, Alexei, no crash program. But we'll go ahead on all fronts just the same. First, we'll find the dog who's been selling our secrets. Penkovsky thinks he knows who it is."

Khrushchev stopped pacing and sat down.

"Suppose, comrades, we took a leaf from the American book. There's a Ukrainian saying: 'You can learn more from your enemies than your friends.' The Americans ring the Soviet Union with rocket bases. Western Europe in front, Turkey on one side, Iran on the other, Pakistan on our tail, Japan above, the submarines below. Someday, we'll have such subs. Until then, should we keep our hands on our asses?

"Here, then, is my plan. We'll secretly install short and intermediate range rocket bases in—where? Guess."

"Cuba," Adjhubei said glumly.

"Cuba's right. No one'll know the missiles are there except we three, Gromyko, a handful of technicians, and Castro. It'll be done without noise. The Americans'll be told only what they should know. They won't object to our installing purely defensive ground-to-air missiles with a range of a few miles, not far enough to threaten the mainland. We'll ship them in during the summer and place them during the American election season, when the government, everybody there, is distracted and confused. The bases'll be well camouflaged in the forest. Their reconnaissance planes won't see a branch out of place. Our men'll be in complete control. A nice situation, eh, if Castro got his hand on some rockets?

"So, comrades, when the time's right we'll spring a little surprise on the Americans. When he finds out, young Kennedy'll raise a big stink. He'll yelp like an injured dog, then lick his wounds and go away. Maybe he'd propose a deal. Fine. But he'd really have to offer something in return. Maybe Berlin. Maybe his foreign bases—a fair exchange. Maybe an agreement on the Polaris subs, our biggest headache. Well, comrades, what do you think? Speak openly. Take me to task if you think I'm wrong."

"One question bothers me, Father," Adjhubei said softly, diffidently, blinking behind his thick glasses. "Can Kennedy or any American President accept missile bases on Cuba without losing face at home? The rightist lunatics—"

"Wait!" Khrushchev broke in. "You bring this up every time I propose something. You gave the same argument during the squeeze on Berlin. Why do you always look at life from their point of view? It's the road to paralysis and defeat. I told you last year and I tell you now, I'm not in business to solve America's domestic problems. When they built those bases around us, when they made those alliances, they didn't ask us what we thought. When they made those subs they didn't ask us.

"Listen, what's sauce for the hen is sauce for the cock. The American fascists? They'll behave only when certain lessons are knocked into their heads—that we're strong and resourceful and can give two blows for one."

Mikoyan, who knew Khrushchev better than anyone, quietly asked how long the whole operation would take, from the shipment of the missiles to the establishment of the bases.

"Pushnikov, who's in charge, has told me the parts could be crated and the men organized in a few weeks. The operation'll get under way in late June, early July, and should be completed sometime in November."

Mikoyan smiled and gave his hand to Khrushchev. "Success, Comrade Chairman. Nothing succeeds quite like it. If all goes according to plan you will be a hero in the Soviet Union and to all Communists, and posterity will salute you."

"Let's drink to that," Khrushchev shouted as he bounded over to a cabinet, from which he removed a canister of vodka and three large glasses. He poured the drink and raised his glass high above his head. "A toast to our success, comrades."

The delicate "operation" proceeded on schedule. Beginning in late June, two and three ships a week, sometimes more, left Soviet ports carrying missile parts, fuel, and technicians to Cuba.

Before long some American politicians were complaining about the "build-up." Senator Chapman Homer of Indiana, ranking Republican on the Foreign Relations Committee, declared that "the Cuban Communists were preparing to attack the Panama Canal," and he accused the administration of "sacrificing the security of this country and this hemisphere on the altar of appeasement."

Cuba became the dominant issue in the fall congressional campaign. Expressing the sentiment of the Republican Party, ex-President Eisenhower delivered a series of speeches across the country denouncing Kennedy's "Caspar Milquetoast policy." One prominent Republican senator even claimed to have "evidence from impeccable sources that ballistic missiles were being installed only ninety miles from our shores."

Kennedy stoutly denied that Cuba posed "a threat to the security of the United States." However, he warned in a speech at the Harvard Club, "if such a threat did arise our response would be swift and decisive." At a news conference he explained the recent increase in the shipment of Soviet arms and personnel to Cuba. "We are satisfied that what is being installed there are ground-to-air missiles, with a range of twenty to twenty-five miles. They are defensive, and we have no objection to their presence, though we regard the need for them as superfluous."

The Republicans, nonetheless, pursued the Cuban issue. It was the only one they had.

Khrushchev took notice of the gathering tempest in the United States, and he gave out reassuring statements. "We're not insane," he told a visiting American businessman. "We've got enough rockets here, where they're well positioned and concealed. Why should we need them on your continent? Our only motive is to help the Cuban people help themselves. This is their natural and their legal right. Tell me, how's it possible for a great nation like yours to worry itself silly over a tiny island, a wisp of a country trying to live its own life?"

On Tuesday, October 16, 1962, at 8:30 A.M., as he was dressing for breakfast with congressional leaders, Kennedy received a call on his "blue" phone (a direct line used by his closest aides only in an emergency). It was MacGeorge Bundy, his special assistant on national security, speaking very slowly and precisely.

"Mr. President, the crunch is on. Pentagon developed a new set of pictures from Cuba. The evidence is incontrovertible. The Russians are building medium and intermediate range missile sites. Colonel Ed Wright, who flew some U-2 missions over Russia, says they are exactly the same kind as he found in the Soviet Union."

"Are we absolutely certain, George?"

"Fairly absolute, sir."

"How many flights do we have over Cuba?"

"One a day."

"Make it five a day. I want a new set of pictures by early this afternoon. Incidentally, where are the sites located?"

"Western Cuba. San Cristóbol, not far from the Bay of Pigs."

"George, when did you find out about this?"

"Late last night, Mr. President. I didn't want to disturb you after you had gone to bed, and I wanted to check it out again."

"Next time don't be so solicitous. I can live with doubts. Now contact everyone on the Security Council and have them meet me at three this afternoon in the Polk Room. Tell them what's up, but don't let on to anyone else, including your family. Tell them that too. Keep the atmosphere calm and normal as though nothing untoward were happening. I'll go through my regular routine, but I'll cancel my appointments this afternoon. Remember, mum's the word."

Kennedy paused before continuing. Then he spoke rapidly, one of his telltale signs of anger.

"That lying, devious son of a bitch. That cocksucker. Pulling a fast one like this. Is he crazy? Does he think he can get away with it? Does he want an atomic war? I can't figure him out.

Maybe he *is* crazy. Yesterday he said the Soviet Union and the United States should lock arms and keep the peace. Isn't that what he said?"

"Yes, Mr. President, those were his very words."

"Well I'd better stop before I work myself up to an explosion. I don't want our congressional friends to see me this way. They'll spread it around that I'm having trouble with my wife. O.K., you know what to do. See you at three. Oh yes, ask Acheson and Lovett [Robert Lovett, a Republican and former Secretary of Defense, now an investment banker in New York] to attend the meeting."

Kennedy chose the James K. Polk Room because it contained a rare old mahogany table, purchased by Jacqueline in London, that could be enlarged to accommodate up to sixty people. Almost that number appeared for the "council of war," as it was later referred to by its participants.

Kennedy, who had just entertained Prime Minister Abu Ngali of Mali in the Rose Garden, strode in at three, Sorensen behind him, and sat in his leather-bound rocking chair.

"Gentlemen," he said quietly, staring into space, "we're at the edge of Armaggedon. I don't think any group of men at any time in history bears a heavier burden than you, than we do here, at this moment in time. Let it be recorded: 3:04, October 16, 1962.

"You know, it's amazing. When you're in a situation like this, all the clichés, the artifices, the formal encumbrances disappear. You can feel the awful, terrible truth in your mouth. It's there. You can't shake it. You simply have to act, to do something, because it just won't go away.

"I'm sorry for going on this way. Now let's get down to work. You've seen the latest pictures. The bases are there all right, and they're going up fast. I'll have hour by hour reports on their stages of development. At the moment they're at least two weeks from completion. That's the time we have. The question, gentlemen, is what we should do. You've had a chance to think it over, at least a little bit, and I notice some of you have put down your thoughts on paper. For posterity, I suppose—if there is one.

"In this conference, it goes without saying, each of you is equal.

There's no rank, one man's opinion is as good as another's. That's your compensation for the misfortune of having been invited here."

"But, Mr. President," Dean Rusk said, smiling hesitantly, "is it a misfortune? Like the knights at Agincourt we can say that we have lived, that we bore witness, that we were there."

"Aren't you being a bit premature?" Treasury Secretary Douglas Dillon asked. "The crisis has hardly begun and you're writing its chronicle already. Besides, there may not be anyone around to care."

"O.K.," the President said brusquely, tapping his temple lightly with his forefinger, "let's get down to business. Go ahead, Bob."

"I appreciate the gravity of the moment," MacNamara said, leaning forward, his arms on the table, "but I don't think we're near having a battle of Armageddon or even Agincourt, though on Shakespeare I defer to you, Dean. I frankly don't understand what the fuss is all about. If you examine the matter closely what have the Russians done? They've put, or are about to put, intermediate range missiles up close to us. That doesn't give the Russians much of an advantage in anything. They can now throw nuclear missiles at us, plenty of them, from the Russian mainland. And they couldn't start anything from Cuba and avoid direct retaliation at home. If they mounted a rocket assault against us from San Cristóbol, they'd have to expect a rocket in Moscow within an hour. That means, of course, they won't turn any of their bases over to Castro. They certainly aren't going to give him the power of life and death over them."

"What you say sounds reasonable, Bob," the President said. "Tell me this. Khrushchev knows exactly what you and I know. Why, then, has he put the goddamned missiles into Cuba? It couldn't be because he has nothing to gain."

"That question's on my mind, on everyone's mind in this room, Mr. President," MacNamara replied even before Kennedy had finished. "My own feeling is this. Khrushchev is trying as cheaply and as easily as possible to redress Russia's inferiority as a nuclear power. He realizes that we have him by the short hairs. There's nothing the Soviet Union can do, not for a long time anyway, to catch up with us. If I'm correct in my contention then we'd be better served if we allow those damn bases to be built in Cuba. When Khrushchev's a little more confident of Russia's equality he may come to terms with us on disarmament and other issues. He never will as long as there's a missile gap."

"Rot and balderdash!" CIA director John A. McCone asserted angrily, upsetting his cup of bourbon and water. McCone, known in Washington circles as the "hawk's hawk" because of his uncompromisingly tough anti-Communist position and his gruff, curt manner, had replaced Allen Dulles some months before. McCone had long suspected a "nefarious Soviet plot" in Cuba and had urged Kennedy to triple the number of intelligence operatives on the island.

"Secretary MacNamara, you seem to think that Mr. Khrushchev, or any Communist leader, is nice and reasonable, like your neighbor down the street in Chevy Chase. My God, what folly! Let the Communists think they're your equal and they'll be on top of you in a trice. Only our greater firepower keeps them in line."

"Maybe so," MacNamara argued, "but where does your reasoning lead, Mr. McCone? Why should the Russians supinely accept their inferiority? It's entirely possible they trust us as little as we trust them. When you begin with the devil theory of Communism you're forced to say about them—as good Christians were once taught to say about the devil—they *know* they're evil because they're evil objectively, and we're righteous objectively, and by destroying them we'd be doing God's work."

"I'm not talking abut evil and righteousness, damn it," McCone shot back, "I'm talking about power and world domination. Communism is expansionist. We're not. Only our superior strength stops them and therefore maintains stability. Give them parity and the world will have nothing but instability."

"See here, Mr. McCone," MacNamara said impatiently. "Events have disproved your thesis. Despite our tremendous superiority the Soviet Union has just done something that's unsettling, to say the least. Why isn't the world stable? If it were, we wouldn't be here now."

"May I get back to the track again?" Acheson, who had been doodling, asked tartly. "Mr. MacNamara, you see the issue from a very narrow spectrum. The laws of optics tell us that a narrow spectrum set against a wide field blurs the colors and destroys the image—"

"You sound like my opthamologist, Mr. Acheson."

"Merely a figure illustrating the point. And the point is this. The Soviet Union always acts within a total context. It does nothing in separate packages. It undertakes no specific strategy independent of its over-all interests. The Soviet mind, the Russian mind, is not empirical and inductive, like ours. It is ruthlessly rational and wholistic, if you know what I mean. It assumes the existence of a block universe, as William James once described such a mentality. So that the installation of missile bases in Cuba cannot be seen in isolation from other facets of Soviet policy. To me it is obvious that Khrushchev will use Cuba as a fulcrum by which to pry us out of Berlin or break up NATO. I propose, Mr. President, that you do not wait to find out."

"I would like to address myself to the Secretary's remarks also," Theodore Sorensen said. Though only thirty-four, he was Kennedy's most intimate political counselor, and everyone in the room attended to him carefully.

"Permitting the Soviets to place missiles in Cuba may be technically justified, and it may even bring long-term benefits in Soviet-American relations. But what President could survive the political consequences of such an act of statesmanship? Not even Eisenhower. The President has been pilloried by the Republicans for months now simply for letting Castro live. Contemplate what they would say when they learned that the President has given his tacit approval to the installation of Russian missile bases there. If we are going to have political martyrs they should serve better causes than this."

"I second that, Ted," Robert Kennedy added. "And something else should be emphasized. What would become of us in Latin America if the Soviets gain a foothold this way in Cuba? I think we would lose everything. The Alliance would go to smash. One Castroite uprising would follow another. The time might come when there are Russian sites in Nicaragua, Colombia, Guatemala, etc."

"Just as we have sites in Turkey, Italy, Germany, etc.," Mac-Namara replied sharply. "Why, unless you accept the devil theory of Russia, should missile sites be right for us and wrong for them?"

"I think I can settle the dispute amicably," the President said. "You have a point, Bob, and we would be advised to see it from the Soviet side. However, apart from the arguments already presented on the political and international consequences of Russian bases in Cuba—all of which see the issue from our side—there's this to keep in mind. The American missile bases in Europe and Asia have been up for some time. Habit and convention, after all, render them acceptable, if not necessarily legitimate. The Soviets know they'll never be used except in a general atomic war. Then, all at once, Khrushchev introduces a great change. The calculations are upset, the equilibrium seriously disturbed. Suddenly everything's up in the air. The world, the American people, don't know what to expect now. Our obligation is to restore the *status quo ante*. We want a return to normalcy."

"I perceive your point very clearly, Mr. President," said Undersecretary of State George Ball, a long-time associate of Adlai Stevenson and a highly placed New York corporation lawyer. "But suppose restoring the *status quo ante* involved a nuclear exchange? How would we then serve the well-being of our people and mankind?"

"Now, George," the President replied, a note of irritation creeping into his voice, "I certainly don't think we'd be serving them if we backed off. I would rather give up my life than see a nuclear exchange—if that was my choice. But it isn't. The choice is whether we stand up to Khrushchev's nuclear threat or knuckle under to it. How the hell will we be able to live with ourselves if we submit to him? What would our allies and friends, not to mention the neutrals, think of us? If we resist, yes, we run the risk of atomic war. I believe we must run that risk."

Silence followed. Then the Chiefs of Staff (led by Air Force General Curtis LeMay) broke out in applause. Finally everyone in the room applauded. Kennedy smiled sheepishly. He thanked them after it had subsided.

"But no more rhetoric or emotion, if we can help it," he said. "Let's be cool and controlled. It's the only way we'll see our way clear."

"Mr. President," General Maxwell Taylor said, "we have only one course, and that is to conduct strikes immediately against the missile bases, and then back up the bombings with airborne landings. I think we can complete the job that we began at the Bay of Pigs last year. We can kill two birds with one stone: the bases and Castro."

"May I ask the Joint Chiefs a question or two?" Adlai Stevenson asked. "How certain are we that we can demolish *all* the bases."

General LeMay answered: "We would get almost all of them. You can be sure of that, sir. No, there's no certainty we would get absolutely all of them."

"Tell me this, General, how many people in your estimation might be killed in such an airstrike. Hundreds, thousands, how many?"

"We estimate that each intermediate base, if fully operational, with all its required personnel on hand, has about a thousand people. If there are fifteen to twenty bases and the bombings caught them by surprise, about ten to fifteen thousand might die."

"That would include the Russians stationed there?"

"I assume so. If they're there, they'll be hit."

"Mr. President," Stevenson said, "I submit that we should not resort to military extremities until every attempt at diplomacy has been exhausted. If we kill thousands of Russians we will force Khrushchev to act precipitately. Nothing is more dangerous, sir, than to allow events to dominate you instead of you them."

"I can think of a damn sight worse thing," McCone said in a loud voice, "and that is procrastinating until it's too late. At that point—this has been my experience, at any rate, and I admit I ain't no intellectual—action makes things worse. As far as I'm concerned if we don't strike now we shouldn't strike at all. Let them build their goddamned bases."

"How in God's name, then, can we go before the bar of world opinion?" Robert Kennedy declared, throwing his arms up. "We'll kill thousands of innocent people. O.K., let's set that aside. But down to the end of time we, the United States, under the administration of John F. Kennedy, pulled a Pearl Harbor. What a blot on our history! Shame, future generations will say. Can 'America have done that? Is that how we act when the heat's on —we sneak up and drop bombs? That's not our way. That's not America."

Acheson turned toward Robert Kennedy and drew himself up to his full Brahmin height. "Now, Mr. Kennedy, you seem more concerned with world opinion and future generations than with the threat at hand. World opinion and future generations are not going to save us, here and now. They can't make our decisions for us. Nor will they bear our responsibilities. Of one fact I am absolutely certain. If we prevail the world now and to come will applaud us. If we fail, thanks to our abstract and irrelevant standards of rectitude, they will damn us. And properly so. Ruling a great power in a hostile world is not like running the Ethical Culture Society, the Civil Liberties Union, or writing textbooks for children."

"Mr. Acheson, you have a wonderful way of setting up straw men. You make it appear that if anyone disagrees with you he has no understanding of power politics and the ways of the world, no appreciation of America's national interest. Every country has its own definition of its national interest. Not being a totalitarian nation America can't act like one."

"Mr. Kennedy, when my life is at stake I'm not going to scruple about the methods of saving it. When the United States was a small country it could afford to castigate the big powers of the Old World for their imperfections. Yet, when the chips were down we didn't act differently. Lincoln suspended Habeas Corpus when he was President, and he justified it by claiming that he had to cut off a limb to save the body. That's the situation we are in now. I'm for sending our planes aloft at the earliest feasible notice."

"Mr. Acheson, you'll excuse my presumption in saying it, but you seem to have overlooked something," Ball said. "Suppose we succeed in destroying all the bases, and the Russians and Cubans then deny they ever existed. The world won't know the truth. Our version will be suspect. The pictures we show will be ridiculed as another CIA fraud. We will be branded a cruel and heinous aggressor. Withholding military action while pursuing diplomacy will, as the Attorney General put it, win our case before the bar of world public opinion."

"May I interject a word here?" Thomas Llewelyn, ex-ambassador to the Soviet Union asked diffidently. "Soviet leaders, whatever we may think of them, have always been wary of alienating world public opinion. From my knowledge of them I would say this: they are restrained when convinced that their acts are unpopular and emboldened when convinced that their acts are popular. This generalization, I hasten to add, is valid within the limits of what they regard as their legitimate national interests."

"All right gentlemen," Kennedy said, "before we go at each other's throats let me throw this question at you. Let's assume we take the diplomatic approach. What should it be? We're agreed the bases have to come out within a given period, before they're completed. Adlai, what do you think?"

"Well, Mr. President," Stevenson said, reading from a sheet of paper, "it's my view that we should obtain our objectives without driving Khrushchev to the wall. That, I say, should be our immediate, or first-line objective. If that proves unfeasible, then we will have to take the ultimate step. And I believe we should be prepared to take that step. Preparing for it gives us our best chance of avoiding it. What I propose, is this: that we order the removal of the missile sites at the same time as we offer to depart from the Guantánamo Naval Base or give up our missile bases in Turkey. We shall have lost nothing in the process, and Khrushchev will not have been humiliated. And we shall have secured our objective."

While Stevenson spoke Douglas Dillon was heard to snicker, McCone said "crap" in a loud whisper, and Robert A. Lovett moaned.

"Mr. Stevenson," Lovett said, tapping his pencil on the table, "why are you so concerned about rescuing poor old Khrushchev from humiliation? Why would you have the United States be so apologetic? Why do you seem to justify—for that's how I construe your proposal—the installation of the missiles by seeking a *quid pro quo,* as though we and they were equally culpable?"

"Hear, hear," Acheson shouted.

McCone stared at Stevenson contemptuously. "Some intellectuals, so-called, see our enemy's position more clearly than ours. I find your proposal disgraceful, sir."

Stevenson paused before replying. "I was under the impression that the patriotism and good will of everybody in this room was taken for granted. I find instead that some will readily impugn the loyalty and insult the good sense of those who disagree with them. Mr. McCone, I'm no less interested in the welfare of our nation than you, and whether or not you think my proposal disgraceful is of no moment to me whatever. And Mr. Lovett, I'm as surprised by your acerbity as by your failure of logic. Yes, I do mean a *quid pro quo*. After all, what is diplomacy but seeking *quid pro quos*? Anything else is either submission or conquest. What is curious is that you, an experienced man of affairs, should equate *quid pro quos* with attribution of guilt. Judges hand down sentences to the guilty. Diplomats work out arrangements between contending parties on the basis not of right but of power and interest."

McCone, whose eyes seemed to bore holes through Stevenson, was about to say something.

The President intervened. "Listen, gentlemen, Khrushchev would like nothing better than to have us fight this way, insult each other, question each other's intelligence, integrity, and loyalty. I know how all of you feel. Only we've got to contain ourselves and treat each other civilly. And no further *ad hominem* remarks either.

"Now as to your proposal, Adlai. I don't see how we can negotiate with the Russians under this sort of duress. It won't be a *quid pro quo,* even if we wanted one, because they'll have acquired a trump card and will demand a much higher *quo* for our *quid* than Guantánamo. I might want to talk to the Russians about these matters some day—but only after they've unconditionally liquidated their missile sites. What we have to take up now is how we can get them to do that."

It was Roswell Gilpatrick, a distinguished Wall Street lawyer before his appointment as Deputy Secretary of Defense, who first came up with the idea of blockading Cuba.

A blockade, Gilpatrick said, would have the "salutary effect" of giving Khrushchev time to "think things over" while the United States called international attention to the "provocation." He also explained that a blockade in "our waters" would place the Soviet Union at a disadvantage. "There is no way they could break a naval blockade short of war. But that decision would be theirs, not ours."

George Ball said he very much favored a blockade. Only, he added, it would have to be "artfully executed." "Our warships must be polite and correct. When they stop Soviet and East European merchantmen they must give ample warning, turning back only those vessels that contain parts or fuel for offensive missiles. The others should be allowed to go through."

"Admiral Anderson," Kennedy said, addressing the Naval Chief of Staff, "can your men artfully execute such a blockade?"

"Yes sir, they can. But what should our men do if the enemy fails to heed the warning?"

"Well," Kennedy said, "I guess a shot across the bow would be sufficient. If that doesn't work, then, well, you'll have to play it by ear. In any event I would exert a minimum of violence, if it could be avoided. But that decision would be up to the Russians, wouldn't it?"

"I gather, then, Mr. President," Acheson said, "that you have settled on a blockade. If you think you have that much time, and if you have that much faith in Khrushchev's reasonableness, so be it. However, let me remind you, sir, that the irritant will not have been removed even if the Soviets honor the blockade, as they probably will. In fact, honoring it may give them their opportunity to complete the building of the bases. Then we will be back where we were."

"I think I can answer that," Robert Kennedy said.

"The Attorney General will set me straight. I'm flattered."

"That's all right, Mr. Acheson, setting people straight is my life's vocation," Robert Kennedy replied with a grin, as the room broke into laughter. [Acheson sat expressionless.]

"If after the blockade has been in effect our reconnaissance planes bring back pictures showing that the bases are still going up, then we—the President—can decide on the next step. At that point we'll be authorized to strike at the sites. The world will have been satisfied that Khrushchev provoked the attack. All diplomatic means will have been exhausted by then."

President Kennedy concluded the Security Council meeting with the tacit understanding that he would announce the blockade during a brief and dramatic speech to the nation on Sunday night, October 21. Until then, he said, "appearances will have to be kept up by everyone here." For the plan to work, Khrushchev had to be taken by surprise, "caught off balance, his lies and deceits exposed."

Kennedy emphasized that "no one outside this room, including our loved ones, wives, children, and girl friends, can be told." He had noticed that some reporters had already "gotten wind of something" and were "sniffing around the corridors, asking questions." If, by chance, some reporters did learn what was "afoot," he said, "they should be told everything and forcefully asked to keep quiet until my speech."

Between Tuesday and Sunday appearances were fastidiously kept up. Officials routinely performed their duties and attended parties and dinners—and, late at night, clandestinely met in the basement of the Executive Office Building, the ninth floor of the State Department, and the "inner ward" of the Pentagon. Secret orders went out to alert American forces in Germany and Korea and at every base in the world. The Strategic Air Command increased the number of B-52 bombers flying around the clock with their complement of hydrogen bombs. Tests of intercontinental rockets were conducted daily. Three squadrons of fighter bombers landed in Florida. When asked what all the activity signified, Pentagon spokesmen offhandedly said that "intensive maneuvers of a routine nature" were taking place. Various cabinet members went off on speaking tours for congressional candidates. Kennedy himself left for the Midwest on Friday, October 19, having decided that he would contract a cold early Sunday morning, when the National Security Council was scheduled to reconvene for a final review of the speech and the strategy ahead.

Before departing for the campaign trip Kennedy received a distinguished visitor from abroad—none other than Andrei Gromyko, the Soviet Foreign Minister. Gromyko had requested the talk in the hope, as he described it in his flawless English, "of facilitating an improvement in relations between our two countries."

"There is no reason why we should be at odds over Berlin," Gromyko said lubriciously. He went on to indicate that Khrushchev would probably come to the United States later in the year to attend a session of the UN's General Assembly, and would appreciate an invitation to the White House.

Nodding slightly, Kennedy said he would invite Khrushchev, though he failed to see "what useful purpose a meeting would serve at this time."

In passing, he asked Gromyko what was going on in Cuba.

"Is there any substance to reports that you're sending Castro offensive weapons against us?"

Gromyko scoffed at "those silly reports." "As Premier Khrushchev has said over and over, the Soviet Union has not, is not, and will not provide Cuba with offensive weapons of any sort. Besides, Mr. President, how can an infant, a little baby like Cuba, harm a great country like the United States? Lay your fears to rest. In moments of stress Premier Khrushchev often cites a Ukrainian proverb to us which may be useful to you too. 'Fear nothing, eat well, make love to your woman, sleep soundly, and the world will be at your feet.'"

"Excellent advice. I hope soon to be able to follow it. First I must get rid of a few trivial problems."

On Sunday morning Kennedy developed his cold and flew back to Washington. He spent the day going over his speech with Sorensen and his brother, and, after many corrections, with the National Security Council, which recommended still more corrections.

At 7 P.M. (Eastern Daylight Saving Time) he went on television before an audience estimated at 120 million. Never had he looked so somber (he had refused to wear make-up, and the shadows cast by the lights deepened the lines that had newly emerged on his face). And never had the American people heard such a somber speech.

Wasting no time on preliminaries Kennedy began by reciting the recent history of Soviet involvement in Cuba: the large shipments of military goods and personnel which the United States had been deceived into believing were sent for defensive purposes; the reassuring statements by Khrushchev and Gromyko, all of them "bald-faced lies"; and then the discovery, drawn from "incontestable evidence, verified by daily reconnaissance flights" that offensive missiles of both medium and intermediate range were being deployed "a short distance from United States shores." "They could strike at targets in an area from Rio de Janeiro in the south to Montreal in the north. Never in our history have we faced such a threat. The existence of the United States is at stake."

He explained why the placement of such missiles was intolerable. He acknowledged that the United States had bases elsewhere in the world, some of them close to the Soviet Union. But he claimed that they were operated openly and aboveboard whereas the Soviet Union had embarked on building these bases in stealth, behind a cloak of deception and prevarication. Obviously its intention was to dominate the world, and its actions presented a clear and present danger to the security of the United States and the peace of the world.

But, he continued, the United States would not permit this invasion of the Western Hemisphere. It would honor its commitments. The United States, he emphasized, sought good relations with the Soviet Union and a settlement of outstanding issues, but only after the missile bases had been removed promptly and unconditionally.

Kennedy then outlined the steps he would take at once. By Tuesday, October 23, the blockade of Cuba—which he called a "protective quarantine" (a blockade, according to international law, being tantamount to a declaration of war)—would be in force. Reconnaissance flights would be increased. And the United Nations and the Organization of American States would be informed of America's response to the "aggression" and their support solicited.

The conclusion of the speech was full of the direst portents: Should an attack be launched from Cuba on any country in the hemisphere, the United States would retaliate instantaneously upon the real source of the attack—the Soviet Union. Although the last thing in the world that the people of the United States wanted was nuclear war, if such a war was forced upon them they would fight it as they had fought their wars in the past. The choice thus rested with Khrushchev.

And so what mankind had feared since the nuclear age began in 1945 had come to pass. The two superpowers, each possessing the capacity to destroy the other, the human race, indeed all life on earth, now headed for a showdown. Suddenly, all the extraneous issues, all the complexities of international politics, disappeared. Cuba counted for nothing in the balance (Kennedy had scarcely mentioned it in his speech). The various military alliances counted for nothing. What alone counted was the showdown. If neither side retreated, there would be atomic war. Who, then, would retreat, and how? This was the question that forced itself on the minds of everyone who heard Kennedy's historic speech.

Khrushchev learned of Kennedy's speech at 3 A.M. Moscow time. Alexei Adjhubei woke him from a deep sleep, induced by the vast quantity of slivovitz (plum brandy) he had drunk the night before at the Romanian embassy. Though his head throbbed painfully, and he could hardly keep his eyes open, Khrushchev sprang to his feet when told: "The Americans know about the Cuban bases."

He dressed while Adjhubei summarized Kennedy's speech. After throwing water on his face and drinking a large glass of lemon juice, Khrushchev summoned Mikoyan, Gromyko, Malinowsky (the Minister of Defense), and Admiral Pyotr Pestel (the Chief Naval Officer), to come to his office at once.

"How did the Americans find out?" Khrushchev asked Malinowsky.

"They have developed new photographic devices that can reveal what is written in a newspaper from five miles up. They first used this equipment in the U-2 flights over our country."

"Why don't we have such equipment?"

"I expect the Leningrad Technion to have even more advanced photography by the end of the year," Malinowsky replied.

"Anyway," Khrushchev said, pouting slightly, "I didn't expect them to find out so soon. Our camouflage experts weren't so expert. They're going to be held to account for this. See to it that they are, Malinowsky."

He turned to Gromyko. "Didn't Kennedy let on anything to you when you spoke to him on Thursday?"

"Not a word, not a hint, Comrade Chairman. He showed no special interest in Cuba, and he nodded his head when I told him what our policy was."

"But he knew then. What a schemer! And our intelligence in Washington smelled nothing? How strange! Anastas, look into it. What was our diplomatic staff in Washington doing this last week? They live too well, that's what. Too many parties, restaurants, girls. Maybe we'll have to go back to Stalin's methods. Our people are sinking too deep into the fleshpots of Western decadence. What happens to their children when they come back? I want that investigated also.

"But I can't worry about these things now. What worries me is that young lunatic. Why, he's talking war! That's what his speech amounts to. Doesn't he realize that events can get out of hand, that we, he and I, won't be able to control them after a certain point? Maybe he's too young, too callow, too foolhardy, to realize it. Maybe he wants to commit suicide. Maybe he wants to drag everybody down with him. I've known such people. There's nothing to be done with them except put them away or dispose of them. They're nihilists.

"Or maybe there's another explanation. Maybe he lost his head, overreacted. The crisis was too much for him. Why should he provoke a conflict because we put some missiles in Cuba? Did we provoke a conflict when they surrounded us with their bases? Instead of dealing with me in a businesslike way, instead of asking me why I decided to install the missiles, he creates a crisis of life and death, as though it were no great matter to him that our civilization might go under. That's the sort of person I have to deal with. And to tell you the truth—"

"Comrade Chairman," Mikoyan broke in, "I would like to point out that the situation is not as bleak as it seems at first glance. If you read his speech carefully you'll observe that the blockade does nothing more than freeze the status quo. Only if our ships challenge the blockade will force come into play. He's vague about the bases themselves. If we ride out the blockade the whole crisis may blow over."

"You might be right, comrade," Gromyko added. "Kennedy might have raised a hue and cry against us to help his party in the elections next month. He has to prove how tough he is. When the election is over and the dust settles Kennedy will probably drop the issue."

"I think we're allowing ourselves to fall into a dangerous trap," Adjhubei said heatedly. "That trap, the deadliest of all, is wishful thinking. Why will he drop the issue now that he's raised it? His aim, comrades, is to have us remove the missile bases. That can't be wished away. Now that he has a pretext, do you think he'll hesitate very long to bomb Cuba, invade it, oust Castro? Yes, I know, the Cuban masses will fight bravely, they'll go into the hills, etc. But Havana will be occupied, an American puppet government will be put in, and so on. We have to face the question, comrades. If we don't comply with Kennedy's ultimatum, the blockade being the interval between the announcement of the threat and the decision to carry it out—if we don't comply, are we ready to see Castro fall, or are we ready to fight an atomic war, limited or total? Early as it is in the morning these are the choices we must think about. I haven't even had my tea."

"I agree, I agree," Khrushchev said wearily. "But Alexei my son, do we have to confront those choices now? The Americans aren't about to attack. Who knows? Maybe they won't. Maybe they'll back down. They don't know what we'll do. Right now, I grant, they have an advantage. We're not going to challenge their stupid blockade. How can we? Admiral Pestel, order all ships carrying missiles to Cuba to turn back. Order the other ships to submit to searching parties. If they gratuitously attack one of our ships, well, we'll see. Iran and Berlin and Turkey are more valuable than a ship or two. Meanwhile, we'll obey the blockade. As for the rest, we'll see."

Even as the Soviet press and radio denounced the blockade as "an extreme provocation," a violation of Soviet international rights, an act of "brigandage" and "criminality unprecedented in recent history," the Soviet and East European ships heading for Cuba were turning back or submitting to American naval inspection. UN Secretary General U Thant, a gentle diplomat from Burma, proposed negotiations leading "to the termination of the blockade." He urged, as a start, that a "truce" go into effect. The United States would "suspend" the blockade for two or three weeks, during which time no Soviet ships would enter the Caribbean blockade zone. On Thursday, October 25, Kennedy and Khrushchev sent brief notes to Thant accepting his terms.

Tensions subsided so sharply that many believed the crisis was over.

In fact, the crisis had entered its climactic phase. The latest reconnaissance photographs showed "a marked acceleration in the erection of the missile bases," as the official memo to Kennedy described it. Accordingly, on Thursday evening, Kennedy and his advisers decided, with no dissent or reservations, that early the following week, "by Wednesday at the latest," the bases would be bombed and upwards of 100,000 soldiers and Marines would be landed in Cuba.

"Khrushchev thinks we're going to be diverted by the sillyass blockade issue," Kennedy said. "Thant has been taken in by that fourflusher. Don't they understand I don't care a fig about the goddamned blockade? Bobby, I want you to go right away to Ambassador Dobrinin. Impress him with the gravity of the situation. Dean [Rusk], have Stevenson issue a warning that we're going to bomb them to smithereens. I want Khrushchev to get the message, and pronto."

By Friday, October 26, the message had been communicated to the world. "The minutes are ticking away relentlessly," a columnist for the New York *Chronicle* wrote, "and we are like the man who helplessly sees his life ebbing away. Tomorrow, or the day after, or the day after that, the assault on Cuba will begin. What will the Soviet response be? Awaiting the answer, we count the minutes." Secretary Rusk was heard to say to a visitor, as they left his State Department suite, "I guess it's better to go with a bang than with a whimper."

Throughout the United States cities were storing food, recruiting air-raid volunteers, working out "contingency plans." In southern California whole communities became ghost towns overnight, as their inhabitants disappeared into family-owned caves and bunkers, many of them stocked with rifles, machine guns, bazookas, and other weapons necessary to keep out predatory strangers during the period of Armageddon. Elsewhere, crowds silently gathered in public places to hear the news. New York's Grand Central Station seemed to be full at all hours, night and day, as people stared vacantly into the enormous television screen that hung down from the four hundred-foot-high ceiling. "America hasn't panicked," a correspondent of *La Terre* cabled from Washington, "it's merely comatose."

President Kennedy and his aides remained in the White House Communications Room, waiting for one thing—Khrushchev's answer.

Late Friday evening, after waking up from a catnap (his only form of sleep), Kennedy told of a "wish-fulfillment" dream he had just had. "I was sitting in my office when I heard a knock on the door. It opened and in walked Khrushchev, his hat in his hand, his head bent low. He said, 'Please, sir, don't ask me to sit. May I kneel before you and kiss your ring?' Before I could say anything he flung himself at my feet and grabbed my hand. All he said to me was, 'You can have everything. Only don't harm my family. Let us live. Let us all live in peace. You can have everything.' I tried to assure him I had nothing against his family, but he continued to press my hand against his cheek, which was wet with tears. Then I got up."

"Oh God," Sorensen said, shaking his head, "if only dreams were the stuff of which reality is made."

"Here's a message from State," someone in the room shouted. "It's a translation of a letter addressed to . . . President . . . Kennedy. Hurry, Mr. President, it's from Khrushchev."

Kennedy rushed over to the teletype machine. He read the following letter.

Mr. Kennedy:

Is it conceivable that our countries are on the verge of war? Do you know what war is? I know you served heroically against the Japanese fascists. I know you were injured rescuing your comrades. We Russians honor you for it. But do you have any idea what *total* war is like? How can you! America has been spared that horror. She fought on other continents, in other peoples' homelands. I do not hold that against you. If the Hitlerite aggressors had not been stopped in Europe, you would have had them in your country. The Soviet Union does know what war is. Forty million of her sons and daughters died in the Great Patriotic War. I myself lost a son, a fine, beautiful lad, who was just entering life. Do you have any idea what happened to our cities—those that lay in the path of the Hitlerite sadists? You can count on the fingers of one hand those they failed to level, a mass of rubble and rats. That's what our victorious sons and daughters came home to!

We have worked hard since 1945 to rebuild our beloved country. Mr. President, you may not like Communism any more than I like capitalism. But our peoples, regardless of their ideologies, have a right to live, to raise their families in peace and hope. This is what the Soviet Union has done in the last seventeen years. We are creating the conditions for a life of abundance and leisure and happiness for our citizens, especially for our young people, for our children. We have endured everything for them. We want them to know a different life, without wars, the threat of wars, armaments. You are a humane man, Mr. President, and you have a family of your own. I am sure you understand what I am saying.

But I am not trying to appeal to your sentiments. My intention is to let you know that I am willing to make the ultimate sacrifice for peace—and not only the peace of my people but yours as well. We Communists have been taught to value man, humanity, not our own idols and fetishes.

For the sake of peace and humanity here is what I will do. I will dismantle the missile bases and ship them back to the Soviet Union. The UN can send inspection teams, though your airplanes seem to know everything. In return you must promise to leave Cuba alone. That promise will negate the necessity for establishing the bases. You realize, Mr. Kennedy, that the missiles were defensive, nothing else. When the crisis is over, we, our two governments, we two men, can sit down and work out arrangements for general and universal disarmament. We can settle the German question—all questions.

I await your reply.

"I think this is it," Kennedy said, smiling broadly.

"Your dream's come true. It's fantastic," Bundy said, looking at Kennedy in awe and wonderment. The others soon gathered around the President and congratulated him too.

Bottles of liquor and champagne appeared from nowhere. Shouting and laughter and cheering filled the hot and noisy Communications Room. Kennedy held up his hand to speak.

"Listen, let's wait until tomorrow before we celebrate. This is an unofficial letter. We've got to hear from the Russian ambassador. So far it seems good. But let's hold off until the agreement's confirmed. Meanwhile, go home and get some sleep. I'll call you back the minute I get word."

Kennedy's caution was justified. He had no way of knowing what was going on in the Kremlin. Khrushchev had sent off the

Friday night letter against the wishes of a majority of the Presidium. Led by M. A. Suslov, the "theoretician," the majority had insisted that before "capitulating" (Suslov's term), Khrushchev should ask to negotiate.

"The Americans feel strongly about these bases," L. M. Brezhnev had stated. "Why shouldn't they give something up for them?"

"But if I ask them that," Khrushchev had replied, his face a kaleidoscope of colors, "they might start bombing at once. Dobrinin thinks they'll start on Saturday morning. I must stop them at any cost."

But within minutes after writing the letter Khrushchev learned from Soviet intelligence that the assault on Cuba was to go off on Tuesday, October 30, at 0600. He had three days, then, instead to a few hours (Dobrinin having been misinformed by Robert Kennedy).

"All right," Khrushchev told Brezhnev, "you might be right. 'Even a fool hits the mark.' In a few hours I'm going to send Kennedy another letter, asking that he trade his Turkish missile bases for my Cuban missile bases. That'll give him a surprise. Chmelnitsky once said, 'Surprises endear you to your friends and unnerve your enemies.'"

Kennedy was surprised—more accurately, crestfallen—when he received Khrushchev's second letter. Its tone was impersonal and officious, as though it had been composed by a clerk in the foreign ministry. It expressed "the Soviet Union's willingness" to remove the bases on condition that the United States remove its "Jupiter missile installations in Turkey." This would be "an equitable and satisfactory solution to our current problem."

"What is this problem?" Kennedy exploded in anger before a hastily summoned meeting of the National Security Council. "He now treats it as if a drunken GI had strayed into the Russian zone of Germany. And what the hell is this about Turkish bases? I'm getting sick and tired of it. Dean, I thought we'd gotten rid of our Jupiter missiles there some time ago. Did we?"

"I don't think so, Mr. President," Rusk replied, flushing.

"You don't think so! Didn't I instruct you to a while back? About a year and a half ago? And they're still there? Arthur, look up the files for the exact date of my instructions to Secretary Rusk. We'll wait until it's located."

Five minutes later Schlesinger returned with the date: May 18, 1961.

"Now, Dean, why the hell hasn't anything been done since then? I thought the President of the United States had full authority in these matters. It appears the bureaucracy has full authority, and I'm only its servant. Jesus Christ, it's more than a man can take."

Kennedy walked out of the Polk Room, his hands clenched at his side.

"It's all right," Robert Kennedy said, "he'll be back in a few minutes. He's just letting off steam."

"O.K., I'm sorry I blew up that way," the President said after returning, a shy grin on his face. "I take it we have to reject Khrushchev's letter. We can't wait while the bases are being built in Cuba. I don't want the situation to crystallize. Nor do I want to do anything under duress. Once the negotiations begin he'll raise the ante. Oh well, we're back where we started from. So close yet so far. Let's slog on."

There was a long pause as Kennedy stared out the window. It was a gloriously clear and bracing fall day, and he took a deep breath.

"Mr. President, I have an idea," Robert Kennedy said in his low, plangent voice. "Why don't you disregard today's letter and address yourself to yesterday's? In other words, accept his offer to scuttle the bases in exchange for your promise to leave Castro alone. You needn't say a thing about Turkey. Meanwhile, I can see my buddy Dobrinin and tell him we must have an answer before Monday."

"Does anyone object to Bobby's proposal? I don't object to it either. It's worth a try. Before you see Dobrinin, why don't you draw up the reply yourself? Then we'll go over it."

Both the letter and Dobrinin's warning that "only thirty-six hours were left before the attack" arrived in Moscow early Sunday morning, interrupting a heated debate in the Presidium between Mikoyan and Suslov.

Suslov argued that the Soviet Union should "yield not an inch more." "If it comes to it, let the Americans invade Cuba. We will provide arms and material support for Castro's army. The Americans would have to keep a force of half a million men there. What would the rest of Latin America, Asia, Africa, the neutrals—what would they say of an American invasion of little Cuba? The long-term advantages to us would be very great."

"You always take the long-term view, Comrade Suslov," Mikoyan asserted, his coal-black eyes flashing in anger. "How can you be so certain the struggle in Cuba will last? Maybe the American operation will take a few days. Remember Hungary? In the meantime, Castro would be out, and Cuba destroyed. A nice situation! Yes, the Americans will be blamed, condemned. But we'll be blamed too for not coming to Cuba's defense. The world will point a finger at us and say, cowards. And if we prefer not to be cowards? Do we send volunteers to Cuba? Do we invade Berlin, Iran, declare war? Finally, what about our Chinese comrades? Why give them more ammunition to use against us?"

"But Comrade Mikoyan," Suslov replied serenely, "if we yield to the Americans now, won't our Chinese comrades call us cowards? I can sit down right now and write Mao's speeches."

"So can I," Mikoyan said. "But if the Americans invade Cuba we'll lose the bases *and* Cuba—in the short run. I leave it to you to tell us what the long run will bring."

It was at this moment that Kennedy's letter and Dobrinin's message arrived, and Khrushchev, who had been listening to the debate with half-closed eyes, came to life.

"That settles it," he shouted, pounding the table. "Kennedy promises not to attack if I give up the bases. That's an iron commitment. Comrades, I'm going ahead, come what may, even if it means my ass. I can't sit here in the Kremlin, day after day, and watch events ride herd over us. We can't lose control. Let the Americans invade Cuba and we lose control. The conflict will escalate. It must. What then? Do you want China to inherit the earth? Oh, Mao would love a little war between the Americans and us. Comrade Suslov, would you want to be responsible for bringing this about? Our children and grandchildren must not say: Marxism-Leninism ended in the year 1962. Then we had Maoism."

The President received Khrushchev's "acceptance letter" on Sunday afternoon, Washington time, while he was lunching with the British ambassador, an old friend of the Kennedy family. Smiling broadly, Kennedy asked for a "large shot of vodka" and said, "Now it's over. I think it's over for good. Now we can celebrate."

He excused himself, went over to the Communications Room, his smile never leaving his face, and told his aides there that they could now hold their party. They cheered him lustily, embraced each other, and danced.

Rusk called to say that Dobrinin had come over to the State Department to "formalize" the agreement. "The bases will be dismantled at once, crated, and sent back," Rusk said jubilantly. "He says they've begun tearing them down already. Congratulations, Mr. President. You handled it beautifully. It's the finest hour of my life, and, I think, the history of our country."

The great Cuban missile crisis was over. The United States and the Soviet Union no longer confronted each other "eyeball to eyeball," as Robert Kennedy later described it, with the fate of humanity hanging on the outcome.

One problem, however, remained: Castro. He was unhappy with Khrushchev's "capitulation," and he did not hesitate to say so. He refused to permit UN inspection teams to report on the destruction of the missile sites. But, thanks to the reconnaissance flights and the advanced photographic techniques, Kennedy made no issue of it.

More serious was Castro's refusal to surrender to the Soviet Union the Ilyushin-28 bombers, which could travel as far as a medium-range missile and were therefore considered an offensive weapon. In mid-November Khrushchev dispatched Mikoyan to Cuba to "apply the carrot and the stick." "If Castro refuses to give back the Ilyushins cut off all aid. If he accepts, increase the amount to four hundred million and all the defensive arms he needs."

The carrot and stick method worked, and the Ilyushins, too, returned to the Soviet Union.

Kennedy gloried in his refulgent triumph. At year's end, according to polls, over 70 per cent of the electorate thought he was doing "an excellent job." But the Cuban missile crisis gave the American people—and the rest of the world—some disturbing questions to ponder. Could another atomic showdown be expected at a future time? Suppose two John Kennedys one day faced each other across the atomic divide, each incapable of retreating, each equally resolute, each equally concerned about his manhood and dignity and public standing? What, then, [. . .]*

* A page in the manuscript is missing.—N.F.M.

8

THAW REDIVIVUS*

A. Missile crisis and split between Soviet Union and China.

1. China's reaction

Chou En-lai's speech in Peking: Khrushchev both adventurer and coward. Started what he couldn't finish. Defeated by American paper tiger. . . . Liu's blazing invective: practically declaration of ideological war. Soviet Union white racists and imperialists. Must be opposed down line in every Communist Party, especially

---

* The remainder of Prescott's study is extremely fragmentary. He was unable to work for sustained periods following a "psychotic episode" on December 18, 1964. Six weeks later he was released from the hospital. According to his brother, C. Willson Prescott, with whom he stayed in the last months of his life, he would frequently "lapse into a state that can only be described as catatonic; he would sit in his favorite wicker chair and stare into space, getting up only to eat, sleep, and care for his personal needs." Periodically, C. Willson Prescott continues, "he would snap out of his state, go into his room, where he kept his voluminous files, and work fiendishly, sometimes for twenty hours at a time."

On September 11, 1968, Julian Prescott collapsed at his brother's home. He died the next day.

Realizing that he had little time left after his illness had set in, Prescott ceased to write a consecutive story. He outlined the topics he would have covered, cryptically noting the manuscripts he would have cited and from which he would have quoted. In several places, however, he did provide a rather full narrative explanation of important events—how important the reader will be able to judge for himself. It was, quite literally, with his last ounce of strength that he did so. The grace and simplicity of his prose may conceal the enormous effort he put into his writing. His achievement, under the circumstances, is nothing short of heroic.

These final fragmentary chapters are published just as Prescott wrote them.—N.F.M.

in underdeveloped countries of world. What issues? Khrushchev traitor, renegade, revisionist. Liu: revolutions everywhere. No quarter given. Neutralism a lie. "Split, split, split, split, split." Better break up Communist movement than sell out to imperialists. . . . Mao's conference with Hoxha, Sukarno. . . . Mao's poem on Khrushchev. . . . The land question: the redrawing of the maps. Mao's meeting with Society of Geographers and Cartographers. . . .

2. Khrushchev's decision

Khrushchev's bathtub conversation with Adjhubei: Mao and China greatest danger to Soviet Union. Would provoke war with United States, destroy Communist movement, take over world. Conclusion? Must reach settlement with United States. "Pact of peace among civilized races." Kennedy man one can go to table with. Kennedy more mature, trustworthy now. Time ripe.

3. Conflict in Presidium

Pro-China faction? Apparently, not really. Suslov and Brezhnev using China as weapon against Khrushchev. . . . Differences over approach to Mao. Brezhnev and Suslov to Khrushchev: one more try. Khrushchev: nonsense, and to prove will make try. . . . Attempt to hold Sino-Soviet conference in Moscow. . . . Breakdown. Increased animosity. . . . Presidium's approval of policy of "rapprochement" with West. . . . Khrushchev's warning to Brezhnev. Brezhnev humbled.

B. Kennedy and Khrushchev

1. Kennedy's self-confidence

Basking in glory of Cuban missile crisis. . . . Right-wing critics silenced. Anyone ever tougher? . . . United States now uncontested Number One power in world. Prestige at all-time high. . . . Kennedy's campaign promises redeemed: glowing future, ebullience, prosperity. . . . Kennedy era unfolding. . . . Evaluation: Emergence of an American world empire. Benevolent imperialism? Woodrow Wilson's ideal of American imperium realized? Opportunity and danger. Periclean Athens. Antonine Rome. . . .

2. Improved prospects for peace

Kennedy's conversation (May 1963) with Rusk, MacNamara, Bobby, Harriman, Bundy, et al. "Peace offensive" now possible. Must try to reach practical, workable agreements as first step. No mishaps. Then other possibilities: arms limitations: no need for such rigorous inspection procedures because of satellite photography. . . . Kennedy's June speech at American University. Most reconciliatory remarks of Cold War. Russia praised. No crusade against Communism. Peaceful coexistence. Etc. . . . Speech much appreciated in Moscow. . . . Khrushchev's talk with ambassador. Ukrainian proverb: No friend as fast as former enemy, no enemy so terrible as former friend (China).

3. Breakthrough

a. Test ban treaty (no testing above ground)

Harriman's negotiations, Moscow, July 1963. Meetings and talks with Khrushchev. Promise of general disarmament. End of Cold War. Technology for peace. Improvement of conditions of life. Much vodka, cognac, toasting, witty exchanges. . . . Snag: Khrushchev's wish to link treaty with non-aggression pact between NATO-Warsaw Pact. . . . Kennedy's rejection: United States cannot allow permanent division into empires. Defacto division into empires? Better left unspoken. . . . Khrushchev's unconditional acceptance. . . . Sweetness and light. . . . More conversations with Harriman: drinking, toasting, etc. . . . Treaty ratified late July by United States, Soviet Union, Great Britain. . . . China's angry rejection. . . . France's rejection. De Gaulle's press conference: France's greatness affirmed. Caustic comments on Anglo-Saxon righteousness, hypocrisy, chauvinism. . . . Supreme importance of treaty.

b. Hot-line agreement, June 1963

Direct line of communication between Soviet and American leaders. No need of intermediaries. . . . Secret exchange of letters between Kennedy and Khrushchev: how both hate bureaucracies, unwieldy machinery of government, "pigeonholers," "careerists," "jobbers," "opportunists," "mediocrities," etc., etc. . . . Another reason for hot line: Reach each other in event of accident. How safe can fail-safe mechanism be? . . . Agreed: Only disarmament the guarantee of peace. No other true guarantee. . . . At any rate, new era launched. Generally accepted judgment: slow but certain progress toward detente. . . . However, some "hawkish" reservations: must keep up guard. Should have no illusions about Soviet Union. Power only real security. Disappointment in Kennedy. . . .

c. Kennedy's problem: Vietnam

Stepped-up war in South Vietnam. . . . Kennedy's decision, March 1963: send yet more advisers, training personnel. . . . Prosecution of the strategic hamlet campaign. Increasing disaffection of peasants. Increasing number of Vietcong guerrillas. Professor Smith's prophecy fulfilled. . . . American public told of failure in Vietnam. Corruption of government officials. Unwillingness of South Vietnamese troops to fight. Lies of American mission in Saigon. . . . Kennedy's attempt to suppress news. Pressure on media. "Halberstam case." . . . Deteriorating situation in South Vietnam. . . . Kennedy's decision: press for new, more democratic regime under Diem. . . . Warned repeatedly of quagmire, endless conflict. . . . Smith's plea for negotiations with North Vietnam. Neutralization of South. Proposal dismissed again by Robert K., MacNamara, Bundy, Rostow, et al. Same old arguments. . . . Diem regime untenable. Kennedy to McCone: "Dump Diem." Fall of Diem, November 1963. His death, flight of family. . . . Turmoil. . . . Kennedy's lament: Vietnam my Waterloo . . . ?

9

INSURGENCY IN AMERICA

A. Insurgency from below
1. Black America
a. Historic background
Oppression since Reconstruction. . . . How United States went back on commitment to blacks. Reversal of Fourteenth Amendment of Constitution. "Separate but equal." Meaning of second-class citizenship: non-citizenship. . . . Slow development of black egalitarian movement. A tiny minority. Middle class. Help of philanthropic whites (NAACP, Socialist Party, etc.). . . . Race question too deep, too divisive. Most Americans preferred to forget. Conception of blacks: not *men:* marginal, interstitial, anonymous. . . . World War II and after: heavy migration of blacks to North. Urban concentration. . . . United States as great world power. Relations with colored peoples of world. Choice: racism (à la South Africa) or equal rights. Formal choice: equal rights. How extensive and deep? Another matter. . . . Truman's civil rights program. His desegregation of armed forces. . . . Black rejection of separate but equal. Insistence on full protection of laws under Fourteenth Amendment. Recognition by more and more federal courts. Finally, 1954 Supreme Court decision: No more second-class citizenship (formal, however). . . .
b. Civil rights revolution
After 1954, protests against segregationist local laws. Justification? Conflict with law of land. . . . Turning point: Montgomery bus strike, 1955. Emergence of Martin Luther King, Jr. Background and personality. Disciple of Gandhi. Non-violent protest in name of Christ, higher law of universal love and brotherhood.

. . . Black student lunch counter sit-ins, 1961–62. Success. . . . Desegregation of Jim Crow bus and train stations. Violence. Success. . . . White racist response: Citizens' Councils. Ku Klux Klan murders. Preservation of white Southern way of life. Alabama's George Wallace: Bantamweight boxer vs. federal government, liberals, twentieth century. . . . By 1963 full-scale black uprising against segregation. Militancy in North too. Irresistible momentum. How far? What form? What meaning? Unanswerable: kaleidoscopic pace of change. . . .

2. Student America

New phenomenon: In wake of Sputnik, millions of college students, ages 17–30. . . . Probers of American norms: demand consistency between ideals and practices. Equality, rights, justice available to all. Defects of American system. . . . Incalculable consequences of student insurgency. . . . Nothing like it in human history. . . . Reaction of public at large? Imponderable. Reaction inevitable. . . .

B. Insurgency from above

1. Kennedy's solicitude for "underprivileged"—economic, racial, ethnic, etc. . . . Robert Kennedy's effect on Justice Department. . . . Attempts to deal with juvenile delinquency. . . . Realization of magnitude of poverty 'midst affluence. Poverty in some ways worse than before: immobility, despair, self-contempt, indifference of middle class. . . . What to be done? Kennedy aware but perplexed. . . . Desire to help powerless groups: farm workers, Mexican-Americans, Indians. Result? Encouragement of insurgency from below. . . .

2. Kennedy's decision to support civil rights. Birmingham outrage: Dogs unloosed on black protestors. "Bull" O'Connor, symbol. . . . Kennedy's speech, May 1963, calling for federal law against Jim Crow. How black Americans suffered: lack of opportunity, high mortality rate. Must redress grievances legally, lest street action, violence, racial warfare. . . . Conservative Congress: little chance of passage of such law. . . . More protests: School boycotts. March on Washington. Greatest mass unrest in memory. . . . Ultimate unspeakable outrage: four children killed in bombing of black church, Birmingham, September 1963. Coun-

try shocked. Provisions of Civil Rights Bill strengthened. Chances of passage improved. . . .

One evening in early October 1963, while the Civil Rights Bill was being debated in the House of Representatives, President Kennedy asked his brother Robert and Martin Luther King, Jr., to join him in the Thaddeus Stevens Library for a "freewheeling and open-ended discussion of the problems confronting us," as he phrased it in his handwritten invitation. The President looked tanned and refreshed after a trip to the West Coast and Hawaii, where he was repeatedly cheered by great throngs of people. He leaned far back in his rocking chair as he spoke.

"Dr. King, I've asked you to come because I'd like your frank personal opinion. Do you think we'll have racial peace in this country? Do you think the Civil Rights Bill, if it passes, will help bring racial peace?"

"I am flattered by your invitation, Mr. President, and I will be candid and open. Let me say again, as I have said on many occasions, I approve of the Civil Rights Bill, although, as you may know, I have criticized it for not going far enough. Still, it is the first genuine effort of its kind by the federal government in ninety years, and for that, I and the black people of America are of course grateful. Never has a President of the United States recognized and called attention to the sufferings and subjugation of black America as you did in your May speech. That is a milestone, Mr. President, and for that, too, we honor you.

"Now, do I think our country will have racial peace? Well, I would reformulate the question. Peace itself means little if unaccompanied by justice. White America had racial peace during the slavery and post-Reconstruction eras. The peace was punctuated by lynchings, whippings, immolations, and race riots, which kept Negroes in line, you see, just as Sparta gratuitously hunted down helots to keep them obedient. So, to rephrase the question, Can America have racial peace provided America does justice to Negroes and other oppressed minorities? My answer is yes, emphatically yes."

"Then I would ask you this, Dr. King," Robert Kennedy said,

leaning forward in his chair. "Do you believe that America *can* do justice to Negroes?"

"Ah, Mr. Kennedy, that is really a question. How often I have asked myself that question. How often I have set my teeth on edge trying to answer it. One of the reasons I find it so difficult is that I have such grand hopes for America. I have always known that I was subject to illusions, the line of distinction between illusion and hope being exceedingly fine. You know, Immanuel Kant, the philosopher, described pure reason, man's inner voice and conscience, as an illusion, by which he meant that it transcended worldly reality. But to me no ideal or act of conscience has meaning unless it applies to this world, to fallen man, to sinful creatures like ourselves. I do not think Jesus embodies a hope fulfilled only in death. No, the Kingdom of Heaven is here and now, or it is nowhere. So I run the risk of such illusions because I have continued to hope. Perhaps Malcolm X is luckier than I. Having no hope, he has no illusions about America.

"But I must tell you this. My vision, my dream is in direct conflict with a deep, almost visceral feeling that I cannot suppress. It keeps coming up from the depths of my being. And that feeling, Mr. President, Mr. Kennedy, that feeling is despair, the opposite of hope. I have to be honest with myself and with you. I have often wondered why I feel that despair so persistently, even as I hope and glorify the future. May I tell you what I think? It might interest you."

"Yes," both Kennedys said at once.

"Has it ever struck you as a coincidence that the progress Negroes have made in the twentieth century has occurred while the United States was becoming a great power in the world? To me it is no coincidence."

"Could you explain that?" the President asked, staring intently at King.

"I mean this. The United States announced itself as a great power in the First World War. It was a war fought for democracy and peace, to be secured by the League of Nations, which President Wilson single-handedly created. Then we retreated back into the wings. We withdrew into isolationism. The Second World War brought us back to center stage permanently—we and Russia. That war was undeniably a struggle between the children of darkness and the children of light. Fascism represented death. The United Nations renewed the hopes defeated in the 1920s and 30s.

"So there we were after 1945, the Jerusalem of democracy, engaged now in a struggle against the Communist Babylon, which also called itself democratic. Here were two universal ideologies competing for supremacy, both standing for equality and the rights of man. Now the rest of the world, all but a handful of privileged European colonialists, professed to favor social and economic democracy too—an ideal, after all, built into the United Nations Charter. The world arena in which this competition of universal ideologies was acted out is colored and poor. The great question of our time is whether these masses will choose Communist democracy or free democracy."

"I deny that Communism can be democratic," Robert Kennedy interposed. "No Communist society offers free elections or civil liberties."

"Well," King replied, "I certainly do not want to quarrel over words. I agree with you. I am only going by what the Communists themselves say or claim. Fascists never *claimed* to be democratic. And you must admit that Communism does offer social and economic equality, if not political rights.

"That is the point I am suggesting. Will masses of people care very much about free elections and civil liberties when they do not have enough to eat, when they are exploited by a tiny, callous oligarchy? I thought the Alliance for Progress was set up to help provide the economic conditions that would make the luxury of political democracy possible in Latin America."

"True, precisely true, and very well put," the President said.

"I'd like you to get back to what you were saying about civil rights and America's world position, Dr. King," Robert Kennedy said, leaning further forward in his chair.

"The answer is self-evident, Mr. Kennedy. As a world empire resting on a democratic ideology—I use the term 'empire' advisedly, though, again, I would not quibble about it—the United States has been forced to acknowledge, in its legal and ethical norms, the claims for justice put forward by its historically oppressed or disfranchised minorities, above all its black folk. It has done so despite the overwhelming racism of white America.

Had the United States remained a small or moderate-sized nation, on the order of, say, Canada or Australia, it is inconceivable to me that the position of Negroes would have improved. They, we, would have remained a caste, neither slave nor free, in the midst of a free society."

"I'm a little confused here, Dr. King," Robert Kennedy said. "First you tell us that you feel this despair. Then, in explaining your despair, you tell us that the lot of Negroes has been getting better because America is a universal empire. Why do you feel despair in that case? If America maintains its empire—I use the word for the sake of argument—shouldn't the lot of Negroes improve still further?"

King smiled. "That is the critical question, the decisive question. When I talked of America's imperial greatness I was referring to one aspect of it, the normative or idealistic aspect. Remember, the other empires of the past—and I am not making an invidious comparison here—had universalistic ideals that they contributed to mankind. This was their patrimony. Monotheism, we are told, first arose among the Babylonians and Egyptians of the ancient Near East. The Code of Hammurabi predated the Pentateuch. The Hebrew prophets, Buddhism, Confucianism, Zoroastrianism, were all products of empire-civilizations. Greek philosophy and Roman law, incorporating the Stoic view of life, were carried to the distant shores of Europe and Asia by conquering armies. Christianity, we know, grew out of the confluence of these universal empires and came to be the official religion of Rome. Consider what the European empires of our own day have given to the world. All empires that have endured have had this benevolent aspect.

"Domestically, I might add, the empires at their height have tended to be tolerant and pluralistic and refined in taste, manners, and intelligence, with many and diverse peoples living side by side, with races, classes, national, ethnic, religious groups, and philosophical sects thrown together in a great jumble. Rather like our own society. Ancient Rome and Alexandria, Nineveh, Ur, Thebes, Jerusalem, and the others were, from all accounts, similar to Paris, London, New York today.

"But now we come to the other aspect of world empires. What has kept them together essentially is a ruling body made up of aristocratic warrior-statesmen-priests. I will not bore you with the details, and, despite my pomposities, I am no great authority on the matter. One does not have to be a great authority. For what was true in olden times is true today. Very little is new under the sun. To bring the question close to home, who ran the British empire in the nineteenth century? A small group of the well-born and the rich. As they did so, they threw sops to their own lower classes, who demanded some of the freedoms and happiness the English were supposedly bringing to the rest of the world. Hence the electoral reforms, factory legislation, trade unions, and the like. The rulers did not surrender their power to rule. They held the commanding heights as securely as ever. So it was in every other European imperial society.

"We find the same pattern here in the United States in the mid-twentieth century. We have a gigantic military-industrial complex that underlies America's imperial position in the world. A small group of men, really an oligarchy, defines our national— if you will, imperial—interests throughout the world, on every continent. I will forbear from calling them cynics, but I am convinced that they use the universal ideology of American democracy for pragmatic and instrumental reasons, as a weapon in the struggle for mastery. They regard it as a means toward an end, that end being expansion, dominion, power."

"Dr. King, this is quite edifying," the President said indulgently, "and I'm really fascinated, but aren't you drifting away from the issue that you posed? How is the division between these aspects of empire relevant to the race problem in America?"

"This is how, Mr. President. When Negroes and others who had once been second-class citizens demand complete equality under the law, in accordance with the norms of a crusading democratic ideology—and by complete equality I mean social and economic rights as well as those adumbrated in the Constitution and the courts—when they assert those demands, they set up a tremendous tension at the very heart of the empire principle.

"Before I go on let me say again how much I appreciate your kindness in putting up with my feeble and presumptuous attempts to articulate these thoughts. I know how preachy and didactic I am. But you must have known what you were letting yourselves in for when you invited me."

"You're too modest, Dr. King," Robert Kennedy said. "I find this terribly interesting, though I won't say I agree with you."

"That goes for me too," the President added. "Please go on."

"Thank you. What I am trying to do is indicate the opposition, or contradiction, that is festering within the American nation now that it stands at the summit of world power and influence.

"There are those who have been encouraged to take American democratic ideals seriously—the ideals that guide its destiny in the world, in history. These, I repeat, are the neglected, the poor, the dispossessed of body and spirit, the victims of social injustice. Chief among these, of course, are the twenty million black Americans. They no longer accept their submerged condition and they press forward. As they win concessions from the power elites they demand yet more rights, for they come to regard their suffering as intolerable. They want and expect more and better housing, schools, jobs, a happier environment, their birthright, and they want and expect these things now.

"The promise of American democracy will not be delayed. Mr. President, you might not care for their impatience, their insistence, their ferocity. I might not either. But the people have hearkened to the words spoken over and over by their leaders, that the United States of America guards the ramparts of freedom and is the champion of democracy against the forces of despotism.

"And so the strain on the country's resources begins to be felt. Where is the money to come from for all the programs that the poor demand? How will middle class whites take to Negroes and other minorities who demand equality where equality counts— in the neighborhoods, schools, places of work, leisure, and entertainment? These social and personal adjustments also require the expenditure of money—if, that is, the adjustment is to be based on love and good will rather than violence and suppression. Make no mistake about it, the mood of the Negroes is changing swiftly, ominously. They will not abide suppression much longer. There is no telling what the young people will do in a few years. White as well as black.

"But I do not want to stray from the point, which is that the pressure is building up. The once lonely and despised are calling

for a definite commitment from the country. Honor your professed ideals of democracy with concrete deeds, they are saying.
Don't *tell* us about the Declaration of Independence and the
Constitution and America's role in the world. Act as if you
believe your preachments.

"Now let us turn to the other side of the imperial coin and the
need of America to uphold its military and political position in
the world. To maintain that position is very costly, and as far as
leaders are concerned there never is enough money. The interesting fact is that the cost of maintaining that position has continued to grow, thanks to modern military technology, the reliance
on very complex weapons systems, and so forth. You know this
better than anyone, Mr. President. Not that I think we have
become a warrior society or garrison state. Nor are our military
men evil. It is simply the imperatives of modern warfare and
self-defense. I fully realize that. Choose the end and you choose
the means as well. Both we and the Russians have discovered
that the end is by and large chosen for us. We—the country, and
especially you, Mr. President—have inherited a situation that we
did not create. To that extent we are the instruments of a
choice imposed upon us, a choice we are beholden to carry out.
Thus are the sins of the fathers visited upon the children. I blame
no one for the quandary we are in today.

"What I am saying is this. Those who are responsible for
managing the imperial estate—and I am being objective about it,
not critical—these men are going to make demands of their own
on the resources of the country, are going to draw up their own
list of priorities, and to resist with all their might attempts by
others to interfere with their authority to do so. I do not want to
put this conflict on a narrowly economic or material basis. The
authority, or prerogatives I speak of refer to the exercise of
responsibility, the power to make decisions, the power of command, the right to determine what is just and good for America.
For example, a dispute over budget requests between the Pentagon
and the Department of Health, Education, and Welfare cannot be
reduced to mere dollars and cents. It bears a moral dimension.
What is it right to do? What is prior, what secondary? It is a
moral choice, and I am saying that the moral choice is bound to
become more and more contentious. I am also saying that the

choice will decide the soul of America—its objectives, what *kind* of imperial nation it is to be. Will it go the way of Egypt and Babylon and Rome and the other empires that fell because they were destroyed from within?

"Here is where I begin to approach the source of my despair. For what do I find? The opposition, or contradiction, I spoke of is not between the rulers of the imperium, the warrior-aristocrats of the military-industrial complex, and the lowly and despised pressing forward their claims. It is not that simple. Too many Americans have a vested material interest in the military-industrial complex. This goes without saying. Too many Americans also have a vested emotional interest in American power and greatness. The limitless horizons of empire thrill them, quicken their spirit, charge them with energy, enable them to escape from the mean, humdrum, trivial preoccupations of their everyday lives, give them a vision of purpose and destiny. The love of empire, or call it what you will, runs broad and deep.

"Now if a crisis should arise over allocation of resources I do not doubt for a moment that the imperial interest would have the support of most Americans. And if in the name of keeping America's position in the world intact it becomes necessary to put down the noisy, recalcitrant minorities, they will be put down. And if the minorities turn to more strenuous forms of protest, they will be put down that much more ruthlessly. I can see in that event all manner of peripheral self-destructive portents: criminality, drug addiction, absurd, anomic outbreaks of violence. The middle class will move farther away from the cities to the suburbs and will gladly prefer a garrison state over disorder and the breakdown of authority.

"But then what happens to the ideal of racial integration that is the law of the land? What happens to America's democratic ideal. Is it abandoned, repudiated, exorcised, or just emptied of all content—mere tinkling bells? Will Negroes and other minorities lose even the little that they have? That too may happen if American democracy turns into its opposite.

"In my gloomiest moments I see a frightening image of the future coming up from the dark shadows of the dusk. I see a nation that is at once stupendously powerful and pathetically weak, a nation bristling with the most advanced arms, feared by all, a terror to its enemies, yet divided against itself, its soul sick and demoralized, a colossus with feet of clay.

"I think I have said too much, and I will stop. I have been a little too opinionated, I am afraid, and I ask your forgiveness for it. In my roundabout way I have tried to convey my feelings of despair. What you heard was the preacher's lamentation, chapter and verse. The main thrust of my remarks is that the question of the American Negro cannot be separated from the question of the American white, from the question of America."

"You have given us a gloomy prophecy indeed, Dr. King," the President said, leaning back as far as he could, puffing on a cigar he had just lighted.

"I would hesitate to call it a prophecy, Mr. President," King replied. "It is in my gloomiest moments that I see the picture I described to you. Not all my moments are gloomy. As I tried to suggest I also have feelings of optimism and hope."

"Where is your optimism, Dr. King?" Robert Kennedy asked sadly. "There wasn't much of it in what you just told us."

"I will tell you what I am optimistic about. The young people of America, especially the college generation. They are beginning to resist the chauvinism, the hard-heartedness, the racism, the false values of their parents. They alone may change the structure of events before it is too late. It is a race against time, really. I have never doubted that men can intervene in the endless train of cause and effect and bring about a great change, a rebirth. The Holy Ghost is always with us."

"Is it your view then," Robert persisted, "that America's redemption will require a miracle?"

"All redemptions are miracles, Mr. Kennedy. I believe in such miracles. I have staked my life on their possibility. I believe it is the noblest wager a man can make."

"But we still have to depend on reason," the President said, "or what we perceive to be the most desirable, least painful thing to do. One thing's certain: we can't anticipate miracles, wait for them, or act on them. From your analysis, Dr. King, I have to conclude that the United States is headed for a disaster. We're not going to become a small power for a long time, and we're going to honor our commitments abroad, our military, economic, and political commitments. And because we live in a hostile world, those commitments, as you rightly said, are very expensive and are bound to get more expensive. So I must conclude that things will get worse all around before they get better."

"Oh, I agree with you there, Mr. President. That is, I agree with your prognosis of the situation. I do not know of one imperial power in history that has voluntarily renounced its commitments or responsibilities or dominion."

"Dr. King," Robert Kennedy said earnestly, "I very strongly disagree with your evaluation of the crisis in America. First, I don't think underprivileged Americans are as angry and impatient as you claim they are. Second, I don't think white Americans, including the power elites and the establishment, are as averse to helping the underprivileged as you think."

"May I interrupt you, Mr. Kennedy? I did not say they were averse. I said they were not able to, despite their best intentions. I was talking about a structural condition. That is what I meant by a contradiction."

"But you also said that you believed in miraculous interventions. Well, I contend that the American people, properly informed and vigorously led, can undertake the reforms that will heal the divisions in our society. I certainly don't foresee the kind of animosities ahead of us that you do, Dr. King."

"God grant that you be His Prophet," King exclaimed, smiling for the first time. "How I would sing hosannas to your wisdom if you proved to be correct! Now let me ask you a question, Mr. Kennedy. What kind of reforms do you envision?"

"Obviously, I can't lay out a blueprint for you," Kennedy replied. "What I envision are programs of full employment, guaranteed minimum incomes, comprehensive medical insurance, aid to education, the elimination of Jim Crow in every public institution in America, and the equitable administration of justice, irrespective of race, class, and income."

"And when do you think these programs will be enacted? And if enacted, will they be carried out?"

"They won't be enacted in a day, of course. They'll take time, but they'll come as sure as we're sitting here, Dr. King. And yes, they'll be carried out, too. Americans will learn by doing, by trial and error, that racial prejudice can have no place in their lives."

"Mr. Kennedy," King said with a deep laugh, "would you mind if I enlisted your services in my organization, the Southern Leadership Conference. We could use someone with your inspiration."

"I can't let him go for a minute," the President said, grinning. "He's too much of an inspiration for my Cabinet. He delivers the sermonette at the close of our meetings. He's quite good at it."

"I don't think either of you is serious. After November '64 I may be looking for a job, Dr. King. So keep me in mind."

"You might keep me in mind for then also," the President added.

"You are both hired!"

"Talking about '64," the President said, "the election must be weighing heavily on my subconscious. I had a funny dream last night. I was watching what seemed to be a great political gathering, a convention I suppose. Suddenly, all the people waved signs and placards saying 1964, and they pointed at me. I acknowledged them and they cheered. Then, just as suddenly, the crowd disappeared. I saw myself wearing a high hat and tuxedo and looking rather pale and carrying a sign with nothing on it. It was blank. Jackie was at my side, holding my hand. I was pleased that it was only a dream."

"I had a rather frightening dream, too, the other day," King said. "I dreamed that I was on top of a mountain overlooking a deep clear blue stream, like the ones we have in Georgia. A voice kept telling me, 'Martin, you are on Pisgah. Here is the River Jordan.' Then I saw a great number of people, black and white, beckoning to me to come on over with them as they crossed the river. I was about to join them, but I noticed that instead of a mountain I was on the balcony of a building, high up from the ground, with no doors or windows. It was a balcony with no escape."

"Since we're discussing dreams," Robert Kennedy said, "let me tell you a recent one of mine that involves crowds. It's been haunting me. I was sitting on a platform before a crowd of people who looked up to me and said, yes, yes, yes, over and over again. Then I noticed one man, he was blurred and indistinct, speaking in a low voice, saying, no, no, no. And though his voice was low, it rang out over the shouts of the yeses, until all I heard was no. When I got up I wondered who had said no to me that day. I could think of no one."

The President rose from his rocking chair and shook King's hand. "I can't thank you enough for visiting us. I enjoyed our talk immensely, and I hope you'll forgive us our dreams. I'd like to see you again soon."

"I would be honored, Mr. President."

It was the last time they saw each other.

BOOK IV

Hubris [?]*

---

* Prescott evidently had not decided whether to keep this as the title of Book IV. There are question marks on the side of the manuscript and alternative titles which he crossed out.—N.F.M.

I

TRANSITIONS

A. Death of John F. Kennedy

His trip to Texas, late November 1963. His desire to mend fences between conservative and liberal Democrats. . . . His popularity (a "tough hombre"). His welcome in Dallas. Dallas: heartland of conservatism: the new privileged class: insecure, beleaguered, paranoid. . . . Kennedy's death. The shooting. . . . Johnson's initial fear of Communist takeover: what he said to aide Walt Barkham. Ready to spring general alert. . . . Johnson's secret letter: "To Be Opened in the Event of My Assassination." . . . Khrushchev's assurances. . . .

B. Kennedy's assassin: Lee Harvey Oswald

What kind of person? . . . Contrast between Oswald and Kennedy: failure, loser, victim, anomic, vs. Camelot, quintessence of American dream. Contrast typically American. . . . Yet Oswald interesting. Attempts to improve himself. Sought answers: joined radical movements, read books, attracted to Soviet Union, Cuba—failure. Marriage—failure. . . . *Ressentiment*. . . . Plot discounted. Why? Odds million to one against plot germinating. Trillion to one against succeeding. Only demonic urge of single man, pitting self against infinity. . . . But then all this a priori deduction. Who can know? Will it ever be known? . . .

C. Ascension of Lyndon Baines Johnson

1. Career as politician

In House of Representatives: New Deal liberal. Extremely ambitious. . . . Extraordinary Senate race, 1948. . . . Rise to

Senate leadership, 1954. . . . Wheeler-dealer non-pareil. From barefoot boy to millionaire. American success story, Texas style. . . .

2. Personality

Energy, charm, crudity, shrewdness, relentlessness, competence, intelligence, egomania. . . . Typical Texan (?), yet valued "best brains," admired class, Eastern establishment, sureness, confidence of command. Looked down and up at same time. Odd mixture. . . .

3. Accomplishments in first year as President

Continued Kennedy's policies. Retained Kennedy's appointees. . . . Managed laws through Congress. Civil Rights Act most important. Johnson friend of Negroes and poor: "War on Poverty." . . .

4. Defeat of Goldwater, 1964

a. Goldwater

Triumph of conservatism in Republican Party. . . . Goldwater's ideal: return to innocence of nineteenth century, rugged individualism, states' rights. . . . Backed by South, West, arrivistes. . . . Distrusted by Eastern moderates, internationalists. Greatest enemy: New York: mass media, publishing, intelligentsia. . . . Goldwater's chauvinism: Get tough in Vietnam. Get touch with Chinese, Soviets, whole world. . . .

b. Johnson's campaign

More welfare state, civil rights, restraint in Vietnam, pro-UN, agreements with Soviets, sweetness, light, moderation.

5. Johnson's third New Deal, 1965

New legislation. Most liberal Congress since 1936: housing, education, poverty, Medicare. . . . Voting Rights Act: Selma affair. Martin Luther King's conversation with Johnson. Johnson's remarkable speech ("We shall overcome"). . . .

6. Black insurgency: new stage

Militancy, violence, "black power," separatism, urban rioting. . . . King's gloomy prophecy reinforced. . . . King's meeting with Robert Kennedy, now Senator from New York. . . . Air of enveloping crisis: black rage, white fear. Rising wall of steel between races. . . .

D. Fall of Khrushchev, October 1964

1. Litany of failures

Agriculture, industry, China, Titoism, Cuban missile crisis. . . .

2. His decision to purge

Mass arrests of opposition to take place midnight, November 1. . . . Blame for failures to fall on Brezhnev, Kosygin, Ignatov, Suslov. . . . Stavrogin of secret police won over to Brezhnev. . . .

3. Khrushchev's ouster

On vacation, caught by surprise. . . . His bitter comments. . . . Held in house arrest. Argument with Brezhnev, new Party boss. . . . Fate of Adjhubei and Mikoyan. . . .

4. Brezhnev and Kosygin: New leadership, same policies. . . .

2

INDOCHINA

A. Continued deterioration in South Vietnam
 1. Military failure
 Verdict on strategic hamlet campaign: disaster. Expanding power of Vietcong. Their conquest of whole regions (Mekong Delta, Central Highlands, etc.). . . . Superior fighting ability of Vietcong. South Vietnamese soldiers and officers found "ineducable." American sergeant, "Can't make silk purse out of sow's ears." . . . High rate of desertion. . . .
 2. Instability in Saigon
 One government after another following fall of Diem. . . . Corruption all levels. . . . General demoralization. Military vs. civilians, Catholic vs. Buddhists, hawks vs. neutralists. . . .

B. Johnson's concern over South Vietnam
 MacNamara's visit. Rostow's visit. Rusk's visit. Bundy's visit. . . . . Their reports favoring United States intervention well beyond technical and support personnel. . . . Maxwell Taylor's appointment as American ambassador to South Vietnam. Johnson's instructions. . . . Taylor's tough position. His request for "emergency" aid: use of American troops. . . .

On May 30, 1964, a day after Defense Secretary MacNamara returned from his twelfth "fact-finding" trip to South Vietnam, President Johnson summoned his "executive command" for a policy conference in the Harry S. Truman Room (furnished by Johnson's wife in simple, "homespun" American decor). The "executive command" consisted of Kennedy holdovers: Secre-

taries MacNamara and Rusk and presidential aides MacGeorge
Bundy and Walt Whitman Rostow. Present at the conference,
too, was Professor John Smith, the Southeast Asia specialist,
whose every warning had come true.

"This is a grave moment," Johnson said, pacing slowly, his
hands in his pants pockets. "Some darn important decisions are
going to come out of the discussions here in this room today,
and I want your deepest, most soul-searching thoughts so that
you can help me make them. I realize, in all humility, that
I and I alone will make them and I and I alone will be held
responsible for them. But the future of the people of the United
States may well depend on them. That's why I've asked Bob
to give you his assessment firsthand.

"While I'm at it let me welcome Mr. Smith to our council.
Bob asked that Mr. Smith be invited here as a devil's advocate.
We're all familiar with Mr. Smith's criticisms of our policy in
Vietnam. For that very reason we want to hear his comments.
Bob, why don't you begin."

"Thank you, Mr. President," MacNamara said, reading from
carefully typed notes. "I'll have a full report for you by tomorrow.
I wish to present here the gist of my conclusions and recommendations, based on what I observed and my conversations
with the President, the Premier, Ambassador Taylor, and Generals Barkin and McFarland.

"My conclusions, in brief, are: one, that the South Vietnamese
army and civil guard will not be able to defeat the enemy;
two, that time favors the enemy at present, and, according to
Max Taylor's prognosis, will not, even if reinforced with the
latest planes and equipment, be able to hold out for more than
a year; and three, that the present contingent of American support
personnel, numbering eighteen thousand, is useless under the
circumstances.

"The recommendations follow logically. Either we evacuate
our personnel at once and prepare ourselves for the unification
of Vietnam under Ho Chi Minh, or we take all measures to
defeat the National Liberation Front. If the latter, we must send
in as many American troops as necessary to clear out the
guerrillas from their village sanctuaries. Since these are estimated
at twenty-five to forty thousand, we must commit upwards of

four hundred thousand American men to the operation, perhaps more, depending on the capacity of the South Vietnamese army to assume its burden of the conflict. At the moment that capacity is minimal. But with intensive training the South Vietnamese army may come to replace our men. At the same time I would recommend that we carry out limited bombing missions against the supply lines, communications centers, and depots in North Vietnam. Hanoi is the fount and origin of this conflict, and the war must also be brought to its territory. I would further recommend, as an ultimate step, if these do not suffice, that United States and South Vietnamese forces jointly invade the North.

"These recommendations, it goes without saying, are based on stark military imperatives. They do not take into account the political, legal, social, economic, and humanitarian aspects of the problem, all of which, I realize, must go into the making of the decision. Thank you."

A thick silence enveloped the room. Johnson scrutinized everyone, staring them down with his heavily lidded eyes. "Mr. Smith," he said softly, "Bob would like you to comment on his remarks. We're all interested in what you have to say."

"Thank you, Mr. President. To tell you the truth, I feel as though I had been kicked in the solar plexus. Mr. MacNamara's recommendations took my breath away. As he spoke I tried to imagine what it would be like if, say, half a million American troops were in South Vietnam. My mind boggled. Here is a country of fifteen million Asian people being host, against their will, to a rich, mechanized foreign army one-thirtieth their number. Imagine, if you will, an army of six and a half million Asians in the United States, freely roaming the country. Imagine, further, that most Americans sympathized with the American insurgents against whom the Asian army had been sent over to fight. If you can imagine that you will have some idea of the problems the United States would face if, Mr. President, you were to follow Mr. MacNamara's recommendations.

"Gentlemen, you may remember my suggestions to President Kennedy some three years ago, at one of his seminars. I hate to be a Cassandra. I certainly dislike anyone who calls attention to his foresight and wisdom. I then opposed any move that would drag the United States deeper into the South Vietnamese civil war. I pointed out that to do so even on a limited scale—the scale of our subsequent involvement, as it turned out—would set in motion an inevitable cycle. For short of destroying the villages and hamlets, literally razing them to the ground and herding their inhabitants into concentration camps —a policy urged on President Kennedy—short of that, no force in the world could defeat the Vietcong. The more force applied by the Saigon mandarins, aided by American advisers, the greater the resistance thrown up by the villages, and the greater the assistance provided by North Vietnam. That cycle has been accelerated so rapidly that—and I agree completely with the Secretary's conclusions—the Vietcong are on the verge of bringing down the Saigon regime. The situation, in a word, is infinitely worse than it was three years ago.

"Such being the case, it may be argued, we have nothing to lose by sending a huge army to South Vietnam. At least it might keep the pro-West government alive. That may be true. But then what is our objective in South Vietnam? To prop up an anti-Communist government at any price? If so, we should have no illusions about the price to be paid, Mr. President. The Vietcong will fight back ferociously, as they have fought outsiders for a thousand years. The North Vietnamese will commit more and more of its own seasoned troops. They will take a heavy toll of our men. And what will our military do? Fighting back just as ferociously as the enemy, they will devastate the country. They will show no forbearance. Our men will annihilate the innocent and the guilty alike. For it will be a form of warfare in which it will be difficult to distinguish between friend and foe. The Vietcong melt into villages and hamlets, or hold them hostage. It will be a brutal and sadistic war, and the longer it continues the greater will be the atrocities. It will weigh heavily on our consciences, sir.

"Among the gravest atrocities we perpetrate will be our bombing attacks. Bombing the North and the Vietcong strongholds of the South will not be like bombing Germany, or even Japan, during the Second World War. There are no distinct military targets—communications centers, depots, and so forth—as Mr. MacNamara implies. One of the most dangerous errors we can

fall into is to use fallacious terms and then proceed to act on
them—terms derived from conventional warfare. Besides, from
a strictly military point of view—not my province, I admit—
such bombings have at most dubious value. I would go further.
They tend to be counterproductive. They did not work during
the Second World War—we know that German productivity
rose under the incessant night and day attacks—and they did
not work in Korea. How can they work in the jungles and
rural communities of Vietnam?"

"What would *you* recommend, then, Professor Smith?" Johnson
asked.

"I know full well how hard it is to answer that question, Mr.
President. But I would respectfully urge you to reject the Secretary's recommendation out of hand. If you do not, sir, I fear
you will find yourself in the grip of a monumental and terrible
tragedy. I think the wisest course would be to seek the neutralization of South Vietnam. To do that—and I have no illusions
concerning its hazards—an accommodation must be reached with
Ho Chi Minh and the National Liberation Front. We should be
prepared to sanction some sort of coalition government. If, however, neutralization proves impossible, if the Communists are
bent on all-out victory, I would favor our pulling out. Hard
as that would be, it would be less onerous in the end than the
course recommended by Mr. MacNamara."

"Do you mean, Dr. Smith, that we just cut and run?" the
President asked, tilting his head to one side, as though he had
not heard right.

"I do not believe, Mr. President, that the choice necessarily
comes down to cut and run. It *may* come down to that, though
I very much doubt it. The French, I might add, cut and ran in
'54 and are none the worse for it."

"Mendès-France was the worse for it," Johnson said, smiling.

"I must disagree with you there, Mr. President. Mendès-France
was ousted for other reasons. His Vietnam settlement was quite
popular."

"I can understand my friend Smith's passion," MacNamara
said. "I might feel the same way if I shared his dark prognosis
of things. According to the best military and political information
we have, a large-scale operation such as I suggested would be

feasible. My aides, as you know, Mr. Smith, include some of our finest authorities on Vietnam. They agree, too, that if any supply lines from the North are interdicted, and the Vietcong centers in the South hit directly, the threat can be contained and gradually diminished, at which point the Vietnam army can move in. We did it with an ill-trained, ill-motivated, ill-equipped South Korean army in 1950–53. We can do it with the South Vietnamese."

"May I respectfully remind you, Mr. Secretary," Smith said, "that there was no civil war, no guerrilla movement in South Korea. The enemy came exclusively from without."

"Well, so to a large extent does this enemy," MacNamara replied. "Hanoi's the pivot, the fulcrum. And I think we should keep in mind that our objective is much more limited than it was in Korea. Our objective in South Vietnam is simply to give the government a chance to survive."

"But that government, Mr. Secretary, is what the civil war is all about."

"Mr. Smith," Johnson said solicitously, "we really don't know who represents the will of the Vietnamese people, do we? I don't think the Vietcong have the right to impose their will. What we'd like to see are free, open elections to determine the popular will."

"Of course, I completely agree with you, Mr. President. That's an internal question, however, which, I maintain, the South Vietnamese should settle themselves. Vietnam has never had democracy, and the will of the people has never been consulted by governments. Certainly the American-supported governments since 1954 have not been democratic."

"Well, then, why can't we begin to establish one now?" Johnson asked. "Our own democracy wasn't established in a day."

"Because, Mr. President, I do not believe outsiders can establish a democracy in any country, least of all Vietnam. It is not a task for us to undertake, sir. It would be the height of self-delusion and folly. It—"

"I would like to say one more thing about the feasibility of my recommendations, Mr. President," MacNamara said sharply. "Then I'll be quiet. Our strategy will best succeed—I lay this out in the report, Mr. President—through a system of perimeters radiating out from urban enclaves. As our military operations continue by means of search-and-destroy missions, we will bring more and more of the villages and hamlets within the purview of the perimeters. Eventually they will meet and coalesce. What is at issue, Mr. President, is not the possibility of military success, but the willingness to execute the military plan."

"I'll read it diligently, you can be sure of that, Bob," Johnson said. "Dean, what are your thoughts?"

"I go along with Bob one hundred per cent, Mr. President. As to Professor Smith, I repeat now what I recall saying to him when we met three years ago, namely that we cannot look at the Vietnamese conflict from a narrow perspective. What is our interest there, Professor? The answer is simple. Our interest there rests on our commitments to the countries of Southeast Asia, all of whom would stand in immediate peril if Vietnam fell to the Communists. You can be sure of this, Dr. Smith— as sure as the day is long. If we turn our backs on our obligations to the South Vietnamese people, an obligation that three Presidents have honored, then our friends and foes both will draw the appropriate lessons. They will learn that the United States, the leader of the free world, does not keep her word, that when the going is tough she turns tail and runs away. Mao and his cohorts would enjoy that spectacle.

"Mr. Smith, we must think of South Vietnam in its wider, more inclusive context, just as our enemies do. Having drawn the measure of our weakness they will be encouraged to test us elsewhere, provoking a still more dangerous situation. Had Britain and France stood up to Hitler at Munich there would have been no Second World War. The benefits of appeasement are brief. It's because of our concern for the long haul, for the cause of enduring, not transitory, peace that we must travel the hard road and follow Secretary MacNamara's courageous recommendations."

"May I add my mite to the discussion?" Rostow asked, leaning far back in his chair (a classroom habit signaling his intention to argue or develop a point). "I merely want to elaborate a little on Secretary Rusk's very trenchant and apposite remarks. What I find disturbing in my friend John Smith's exposition, coming especially from a man of his erudite wisdom, is its—how shall I say it?—its abstract and empty moralism.

"Now, John, I mean nothing disrespectful in that. What I mean is that your views are one-sided. They're subjective. Who wants to see the conflict escalated? Do you think, John, that people in high places have less solicitude for the lives of the innocent than you? The issue, however, is not the abstract one: war versus peace, killing versus living, and the like. No, the issue is whether the Communist movement will extend over the whole of Southeast Asia, or be contained by the only force in the world that can contain it, the force of American arms.

"That historic duty has been thrust on us, the most humanitarian of people, the nation least desirous of assuming anything like the role of international peacekeeper. Willy-nilly, that's our destiny now, our responsibility at this moment in time. The United States wishes nothing more than to prevent a serious perturbation in the balance of power. We have no designs on Communist China or North Vietnam. Let them stay where they are and live in peace. I for one wish them prosperity. However, they have foolishly avoided consulting me, and I dare say you too, John. Instead, they are determined to aggrandize, to move forward here, there, wherever they perceive a chink in our armor. Like Secretary Rusk I am convinced that unless we shore up our defenses in South Vietnam the whole edifice will crumble, and all of Southeast Asia, from the Celebes to Rangoon, will inexorably come under the Chinese sphere of influence. These are not abstractions. These are concretions, hard, impermeable concretions."

"I think I understand you, Walt," Johnson said with a warm, crinkly smile, "but you'd be advised to supply us with dictionaries the next time you come here."

"Nonetheless, Mr. President," Bundy asserted, looking over his glasses, "Walt's analysis was, as usual, profoundly correct. It's hard to follow his act. I would like only to call attention to one point that has been neglected here. It seems to me that a defeat in Vietnam would have all kinds of unhappy moral and psychological ramifications. In the last few years the United States has established its pre-eminence in the world, a pre-eminence articulated not through dominion but through order

and justice. I don't think I exaggerate very much when I
say that not since Roman times has there been such a sense
of universal order as there is today. And it has been achieved,
I repeat, without marching armies, a great imperial apparatus.
Our prestige would suffer a grievous blow if the Communists
were to win in Vietnam. Not our prestige for its own sake,
but the prestige of international law, which it is our supreme duty
to uphold.

"One other point. There are domestic considerations to worry
about. The right is champing at the bit, waiting, hoping for an
opportunity to ride free. Would anything suit Nixon and Goldwater and Wallace better than a Communist takeover in Vietnam?
I won't mention the Birchers and Minutemen and fanatics of
their ilk. Personally, I think it would make the McCarthy era
seem like a picnic outing. What I'm saying substantiates Walt's
criticism of Mr. Smith's argument as abstract and one-sided."

"Thanks, George, for putting the icing on the cake," the
President said. "Mr. Smith, I'll give you the last word before
closing up shop here. I don't want you to go away thinking
the Chief Executive is discourteous to his guests."

"Mr. President, you have been very generous," Smith replied,
"although I have a feeling your mind is made up. I find it
rather intimidating to take on such argonauts as you have
assembled here, Mr. President. Each of them is much more
persuasive than I can hope to be, and I do not say that
facetiously.

"Two criticisms of my point of view—of my criticism of Mr.
MacNamara's recommendations—have been presented here, it
seems to me. One is that I overestimate the capacity of the
Vietcong to fight off our army. Mr. MacNamara, of course, cites
other non-military authorities to support his conviction that they
do *not* have such a capacity. We should remember, however,
that North Vietnam has several hundred thousand men in reserve. Ho will not permit the Vietcong to lose. And behind
Ho stands China. Suppose, in an emergency, the Chinese intervene. After all, they might have a right to feel alarmed
with armies of Americans so close to their borders. Will we
then send in yet more armies? Will we fight a full-scale war
on the Asian mainland? Just to preserve the pro-American govern-

ment in Saigon? Just to honor our commitments, as though they were covenants handed down on tablets of stone? The logic is incredible.

"Obviously, we will not know who is right until our army is sent there. But I have already suggested that the very act of testing the situation, the havoc that will be unloosed on the Vietnamese people, must be one of the factors taken into account in making the decision, though I have heard no one here mention it, even in passing. America is not Nazi Germany. Let us assume the war goes on for two or three years. Is it conceivable that all Americans will blithely accept the atrocities our men will commit upon Vietnamese civilians? I doubt it.

"This leads me into the second criticism that Messrs. Rusk, Rostow, and Bundy leveled at me. The question of abstraction and concretion is an interesting one, philosophically and methodologically, and it would be pointless to pursue it here. It's enough to say this: one man's concretion may be another man's abstraction. It depends on the perspective. I contend that you gentlemen have carefully *chosen* your concretions, and in doing so have omitted others that bear on the issue at hand. I therefore charge you with abstractness and one-sidedness.

"For example, what is more important than the morale and political health of the American people? I believe that a sustained Vietnamese war would profoundly undermine that morale and that health. I am thinking not only of atrocities. I am thinking of how our country can meet its tremendous domestic commitments—commitments being one of our favorite terms. I say the government's domestic commitments should be at least as binding as its foreign ones. The cities, the poor, the Negroes, the needs of the middle class as well—these will all suffer irreparably in the event of war. How is the cost of keeping an army of a half million to be borne? At whose expense? We already spend five hundred million a year on Vietnam. Imagine what we should have to spend on such an army. Price and wage controls—are these also in the offing? And if not, won't the country fall victim to runaway inflation, given the fact that production is already near its limits? Won't the lower classes suffer even more, thus exacerbating the tensions still further? These are some of the extramilitary consequences, Mr. President, that will flow from a decision to act on Mr. MacNamara's recommendations.

"If you will allow me, I would like to take up another concretion. I find it astonishing that you gentlemen can justify an undeclared war in Vietnam in the name of international law and order. I am not referring to legal technicalities, which we would not hesitate to honor. I am referring to the spectacle of the greatest power in world history—Caucasian and fantastically affluent—attempting to stamp out a rebellion of very poor, non-white people. Can't you see it in your mind's eye? Our big, beautiful men, our prodigious wealth, our tanks and planes and vast organizations engaging a small number of insurgents, animated by a revolutionary hope, carrying little more than rice and small arms.

"What would such a spectacle do for our image—which Mr. Bundy celebrates so eloquently—as the pillar of world order and justice? In plain words, the world would see us as a great bully. Our ruthlessness—for that is what it will be called—will give tremendous encouragement to lawlessness elsewhere. The strong will say to themselves: If the United States can do it, why can't we? This attitude will be all the more blatant if, in carrying out Mr. MacNamara's recommendations, we bomb North Vietnam. North Vietnam is a sovereign country, and is recognized as such under international law. To bomb or blockade it would be an outright, legally indefensible, outrage. We declared war on Imperial Germany in 1917 for much, much less.

"A final point. I can see, Mr. President, that I have wearied you. I will be done in a minute."

"Oh, that's all right. Go ahead and make your point, Mr. Smith."

"I have stated this on many occasions of late. The assumption that all of Southeast Asia would fall to the Communists and come under Chinese hegemony if the Vietcong won—this assumption is false and misleading and pernicious. Heaven knows how many times Munich is thrown up at us. Few things are worse than historical analogies, invoked arbitrarily to support one's case. Who does not shudder in horror at Munich, at appeasement, the whole arsenal of catchwords? All you need to do is substitute South Vietnam for Czechoslovakia, the Communists for the Nazis, and ergo, the conclusion becomes inescapable. Once again I say, with as much urgency as I can muster, that what we have in South Vietnam is a civil war, a revolutionary uprising, that if the country were to go Communist, it does not mean that Thailand, Malaysia, and the others, 'from the Celebes to Rangoon,' will go Communist too—not unless conditions are ripe for Communism internally in each of these countries. The 'domino theory' is spurious from A to Z.

"And while I am at it, I should remind you, gentlemen, what you no doubt know, that Communism is, in any case, far from being monolithic. No love is lost between Communist China, Communist North Vietnam, and Communist North Korea. The Vietnamese dislike the Chinese, whatever their ideologies. I could easily argue, without laboring a paradox, that the Communization of Vietnam would be a hindrance to China, whose main enemy today is the Soviet Union. Conversely, will it be disputed by anyone that our massive intervention in Indochina will cause the various Communist nations and movements in Asia to draw closer to China? Offhand, I would guess that Mao Tse-tung would place his stamp of approval upon Mr. MacNamara's recommendations.

"I could say more, but I will stop now. Thank you, Mr. President, gentlemen, for your indulgence in hearing me out, and I hope I offended no one's sensibilities."

"I enjoyed listening to you, Mr. Smith," Johnson said, smiling enigmatically. "The councils of government, the decision-makers, should listen to adversary opinions more often than they do. When I decide one way or t'other on Bob's recommendations I'll keep your criticisms very much in mind."

. . . Further deterioration in Vietnam. . . . Taylor's hurried visit to Washington. Plea for immediate assistance. . . . Johnson deeply troubled: "Can't make up my mind." Sleepless nights. Wife, daughters unhappy over his "grumpiness." . . .

Goldwater's nomination, late July 1964. For Vietnam fight to finish. . . .

Military's criticism of Johnson. Attitude: "Fish or cut bait." . . .

Early in the morning of August 1, 1964, Johnson suddenly asked his "executive command" to cancel their plans, if they had any, and be at his White House office at 10 P.M. When Rusk, MacNamara, Rostow, and Bundy arrived, they found him sitting at his desk, which was cluttered with Texas memorabilia—guns of every description, bowie knives, arrows, pieces of rope, canvas, barbed wire, framed proclamations signed by Sam Houston, Davy Crockett's last letter from the Alamo, and so forth. He arose, stuffed his hands in his pants pockets, and, looking down at the floor, began to pace back and forth.*

"You all know how Ive agonized over this decision two months now its kept me awake sometimes Id be with a foreign ambassador or holding a cabinet meeting and damn it to hell Id just think and think about what I should do well yesterday I made up my mind dont ask me how I just did Im going ahead with your recommendations Bob and I expect Defense to prime up for the big push and the bombing assault on the North only Im going to delay implementing the plan until after the election maybe therell be a change in the picture in the next five months though I doubt it Max Taylor was pessimistic as hell but he agreed nothing bad is going to happen now during the monsoons also I want Hanoi and Peking to get a signal or two about our intentions Ill give them a little time to rein in their boys if they dont then all hells going to break loose they cant say I didnt warn them Im going through with it all the way Bob I read your report so often I think Ive memorized it its convincing all right and Im sure the American people will be convinced of it too when I present its arguments to them sometime early next year theres going to be no declaration of war its going to be like Harry Trumans police action in Korea only weve got to go it alone why by the time the UN crawled an inch Ho Chi Minh would be in Saigon waving his flag laughing his ass off behind his beard what Im going to do is get Congress official sanction for me as commander in chief of United States armed forces to take whatever steps I deem necessary to protect the lives of our boys in Vietnam therell have to be some incident an attack by the Communists against us I leave

---

* Prescott obviously wrote the following monologue, or soliloquy, in great haste from his notes, without bothering to punctuate. It is presented here exactly as he wrote it.—N.F.M.

that up to you Bob then Ill draw up a resolution and the Congress
will pass it that ought to do it just fine [. . . .] yes its my responsibility if we dont stop the Communists in their tracks theyll
just go on and on and on and itll be harder to stop them the next
time why dont they negotiate they should know that in me
theyve someone who they can talk to what do they want for
Christs sake but Ill be damned if they get anything by force the
ways always been open to reason and friendly discussion and still
is but reason whats that to them without muscle thats why Im
going to move into Vietnam to give us the leverage for negotiation I agree with you Walt if only Peking and Hanoi would live
and let live I don't care a shit about what our yahoos and
goddamned fanatics say let the Communists run their own affairs
just so long as they dont give us and the rest of the free world
any trouble when they do theyre going to be brought to heel
damn them to eternity Ill do my duty maintain peace the delicate
balance thats been worked out by four Presidents before me if
theyre intent on upsetting the balance if theyre intent on humiliating us making us look like crap were going to fight back
and fight hard theyre not going to find me or the people wanting
Peking and Hanoi will have to learn the hard way this is a
defensive battle were about to wage in Vietnam a battle to give
the people the right to whatever government they want even if
its a Communist government no outsiders are going to shove
anything down their throats thats what this ball games all about
no Im no professional anti-Communist no redbaiter no crusader
for anything but freedom and democracy I didnt build my career
on hatred and division I fought Joe McCarthy I was against any
kind of adventurism on our part Im proud of my record in the
Congress as a moderate a restraining influence Eisenhower always
consulted me and Sam Rayburn and Im proud that I always encouraged him to go ahead and meet the Russians more than half-
way I encouraged John Kennedy too and Ill do the same Im
going to try hard as all get out to consecrate this administration
to disarmament extending agreements with Russians down the
line all the way if I win big in November Ill take some mighty
initiatives sure as shit the right-wingersll squawk and yell and
howl but the American people are ready for a real settlement
with the Russians itll be my legacy to history and I want nothing

from history but the recognition of my desire for peace [. . . .]
and I know what the philanthropists and intellectuals and do-
gooders and nervous Nellies will say theyll point their crooked
forefinger at me and accuse me of unleashing the wraths of war
on children old people the lame the halt and the blind shit fart
and corruption why dont they point their accusing finger at Ho
Chi Minh or Mao Tse-tung or Khrushchev as far as that goes
what in tarnation do they know these purists who never soiled
their hands but dont mind one bit having the fruit of someone
elses labor or getting the benefits of someone elses responsibilities God these people love to criticize and run down but why
in hells name should I answer to them tell me I was born in
poverty and deprivation and I raised myself by my own boot-
straps by the sweat of my brow I earned the right to live from
the time I went into public life as a boy I was with the poor
fighting for them I could have gone over to the fat cats in oil
and gas and cotton and cattle I joined the New Deal and fought
hard skinning myself down to the bone for the plain folks and
Mexicans in my district and I didnt stop when I became a
senator they say I was a wheeler-dealer in those days those
ignorant sons of bitches pardon the strong language but you know
how goddamned insidious those innuendoes are how they assassinate your character I could have betrayed my people in
Texas and it would have been good politics the temptations were
all around me but I stayed true to them I did whatever I could
to help the poor and not only in my own state but remember
Eisenhower was retrenching in the 50s cutting back there was no
social reform yet I saw to it that we had the first civil rights bill
in almost a hundred years and if you think that was easy you
shouldve heard the shit I got from some of my best friends and
Eisenhower wasnt too happy about it either yet I prevailed because I thought it was the right and the decent thing to do and
I knew it was only the start I welcome the civil rights revolution
because we have a lot of catching up to do they dont know shit
from shinola those sunshine friends of mine those people wholl
jump down my neck when they see Ive gone into Vietnam in a
big way all right fine I accept the burden Im in the kitchen
fussing over the stove thats my job no excuses and no explanations but do they know why Im doing this why Im going to order

the shooting to start why Im going to see it through to the end
I want to read you something I carry it with me all the time in
my jacket its Lincolns Second Inaugural the words are burned
into my mind I quote fondly do we hope fervently do we pray
that this mighty scourge of war may speedily pass away yet if
God will that it continue until all the wealth piled by the bond-
mans two hundred and fifty years of unrequited toil shall be
sunk and until every drop of blood drawn with the lash shall be
paid by another drawn with a sword as was said three thousand
years ago so still it must be said the judgments of the Lord are
true and righteous altogether end quote those are powerful words
gentlemen and will ring as true now for our struggle in Vietnam
as they did in the war for the union the war to destroy slavery
will they get it through their heads that its peace I seek and
nothing but peace will they accuse Lincoln of being a war maker
because he sent in the armies too I want to solve the problem
once and for all its the one problem we have now in the whole
world everwhere else theres peace and concord Vietnams the
only place and Im going to bring peace there too and I promise
I swear to you here and now once we get peace there Ill move
heaven and earth to bring happiness and prosperity to those
people in Southeast Asia I mean all the people Communist and
non-Communist and I mean all the countries China and India
and Japan too well have a Marshall Plan a New Deal for those
poor people well take out our troops and bring in our doctors
and engineers and teachers and civil servants well have TVAs
on the Yangtse and Mekong and Ganges well increase their rice
yields cure their diseases build schools and houses thats the
vision of peace I have once weve concluded this ugly war hon-
orably and courageously America the mighty and proud and
beautiful will lead the way men will turn their spears into pruning
hooks their swords into plowshares theyll learn war no more
theyll sit down and work out their differences and shake hands
and embrace each other as brothers and friends this is no vain
hope no false vision no self-deluding prophecy oh no oh no
no [. . .]*

* The rest of Prescott's manuscript is undecipherable.—N.F.M.

INDEX

Acheson, Dean, 15, 35
  Berlin crises and, 29–30, 306–13
  Cuban missile crisis and, 344, 346–47, 349–50, 353
  Korean War and, 40, 43, 49, 50–52
  McCarthy's letter to, 64–65
  report on loss of China by, 36–38
Adenauer, Konrad, 90
  with Dulles, 102–5
Adjhubei, Alexei, 217, 291–94, 314–15
  Cuban missile criiss and, 338–42, 357–59
  fate of, 391
"Agreement of the Three Princes," 326
Albania, 291–92
Alliance for Progress, 269–70
Anderson, George H., Jr., 284, 311, 353
Anglo-Iranian Oil Company, 121
Anti-Semitism in Russia, 32–33, 46, 83–86, 164–65
Anzooz, Mehdi, 120
Arbenz Guzmán, Jacobo, 114, 121–24
Army Times, 216
Asch, Monroe, 288–89
Assassination of John F. Kennedy, 389
Aswan Dam, 184, 186–87, 192
Atlantic Charter, 7
Atomic weapons
  discussed at Potsdam, 9–11
  Nuclear Test Ban Treaty (1963), 370
  obtained by Soviet Union, 30–31

Attlee, Clement, 49–50
  at Potsdam, 8–11
Attorney General's subversive list, 55–56
Australia, 124
Austrian Treaty (1955), 145–46

Baghdad Pact (1955), 124, 185, 190
Ball, George, 348, 350, 352–53
Bao Dai (Emperor of Vietnam), 126–27
Bartók, Ferenc, 169, 174
Barton, Winslow Andrew, 294–96
Baruch, Bernard, 35, 40
Batista, Fulgencio, 268
Bay of Pigs invasion (1962), 275–90
Belgium, 29
Ben Gurion, David, 187, 203
  meeting with Eden, Mollet and, 194–99
Beneš, Eduard, 19–20
Benton, William, 67–68
Bequest, Andrew, 89–90
Berger, Darius, 163
Beria, Lavrenti, 23–24, 26–27, 32, 46
  death of Stalin and, 83–89
  East Germany crisis and, 106–9
  purge of, 109–11
  triumvirate after death of Stalin and, 89–96
Berlin blockade (1948–49), 27–29
Berlin wall (1962), 306–18
Bevin, Ernest, 31
Bierut, Boleslaw, 163–65
Big Four Conference (Geneva, 1955), 146–50

Big Four Summit Conference (Paris, 1960), 238–43
U-2 affair and, 238–43
Birchby, Lemuel, 42
Birmingham Sunday (1963), 373
Black, Hugo, 60–61
Black power, 390
Blacks in America, 372–85
Blockade, Cuban (1962), 352
Kennedy's speech on, 355–57
Blockade of Berlin (1948–49), 27–29
Bluestone, Abba, 253–54
"Blunting the Soviet Threat" (Acheson), 306–13
Boa, Achille, 286–87
Bohlen, Charles, 146, 151
Bolivia, 116
Bone, Maxwell, 306–6
Boun Oum (Prince of Laos), 324–26
Bowles, Chester, 263–64
Bradley, Omar T., 35, 40, 50, 52, 132
Brandt, Willy, 317
Brezhnev, L. M., 363, 369, 391
Bricker, John, 51
British Guiana, 114–15
Brownell, Herbert, 81, 151–52, 154
Bulganin, Nikolai A., 106, 108, 109, 149, 211
destalinization and, 156–58
replaced by Malenkov as Premier, 142–43
visit to Yugoslavia and, 143–45
Bundy, MacGeorge, 275, 277–78, 312
Cuban missile crisis and, 343–44
Indochina briefings and, 319, 322–23, 327–37
visit to Vietnam of, 392–403
Butler, R. A., 201, 203
Buttner, Steven B., 215–16
Byquest, Raymond, 142
Byrnes, James F., 14–15

Cambodia, 127, 319, 321, 323–24
Camp David Summit (1959), 235–37
Canada, 29
"Canal Users' Association," 194
Capehart, Homer, 51
Carnegie Endowment for Peace, 56
Castillo Armas, Carlos, 122–23
Castro, Fidel, 267–69, 276, 366–67
Catholicism, 250

Central Intelligence Agency, 112, 138
Bay of Pigs and, 275, 276–85
Iran crisis and, 119–21
McCone as head of, 346, 349, 351
overthrow of Guzmán and, 121–24
Chambers, Whittaker, 57
Checkers speech (Nixon), 79–81
Chen Yi, 222–23
Chiang Kai-shek, 34–36
China, 34–38
Communists win control of, 34–38
Korean War and, 47–53
Sino-Soviet dispute, 217–27, 291–94, 368–69
Cholent, Murray, 257
Chou En-lai, 52, 135, 219, 291, 368
Christian Militant, 57
Chu Teh, 35
Churchill, Winston, 132, 146
secret agreement with Stalin of, 7–8
at Teheran conference, 5–7
Civil Liberties Digest, 60
Civil rights march (1963), 373
Civil rights movement, 372–85
Kennedy's meeting with King and, 374–85
Clark, Tom, 55–56, 58
Clifford, Clark, 35
Cohn, Roy, 152–54
Committee for European Economic Cooperation (Marshall Plan), 18–19
Committee for Mutual Prosperity, 23
Communism, McCarthy era and, 54–68
See also McCarthyism
Connally, Tom, 35, 43
Cooke, Adrian, 217
Coudert, Serge, 146
Counterinsurgency, 263–64
Cuba, 267–69
Bay of Pigs invasion by U.S., 275–90
missile crisis, 338–67
Cult of personality, 156
Czechoslovakia, 19–22

Daley, Richard, 258
De Gaulle, Charles, 126–27, 240–41
Paris meeting with Kennedy and, 294–99
Decentralization policies of Khrushchev, 205–11

Decker, George L., 335–36
Defense policies of Kennedy, 262–64
Democratic party
  1952 presidential election and, 76–77
  1960 presidential election and, 249–55
Denmark, 29
DeSemino, Ludovico, 249
Destalinization, 155–62
Dewey, Thomas E., 44, 71, 73–74
Diem, Ngo, 320, 328, 329–30
  corruption of, 328, 333, 336
  fall of, 371
  opposition to, 322
Dien Bien Phu, 127–28, 134
Dies Committee, 54
Dillon, Douglas, 275, 351
"Direction of U. S. Policy toward World Communism" (Dulles), 98–100
Dirksen, Everett M., 50, 74
Dobrinin, Nikoli, 363–66
Douglas, William O., 61
Dulles, Allen, 112, 118–19, 121
  Bay of Pigs and, 275, 276–85
  Indochina and, 327
Dulles, John Foster, 44, 82, 147–48, 150
  with Adenauer, 103–5
  Austrian Treaty and, 146
  cold war policies of, 97–105, 113–19
  death of, 228
  Egypt and, 184–92
  elections in Vietnam and, 319–21
  Geneva Conference (1954) and, 135–37
  Guatemala crisis and, 113, 115, 121–24
  Hollings and, 137–38
  Hungarian crisis and, 178–80
  Indochina and, 125–31
  Iranian crisis and, 112–13, 115, 119–21
  National Press Club speech of, 108–9

East Germany, Berlin wall crisis and, 306–13
  See also Germany
Economic policies of Kennedy, 267–70

Eden, Anthony, 7–8, 135
  meeting with Ben Gurion, Mollet and, 194–99
  Suez crisis and, 200, 202
Ehrenbourg, Ilya, 142
Eisenhower, Dwight D., 40, 43, 44–45
  cabinet of, 81–82
  Dulles and, 97–102, 112
  farewell address of, 241–43
  Geneva Big Four Conference (1955), 146–50
  Indochina and, 125–34
  meeting with Kodály, 177–81
  1952 presidential elections and, 71–81
  Suez crisis and, 200, 202
  U-2 affair and, 238–41
  visit of Khrushchev and, 228–37
Eisenhower, Milton, 228, 229–30
Elections of 1952, presidential, 71–82
  campaign for, 77–81
  Democratic party and, 76–77
  Republican party and, 71–76
Election of 1960, presidential, 249–58
  campaign for, 255–58
  Democratic party and, 249–55
  Republican party and, 255
Election of 1964, presidential, 390
Espionage Act (1917), 62
Essinger, Heinz von, 133
European Recovery Program (Marshall Plan), 17–19

Faisal (Prince of Saudi Arabia), 188
Fannin, Stanley, 204
Farkas, Georg, 170
Farouk (King of Egypt), 186
Fedayeen, 185, 196
Federal Bureau of Investigation (FBI), 61
Fish, Hamilton, 37
Ford, Ezekiel, 260
Foreign Ministers Conference (Paris, 1949), 31
Foreign Policy Review, 94
Forrestal, James V., 27–28, 40, 117
Fourier, Arnulph, 149–50
France, 29, 124
  Indochina war and, 125–38
  Kennedy's visit to, 294–99
  Marshall Plan, 16
  Suez crisis and, 184–204

Frankenthaler, Patrick, 73
French Communist party, 161–62
Fuchs, Klaus, 61
Fulbright, J. William, 275, 278–82

Galbraith, John Kenneth, 272–73
Garvey, Abe, 249
Gasperi, Alcide de, 17
Gaza Strip, 198, 203
Geneva Conference (1954), 134–38
Germany, 45
  Berlin wall, 306–18
  dispute after war over, 25–32
  East Germany crisis, 104–9
  Marshall Plan and, 16
  "Master Plan" for, 29–32
  Russian plans for, 90–93
  talked about at Vienna conference, 302–4
Gero, Ernest, 167–68
Giap, Nguyen, 126
Gilpatrick, Roswell, 352
Goldwater, Barry, 390
Gomulka, Wladyslaw, 168, 169–74
Gottwald, Klement, 20–22
Breat Britain, 29, 124
  Attlee and, 8–11, 49–50
  Suez crisis and, 184–204
  at Teheran conference, 3–7
Greece
  end of civil war in, 25
  Truman Doctrine and, 15–16
Gretchko, Andrei A., 30
Grigenko (Soviet analyst), 108
Gromyko, Andrei, 30, 40–41
  Cuban missile crisis and, 357
  meeting with Kennedy and, 354–56
  Nasser and, 188–91
Gross, Herbert, 257
Gruenther, Alfred, 132
Guatemala, 1953 crisis and, 113, 115, 121–24
Guantánamo Naval Base (Cuba), 286
Guevara, Che, 283
Gulf of Aqaba, 198

Hall, Leonard, 152
Hammarskjöld, Dag, 202–3
Harriman, Averell, 35, 325–36, 370
Heller, Walter W. W., 270–73
Heminway, Marcus, 71
Henderson, Elias V., 29

Henderson, Loy, 113, 119–21
Herter, Christian, 200, 231
Higman, Bryce, 49
Hillsman, Bradford, 71, 73
Hin Hum Hump, 326
Hiroshima, 11
Hiss, Alger, 56–57
Ho Chi Minh, 125–26, 136, 138, 320–21
Hollings, J. Horton, 137–38
Holmes, Marvin, 234
Hombrug, Adam, 94
Homer, Chapman, 342
Honduras, 118, 122
Hoover, Herbert, 44
Hoover, J. Edgar, 61, 63
Horvitzer, Hiram, 283–84, 311, 334
Hot-line agreement, 370
Houghton, Everett, 129–30
House Un-American Activities Committee, 55
  Hiss affair and, 57
Hughes, Charles Evans, 63–64
Hukbalahap Communists (Philippines), 114
Hull, Cordell, 97
Humphrey, George, 81
Humphrey, Hubert H., 250–51
Hungary, 163–65
  1965 crisis in, 167–68, 173–84

Iceland, 29
Inchon, 47
Indochina, 114–15, 125–38, 319–37
  "Agreement of the Three Princes," 325–26
  French war in, 125–28
  Geneva Conference (1954) on, 134–38
  U.S. briefings about, 128–31
  See also Vietnam
Indonesia, 127
Inquest, Herbert, 157–59
Internal Security Act (1950), 62–64
International Bank, 184, 192
International Report and Survey, 44, 278, 309
"Internment camps," 63
Iran, 124
  1953 crisis in, 112–13, 115, 119–21
  removal of troops from, 13–15
  Teheran Conference (1943), 3–7

Iraq, 124, 187
Isolationism, 44
Israel, Suez crisis (1956) and, 184–204
Italian Communist Party, 162
Italy, 29
  Marshall Plan and, 16

Jagan, Cheddi, 114
Japan, 3, 11
  Mutual Defense Assistance Agreement with U.S., 124
Jen Min Jih Pao, 218
Jenner, Albert, 78–79
Jews in Soviet Union, 32–33, 46, 83–86, 164–65
Jiminez (Latin American leader), 268
Johnson, Lyndon B., 131–32, 177–78, 228–31, 317
  briefings on Vietnam of, 392–403
  defeat of Goldwater and, 390
  1960 presidential elections and, 251–52
  as President, 389–90
  as vice presidential candidate, 253–55, 258
  visit to Vietnam of, 329
Jupien, Georges, 128

Kadar, Janos, 174, 182–83, 291
Kaganovitch, Lazar, 26, 145, 160–61, 170–71, 205
  East Germany crisis and, 106–9
  fall of, 207–210
  purge of Beria and, 109–11
Kamenev, Lev Borisovich, 164
Kardelj, E. M., 182
Kefauver, Estes, 249
Kennan, George F., 25, 28–29
Kennedy, Jackie, 296
Kennedy, John F.
  assassination of, 389
  Bay of Pigs invasion and, 275–90
  Berlin wall crisis and, 306–13
  career of, 247–49
  Cuban missile crisis and, 342–67
  defense and, 262–64
  economic policy of, 270–74
  Indochina and, 319–37, 371
  Kennedy-Nixon debates, 257–58
  "Kennedy Team," 259–62
  Khrushchev and, 369–70

Latin America and, 267–70
  meeting with King and, 374–85
  1960 elections and, 249–58
  space program and, 264–67
  Vienna meeting with Khrushchev and, 299–305
  visit to Paris of, 294–99
Kennedy, Joseph, 247
Kennedy, Robert F., 248, 253–54, 275, 284
  with Acheson, 310–11
  as Attorney General, 260
  Cuban missile crisis and, 347, 349–50, 353, 364
  Indochina briefings and, 347, 349–50, 353, 364
  meeting with King and, 374–85
Khrushchev, Nikita S., 89–96, 148–49
  Berlin wall and, 315–18
  Camp David Summit and, 235–37
  Cuban missile crisis and, 338–42, 357–59, 362–66
  death of Stalin and, 83–89
  destalinization and, 155–62
  East Germany crisis and, 106–9
  meeting with Kennedy in Vienna and, 299–305
  1955 party symposium and, 139–43
  ouster of, 391
  purge of Beria and, 109–11
  Sino-Soviet dispute and, 291–94, 368–69
  solidification of power of, 205–11
  Suez crisis and, 201–2
  talks with Mao and, 222–27
  Tito and, 143–45
  U-2 affair and, 238–41
  visit to U.S. of, 231–35
Kim Il Sung, 38–39, 41, 94–95
King, Martin Luther, Jr., 374–85
Kingston, Harley B., 28
Klementis, Vladimir, 21
Klosco, Robert, 238
Klosiewicz, Wiktor, 166
Knowland, William F., 131, 177
Kodály, Tibor, 177–81
Komsomolskaya Pravda, 210
Korean War, 38–53
  armistice in, 102
Kornilov Memorandum, 5
Kosygin, Alexei, 391

Kozlov, Frol, 218, 232
Ku Klux Klan, 373

Laniel, Proteus, 132–33, 134
Laos, 127, 319, 321, 323–26
Larouche, Winston V., 36
Laser, Jarman, 264–67
Laswell, Gar, 234–35
Latin American policies of Kennedy,
   267–70
Lattimore, Owen, 66–67
Lebyadkin, Vassily N., 39
LeMay, Curtis M., 312, 348–49
Lenin, V. I., 92
List of subversive organizations, 55–
   56
Liu Shao-ch'i, 218–19, 222, 291, 368
Llewelyn, Thomas A., 275, 350–51
Lodge, Henry Cabot, 200, 232, 247–48
   1952 presidential elections and, 71–
   73, 79, 81
Lovett, Robert, 344, 351–52
Luxembourg, 29

MacArthur, Douglas A., 41–42, 47–50,
   132
   recall of, 51–53
McCarran, Patrick, 62–64
McCarran Act (1950), 62–64
McCarthyism, 54–68
   under Eisenhower, 150–54
   Hiss affair, 56–57
   McCarran Act and, 62–64
   Rosenberg trial, 61–62
McCarthy, Joseph, 64–68, 150–54, 248
   letter to Acheson of, 64–65
   during 1952 elections, 78–79
McCone, John A., 346, 349, 351
McCormack Hall, 73
Macedonia, 25
McElroy, Neil, 177, 179
McGrath, J. Howard, 52, 63
MacMahon, Brian, 65
MacManus, Ivan, 118, 122–23
Macmillan, Harold, 203–240
MacNamara, Robert, 260, 262–64, 276
   Cuban missile crisis and, 345–47
   Indochina briefings and, 319, 321,
   327–37
   visit to Vietnam of, 392–403
Magsaysay, Ramón, 114
Malaya, 114–15, 127

Malenkov, Georgi, 41, 46, 205
   death of Stalin and, 83–89
   East Germany crisis and, 106–9
   fall of, 207–10
   purge of Beria and, 109–11
   replaced by Bulganin, 142
   triumvirate after death of Stalin and,
   89–96
Malinowski, Rudyan, 26–27, 89–96
   Cuban missile crisis and, 357
   death of Stalin and, 83–89
Mallose, Phil, 267–70
Manchuria, 38
Mao Tse-tung, 34, 36, 94–95, 369
   Khrushchev and, 222–27
   Sino-Soviet dispute and, 218–27,
   291–94
Marshall, George C., 17, 34, 40, 52,
   66, 78–79
Marshall Plan, 16–19
Martin, Joe, 131, 177
Marxism-Leninism, 24, 32–33
Masaryk, Jan, 20–22
Masjeeb, Mohammed, 189–92
Masjumi, 119
"Master Plan" for Germany, 29–32
Mather, Cotton, 98
Matsu, 293
Meany, George, 249–50
Medicare, 390
Medina, Harold, 59–60
Mendès-France, Pierre, 134–38
Meyer, Kurt, 105–6
Mikoyan, Anastas, 159, 167–68, 176–
   77, 223, 232
   Berlin wall crisis and, 314–16
   Cuban missile crisis and, 338–42,
   357, 364–65
   fate of, 391
   Sino-Soviet dispute and, 291–94
Militancy, Black, 390
Military industrial complex, 243
"Missile gap," 256, 262
Mollet, Guy, 193–202
   meeting with Eden, Ben Gurion
   and, 194–99
Molotov, Vyacheslav, 30, 135, 145,
   149, 205
   Committee for European Economic
   Cooperation and, 18–19
   Czechoslovakia and, 20
   death of Stalin and, 46

East Germany crisis and, 106–9
fall of, 207–210
1956 Polish crisis and, 170–71
partition of Berlin and, 26–27
in Peking, 36
at Potsdam, 9, 10
purge of Beria and, 109–11
resignation of, 160
Stalin and, 46
Tito and, 23–24
triumvirate after death of Stalin and, 89–96
Montgomery bus strike (1955), 372
Mossadegh, Mohammed, 112–13, 119–21
Mover, J. Scott, 82, 187
Mundt, Karl, 62, 64
Muravchek (Beria aide), 109, 110
Mutual Defense Assistance Agreement (Japan-U.S.), 124
MVD (secret police), 20, 32
My Six Crises (Nixon), 80–81

Nagasaki, 11
Nagy, Imre, 168–69
1956 Hungarian crisis and, 173–77, 181–83
Nasser, Gamal Abdul, 184–87, 203
meeting with Gromyko and, 188–92
nationalization of Suez Canal and, 193–94
National Liberation Front (NLF), 393
National Security Council, 27, 98
NATO (North Atlantic Treaty Organization), 29–30, 42–45, 100
"Natolin Group," 169–70
Negev, 198
Netherlands, 29
New Zealand, 124
Ngali, Abu, 344
Nixon, Julie, 80
Nixon, Pat, 79–80
Nixon, Richard M., 55, 68, 180
anti-communist crusade of, 57
Checkers speech of, 79–81
Eisenhower and, 228–31
Indochina and, 128, 129, 131, 133
Kennedy-Nixon TV debates, 257–58
McCarthy and, 152–54
1952 presidential election and, 74–76, 78

1960 presidential election and, 255–58
Nixon, Tricia, 80
Norway, 29
Novikov, Boris, 200
Nuclear Test Ban Treaty (1963), 370
Nuclear weapons
discussed at Potsdam, 9–11
obtained by Soviet Union, 30–31

O'Brien, Sean, 118, 122–23
O'Connor, Bull, 373
Ochab, Eduard, 166, 169, 170–71
Oliphant, Robert, 142
Ollenauer, Erich, 105
Onassiarch, Thersites, 143
Oswald, Lee Harvey, 389

Pahlevi (Shah of Iran), 119–21
Pakistan, 124
Pall, Morris, 232–33
Panmunjom, 90, 102
Paradise Lost (Milton), 98
Pathet Lao, 324–26
Patofi Tribune, 166
Peaceful coexistence, 141
Peggotty, Peter, 131, 133
Peking, 36
Pestel, Pytor, 357, 359
Petofi Circle, 167
Philippines, 114–15, 124, 127
Piersall, General, 130
Pijade (Tito aide), 23
Pinay, Antoine, 49
"Plan to Reorganize Industry" (Krushchev), 206–7
Poland, 122
Khrushchev and Rakosi, 163–65
1956 strike and, 166–67, 168–73
Polaris missile, 216–17
Potsdam Conference (1945), 8–11
Powers, Francis Gary, 238–39
Poznan, 166–67
Prall, Glenn, 119–120
Pravda, 88, 110, 142, 157
Presidential election (1952), 71–82
campaign for, 77–81
Democratic party and, 76–77
Republican party and, 71–76
Presidential election (1960), 249–58
campaign of, 255–58
Democratic party and, 249–55
Republican party and, 255

Presidential election (1964), 390
Priapus Intercontinental Ballistic Missiles, 216–17
Profiles in Courage (Kennedy), 249
Puerifoy, John E., 121–24
Purges, 32–33, 46, 83–86
Pusan, 42, 47, 49
Pyongyang, 48–49

Quemoy, 293

Radek, Karl, 164
Radford, Arthur W., 116–17, 129, 177
Rajk, Lazslo, 165
Rakosi, Matyas, 163–65, 169–174
    meeting between Mikoyan and, 168
Rayburn, Sam, 131, 177–78
Red Star, 157
Registration of communists, 62–63
Republican party
    1952 elections and 71–82
    1960 elections and, 255
Reuther, Walter, 234
Rhee, Syngman, 38–39, 41
Ridgway, Matthew, 132
Rogers, William, 153
Rojas Pinilla, 268
Roosevelt, Franklin D., 54
    at Teheran Conference, 4, 6–7
Roseland, General, 130
Rosenburg trial, 61–62
Rosenberg, Ethel, 61–62
Rosenberg, Julius, 61–62
Rostow, Walt, 263–64, 275, 280–81, 334
    visit to Vietnam of, 392–403
Rusk, Dean, 259–60, 270, 276, 278, 280
    Cuban missile crisis and, 345, 364–65
    Indochina briefings and, 319, 321, 327–37
    visit to Vietnam of, 392–403

Said, Nuri, 188
St. Jacques, Maurice, 193
Samoza, Luis A., 268
Sansinov, L. V., 318
Saud (King of Saudi Arabia), 188
Saudi Arabia, 187–88
Sawyer, Charles, 58–59
Schine, David, 152–53

Schlesinger, Arthur, Jr., 261, 275, 278, 285
Schwartz, Norman, 151
SEATO (Southeast Asia Treaty Organization), 125
Selma (Alabama), 390
Seoul, 42, 47
Sforza, Henry, 213, 234
Shah of Iran, 14, 119–21
Shepilov, N. I., 30, 160, 205
    fall of, 208–10
Sholokhov, Mikhail, 157
Shrike, Robert, 257
Sihanouk, Noradom, 323–24
Sino-Soviet dispute, 217–27, 291–94, 368–69
Smerdyakov, Semyon, 156, 205, 211–12
Smith, Hiram Beadle, 134–35
Smith Act roundup of alleged communists, 58–61
Snyder, John, 58–59
Sorensen, Theodore, 248, 253–54, 261, 319
    Cuban missile crisis and, 344, 347
Souvanavong (Prince of Laos) 324–36
Souvanna Phouma (Prince of Laos) 324–26
Soviet Union
    Austrian Treaty (1955) 145–46
    crushing of Hungarian crisis by 174–75
    Iran and 112–13
    "Master Plan" for Germany and, 30
    obtains atomic weapons 30–31
    Sino-Soviet dispute, 217–27, 291–94, 368–69
    space achievements of, 213–17
    at Teheran Conference, 3–7
    threats to sign peace treaty with East Germany of, 306–13
    transition of power after death of Stalin in, 89–96
    See also Khrushchev, Nikita S.; Molotov, Vyacheslav; Stalin, Joseph
Space program of Kennedy, 264–67
Speaking Out, 167
Spencer, Brian, 200
"Sputnik I," 213–14
Stalin, Josef, 32–33, 142

Berlin blockade and, 27
break with West and, 12–19
Czechoslovakia and, 19–22
death of, 83–89
destalinization, 155–62
Kim Il Sung and, 39, 41
Marshall Plan and, 18–19
secret agreement with Churchill of, 7–8
at Teheran Conference, 5–7
Stevens, Robert, 151
Stevenson, Adlai, 76–77, 81, 252
as ambassador to UN, 260, 286–87
Cuban missile crisis and, 349–52
Stoff, Willi, 104
Strait of Tiran, 197
Stroessner, Alfredo, 268
Student unrest, 373
Subversive organization list, 55–56
Suez Boat and Waterway, Ltd., 193
Suez Canal, 185
nationalization, of, 193
Suez crisis (1956), 184–204
Supreme Court, 60–61
Suslov, Michael, 145, 176–77, 363, 364–65, 369
report on China of, 217–21

Taft, Robert, 44, 72, 73–74
Taiwan, 36
Taylor, Maxwell, 263–64, 289, 336, 348–49
as ambassador to Vietnam, 392
Teheran Conference (1943), 3–7
Thailand, 124, 127
"Thaw," 142
Thermopoulos, Cleon, 233
Thiebold, Arthur, 29
Thrace, 25
Tito, Josip Broz, 23–25, 116
Khrushchev and, 143–45
Togliatti, Palmiero, 162
Touhy, Emil, 153
Trotksy, Leon, 164
Trunillo Molina, Rafael, 268
Truman, Harry S, 35, 79
aid to Yugoslavia of, 25
Berlin crisis and, 27–29
Korean War and, 40–42, 47–52
at Potsdam, 8–11
removal of troops from Iran and, 14–15

Smith Act and, 58–60
Stevenson and, 76–77
Truman Doctrine, 15–16, 25, 100, 252
Tsedenbal, U., 221–22
Tudeh (Communist party of Iran), 113, 120
Turkey, 124
Truman Doctrine and, 15–16
Tydings, Millard, 67–68

Ulbricht, Walter, 32, 91, 95–96
Berlin wall crisis and, 314–16
East Berlin crisis and, 104–9
United Nations, 13–14, 19
Korean Resolution of, 41
United States, 29, 124
Berlin airlift of, 28–29
Mutual Defense Assistance Agreement with Japan, 124
at Teheran Conference, 3–7
See also Eisenhower, Dwight D.; Johnson, Lyndon B., Kennedy John F.; Truman, Harry S
Urenko, Maxim, 105–6
U-2 affair, 238–41

Vandenberg, Arthur, 35
Vandenberg, Hoyt, 28
Vargara, Gregory, 18–19
Vienna meeting of Kennedy and Khrushchev, 299–305
Vientiane, 324
Vietcong, 327
Vietminh, 114, 125–26, 134, 320
Vietnam, 319–37, 392–405
"Agreement of the Three Princes," 325–26
fall of Diem and, 371
Johnson briefings on, 392–403
Kennedy briefings on, 319–25, 327–37
See also Indochina
Vinson, Fred, 40, 60
Voroshilov, Klement, 212, 214
Vlasav, Gregory, 85–87
Voting Rights Act (1965), 390
Vyshinsky, Andrei, 19, 30, 31–32

Wake Island meeting between Truman and MacArthur, 47–48
Wallace, George, 373

War in Vietnam. *See* Indochina; Vietnam
Warren, Earl, 71, 76
Warsaw Pact (1955), 46–47
Wells, Matthew, 74–75, 79
West Germany, 29–30
  See also Germany
White, Portland W., 184–87, 192
White Citizens' Councils, 373
White House Committee on Freedom and Security, 54–55
Wiefanz, Alex U., 71
Wilson, Charles E., 81, 112, 116, 130, 152
Wilson, Harold, 204

Xuy, Tuang Hoc, 135

Yalu River, 38
Yugoslavia
  break with Soviet Union and, 23–25
  Khrushchev visit to, 143–45
Yunan, 34

Zahedi, Fozlollah, 118, 120, 121
Zambrowski, Roman, 165–66
Zukov, Georgi, 173–175
  consolidation of Khrushchev's power and, 209–11
Ziemens, Ian, 194
Zigorin, Paul, 161
Zinoviev, Grigori, 164
Zorin, Valerian, 20–21